SAILING RIGS AND SPARS

INSTALLATION ▫ MAINTENANCE ▫ TUNING

Matthew Sheahan

A FOULIS Boating Book

First published 1990

Published by:
Haynes Publishing Group,
Sparkford, Yeovil, Somerset
BA22 7JJ, England

Haynes Publishing Inc.
861 Lawrence Drive,
Newbury Park,
California 91320, USA

British Library Cataloguing in Publication Data
Sheahan, Matthew
Sailing rigs & spars.
1. Sailing boats. Gear & rigging. making, maintenance & repair
I. Title
623.862

ISBN 0-85429-753-7

Library of Congress Catalog Card Number 90-83292

Typeset in Frontiera light rom 10/11pt

Printed in England by:
J.H. Haynes & Co Ltd

Contents

Introduction

The rig of a sailing yacht consists of the sails, standing and running rigging and spars. This combination is the source of propulsion and so is equivalent to the engine in a motor vehicle, motor boat or aeroplane.

Like these other modes of transport, if the primary means of propulsion is not correctly installed or is unsuitable for the job, disappointment and perhaps even danger will result. While the rigging, that is all the controlling and "positioning" lines and wires must be correct, the drive is from two main elements, the sails and the spars which project them. This book is all about spars: masts, booms, poles and all their components.

Just as there is an enormous range of engine types for different purposes in cars and trucks, so there are many variations of spars which match particular requirements. Knockabout day boats, light racers, deep sea boats both racing and cruising and spars for special rigs of all sorts abound.

The object of this book is to provide a comprehensive guide to the most commonly used spars and an insight into others. It describes the configuration and setting up, then keeping them going and essential maintenance.

There are a number of persons and firms to whom I would like to express my thanks, who have given generously and unstintingly of their time and experience; these include Robin Tucker and Cliff Norbury of Proctor Masts; Chris Regnart of Riggarna UK; Ben Bradley and Ken Matthews of Spencer Rigging; Clive Garner for the important photographs and special thanks to Caroline Sheahan for wearing her fingers out on all the typing.

Throughout the book, in the interests of practicality, specific instructions for work on spars and rigging are given. But as in reality every boat and its rig varies, neither author nor publisher can accept responsibility for any consequences of particular actions taken.

P.Matthew Sheahan
Itchen Abbas, Hampshire.

1: Rig types

An area of constant development in the sailing world is that of rig configuration. Designs of rigs are as varied as the applications that encourage their development. The common denominator amongst these various designs is that of the balance required between ease of handling and performance. Whether the subject be commercial or recreational consideration has to be given to a wide range of factors which in turn will influence the final design of the rig.

This book is primarily concerned with recreational sailing which can be assumed to include the following types of popular rig although there are many others.

Bermudan sloop
The Bermudan sloop rig consists of one mast and mainsail boom, one mainsail and one headsail. This is by far the most popular configuration and falls into two distinct catagories, masthead and fractional. These are defined by the position at which the forestay is attached to the mast.

On a masthead rig the forestay is attached at the very top of the mast which allows the headsails to reach the same vertical height as the mainsail. The forestay on a fractional rig is fitted at a position on the forward face of the mast below the masthead. The exact position of this attachment varies depending on the type of boat and is usually expressed as a fraction of the height of the spar with the most common configuration being "seven-eighths" or "three-quarters".

Masthead rigged sloop
Traditionally the masthead rig has a relatively short footed mainsail with a large overlapping headsail with most of the rig's power being developed by the headsail. This configuration is very popular due to the simplicity of its rigging arrangement. With the forestay, backstay and cap shrouds meeting at the masthead the mast is subject to compression forces only and setting up the spar is a relatively simple task. Upwind performance is good as a result of the long genoa luff and efficient slot. However when sailing upwind or reaching in strong winds efficiency is lost due to the widening of the slot.

The main disadvantages of such a rig are that (a) a large sail wardrobe of genoas is often required to cope with a range of conditions and, (b) that the large size headsails are more difficult to manage and larger deck gear is required to cope with the higher loads. For cruising boats these problems have, to a certain extent, been overcome with the advent of headsail furling systems although these do sacrifice a degree of performance. When sailing downwind with this type of rig, the masthead spinnaker with its large area provides plenty of power but can prove to be more than a handful in strong winds!

Fractional rigged sloop
This rig has smaller headsails and longer footed mainsails with the result that the latter contributes more to the overall drive of the rig. More emphasis is put on depowering the mainsail with mast bend and hence fewer headsails are required to cope with a wide range of conditions. The sail handling aspects of such a rig are also simplified as fewer headsail changes are required with the mainsail shape being altered to balance the boat. In addition to this, the downwind handling of the boat under spinnaker is also easier and less nerve racking in heavier winds. This is due to the spinnaker being smaller than on a masthead rig coupled with the halyard position being lower on the mast, thus reducing the heeling lever on the boat. Because the mainsail is larger and the spinnaker smaller than on a masthead version the distribution of sail area about the centreline of the boat is better balanced

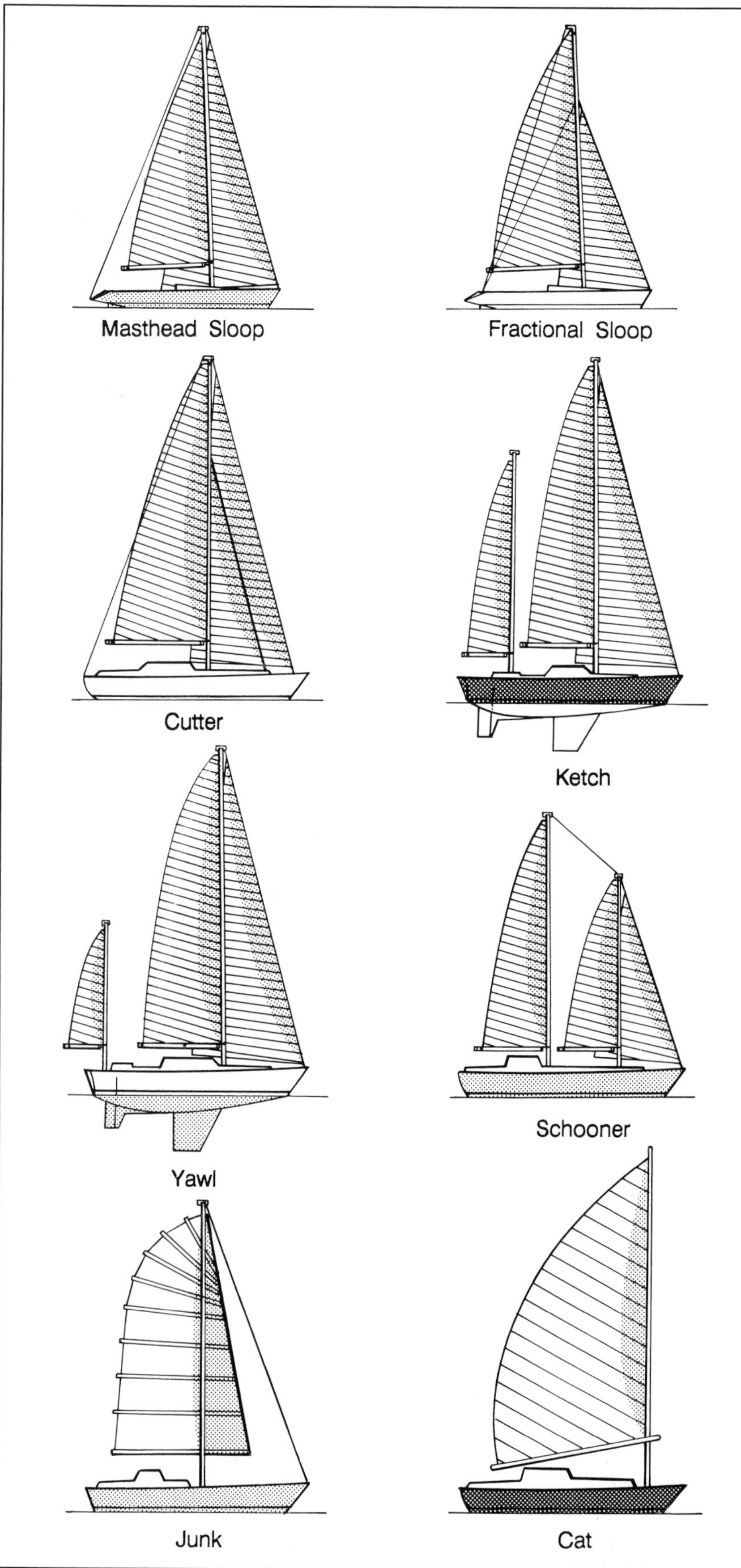

Left: Popular rig types

which reduces the tendency to roll.

As with all types of rig there are however disadvantages, the main one being a compromise with the staying arrangements. With the backstay attaching to the mast well above the forestay, a bending moment results on the topmast. The result is that the forestay cannot be sufficiently tensioned without excessively bending the topmast. Jumper struts are often fitted to stiffen the topmast up but very often this merely moves the bend further down as the mast hinges about the hounds. (This can in fact be used to advantage to control the lower part of the spar and flatten the mainsail in stronger wind strengths, but does still compromise the setting of sails in certain conditions. The problem is most noticeable on racing yachts where upwind performance is very important.)

To assist the tensioning of the forestay, the spreaders can be swept aft to achieve a component of fore and aft support for the forestay. Again, this arrangement has a trade off in terms of lateral support for the spar. As the backstay is tensioned and the mast rakes aft, the tension in the cap shrouds is slightly relieved. The result is that the mast begins to fall off to leeward.

In order to achieve better staying and performance of the rig, the spreaders can be fitted at right angles to the fore and aft centreline of the mast with a set of running backstays attached to the hounds area. The running backstays are fitted at deck level on the transom of the boat and as close to the centreline as possible. By tensioning the windward running backstay the forestay can be tensioned without bending the topmast. This system is common to many racing craft but does not generally find favour with the cruising yachtsmen who are often sailing shorthanded. As a result most fractionally rigged cruising boats are fitted with aft swept spreaders and thus sacrifice some upwind performance.

Cutter
As sloop rig boats get larger, so the genoa area becomes significantly larger, necessitating more power to sheet sails and larger winches to take the higher loading. This can become prohibitive for the shorthanded crew. A means of overcoming this is to utilize a cutter rig.

The cutter rig, in its basic form, is essentially the same as the masthead Bermuda sloop with the exception that the cutter has a double headed rig comprising a high clewed jib or yankee set foremost and a staysail whose tack fitting is further aft. The head fitting for this sail is below the mast head and gains its fore and aft support from a set of running backstays which are fitted opposite the inner forestay attachment. The deck attachment in this case is at either side of the boat and at the gunwhales, aft of the mast step. The "runners", as they are often termed, are frequently viewed as an added complication for the cruising yachtsman. This need not be the case as they can be taken forward and attached to the mast in light airs where they will not interfere with the sheeting of sails. In heavy airs and large seas they are a distinct advantage offering significant support to the mast in the fore and aft plane and preventing the mast from "panting".

This type of rig is much easier to handle for an equivalent sail area to the conventional sloop. The sail area is split and hence so are the loads and very often the staysail is equipped with a boom and can be self tacking as it is usually a high aspect ratio with no overlap. The yankee has a full length luff with a relatively short foot length. The high clew on the sail allows a sheeting angle that minimises twist in the sail. The staying arrangement also offers an advantage as the inner forestay can act as a safeguard in the event of a forestay failure.

The main shortcoming of this configuration of rig is that it lacks the drive of a sloop rig in light weather conditions. If the inner forestay is fitted with a quick release deck fitting this can be remedied by removing the inner forestay and setting a large overlapping genoa. However care must be taken as the mast will have less fore and aft support and could tend to invert (develop a reverse bend) in choppy conditions.

Ketch
The ketch rig consists of two masts and booms, the former being of unequal height. The forward mast is the taller and can be either masthead, fractional or cutter rigged and is known as the mainmast. The aft mast, known as the mizzen mast, is shorter and can fly a mizzen mainsail and a mizzen staysail. By definition the mizzen mast on a ketch rig should be positioned forward of the yacht's rudder (otherwise she is defined as a yawl) with its sheet mounted inboard.

This configuration is again a means of carrying a large amount of sail area while keeping each sail to manageable proportions. It is not as efficient as the cutter rig because the mizzen sail is a relatively poor means of drive upwind and more of a balancing sail. This balancing effect is a distinct advantage when the boat needs to be held into the wind whilst anchored or lying ahull with a sea anchor. If this aspect is particularly required, a flat fully battened sail is most efficient as it will resist flogging and hence chafe. This type of sail however does not possess the required shape for efficient drive and an additional sail may be required for this purpose.

When reefed, and sailing upwind, the mizzen mast and its associated rigging present a considerable drag. Downwind this sail is also a problem as it tends to blanket the sailplan forward of it. However the performance of the boat can be significantly better than that of a sloop, when reaching, especially when a mizzen staysail is set.

Deck space for staying such a mast is frequently a problem. The mizzen mast is usually stepped in the cockpit with the result that both the mast and the rigging are often in the way of the crew on all but large yachts. The positioning of the mizzen forestay attachment at deck level often causes problems where space is concerned. One way of supporting the mizzen mast fore and aft is to take the backstay from the mainmast and attach it to the forestay fitting of the mizzen mast. This is referred to as a triatic stay. The aft support for both spars is then effected by the mizzen backstay. The drawback is that in the event of a failure of the triatic stay, both masts are jeopardized. The safest means of support is to have a conventional backstay for the mainmast and use twin forestays for the mizzen mast. These stays can be fitted to the top of the mast, if the mast is relatively short, or attached at a position further down with jumper struts providing the support for the topmast. These forestays are then attached forward of the mast step, at or near the gunwhale, port and starboard.

Yawl
This rig is almost identical to the ketch, but carries its mizzen sheet on a stern spar known as the bumpkin. Generally the mizzen mast is positioned aft of the rudder stock. The yawl rig can be a better option than the ketch rig as:

a) The mainmast can be positioned further aft which allows a wider chain plate base thus

reducing the compression loads in the mast.
b) With the mainmast further aft the foretriangle can be larger allowing better light airs and windward performance.
c) The mizzen sail on a yawl is generally smaller than that of a ketch rig and as a result there is less of a sacrifice in downwind speed when the mizzen sail is lowered and less of a blanketing effect on the mainsail if it is left up.

As with the ketch rig the yawl's mainmast may also be masthead, fractional and or cutter rigged.

Schooner
The schooner rig is mainly found on yachts over about 55ft (16.76m) and consists of at least two masts with the aft mast(s) equal or taller than the foremasts but not usually to the same extreme proportions as on the ketch or yawl. Again the objective of this type of rig is to reduce the individual sail areas to manageable proportions. The sailplan consists of a foresail(s) (on the forward mast), staysail(s) between masts and a mainsail (on the mainmast which is aft). In addition to these, often some form of additional sail can be flown between the masts which may include the following:
a) Mainsail with mainsail boom.
b) Staysail with or without a staysail boom.
c) Fisherman; a rectangular sail whose luff runs up the aft face of the forward mast with its foot well above the deck. Its sheets run from the upper and lower clews to the forward face of the mizzen mast where they pass through turning blocks and are led down to deck level.
d) Gollywobbler, which is a more modern equivalent to the fisherman and considerably larger with its foot being close to deck level.

As with the ketch and yawl rigs there are problems with a large blanketing effect on the forward sails when sailing downwind. The upwind performance can also be lacking due to the relatively small headsails as well as the large windage factor from the two (or more) large masts and their associated rigging. The financial effect of a cutter rig can also be felt with two sets of spars and rigging to purchase and maintain!

Having said that there are of course advantages such as:
a) The well balanced nature of the rig.
b) The ease of handling.
c) Good reaching performance.

These factors make it a popular choice for 'Blue Water' cruising and charter yachts. In addition to this the centre of effort of the sail plan can be kept relatively low resulting in a lower required initial stability and hence lighter boat. (There will be more about stability considerations later.)

Junk
This type of rig is perhaps the oldest traditional type of sailing rig in existence and has more or less retained its original form. Although it is rarely seen on modern sailing yachts it does gain favour with yachts that are sailed short handed for passage sailing. The reasons for this are that it is an extremely well balanced rig which is very simple to reef with no necessity to change sails and thus additional sails do not need to be accommodated below deck. The mainsail is a fully battened type with a large roach and is semi-balanced. Each batten has its own sheeting line which allows the sail to be set at various heights in much the same way as modern day slab reefing. The panels in this case are however between battens as opposed to reefing points. Because the sail is balanced the loads are relatively low and tackles are used in preference to winches.

The mast is usually unstayed, which, as well as leaving a very clear deck, allows the sail to be hoisted on any point of sailing. This does however mean that the masts are usually heavier than their stayed counterparts and tend to whip in a choppy sea, especially when the sail is down and the boat is motoring. With the higher number of control lines required chafe can also sometimes be a problem.

Cat rig
This can be considered to be a contemporary version of the junk and is also unstayed. It resembles a large sailboard rig with a wishbone arrangement being used for the boom. This wishbone is mounted high at the tack area and slopes downwards to the clew where the mainsheet attachment is made. This angled boom acts in a similar way to a conventional kicking strap arrangement and prevents the clew lifting and twisting the sail. The luffs of these sails are generally of the wrap around type although there are some which incorporate a track up the aft face of the mast.

The main advantage of such rigs is their ease of handling coupled with the uncluttered deck. The disadvantages are that they do not perform as well as sloop rig yachts when sailed to windward and suffer the same problems as the junk rigs with their unstayed masts. Indeed from a spar manufacturer's point of view unstayed masts are often a concern in terms of fatigue strength.

2: Mast design

As with most design, there are many theories as to how one should calculate the loads experienced for a particular structure. The method(s) employed will depend entirely on the context of the operation and which features are particularly required. This process is rarely an easy one and in the case of yachts, mast design is made more difficult by the fact that there are high additional loads as a result of the motion of the yacht. These additional loads are very difficult to measure without the use of expensive measuring equipment and even then it is virtually impossible to predict exactly all the conditions that a yacht may encounter.

Over the years mast design has been based on a mixture of calculation using established engineering principles and case histories. Classification Societies such as Norske Veritas, Bureau Veritas, Nordic etc. have developed guidelines for spar design which offer ways of establishing spar sizes. These rules are relatively complex and lengthy. They require detailed knowledge of yacht design principles. This chapter concentrates on the basics of establishing the influencing factors and the way in which to choose a set of spars.

It is important to note that in most cases the mast manufacturer will calculate the required mast sizes for a particular yacht and you will not need to carry out any detailed calculations. When obtaining a quote or ordering spars you will however need to supply the manufacturer with some essential information. This chapter is mainly concerned with:

a) the influencing factors on mast size

b) establishing the type of specification that you will require for your particular project

The Mechanics

There are a number of fundamental factors that influence the size of spars required:

a) Height of the spar

b) Type of rig, masthead or fractional

c) Width between the chainplates (the positions where the shrouds meet the deck)

d) Number of spreaders

e) Righting moment of the yacht

f) Deck or keel stepped

g) Application (eg. racing/cruising)

These factors are the minimum that a spar manufacturer will require to establish the spar sizes. Let us look at each one individually.

a) Height. This is the hounds height from deck commonly referred to as the 'I' measurement.

b) Rig type. If the mast is fractional the amount of topmast will be required.

c) Chain plate width. This affects the angle between the shrouds and the mast and is very important. As the angle decreases so the total compression forces in the mast increase and the component of support decreases. If the angle is too small it may result in excessively high compression loads which in turn will cause the mast to buckle and fail. The chain plates need to be as far apart as possible to reduce the loads in the mast and hence the amount of material required. This reduces the weight of the spar. However there are often constraints on the width of the chain plate base due to either the beam of the boat and/or the need for overlapping headsails. Another consideration is that of the sails. In order to achieve good windward performance the sheeting angle of the headsails may conflict with the shroud base dimension and a compromise may need to be struck.

d) Number of spreaders. In some cases the width of the chain plates and the height of the mast mean that the shroud angle is too small. Multiples of spreader sets are then employed to maintain the shroud angle for the same shroud base. This increase in the number of

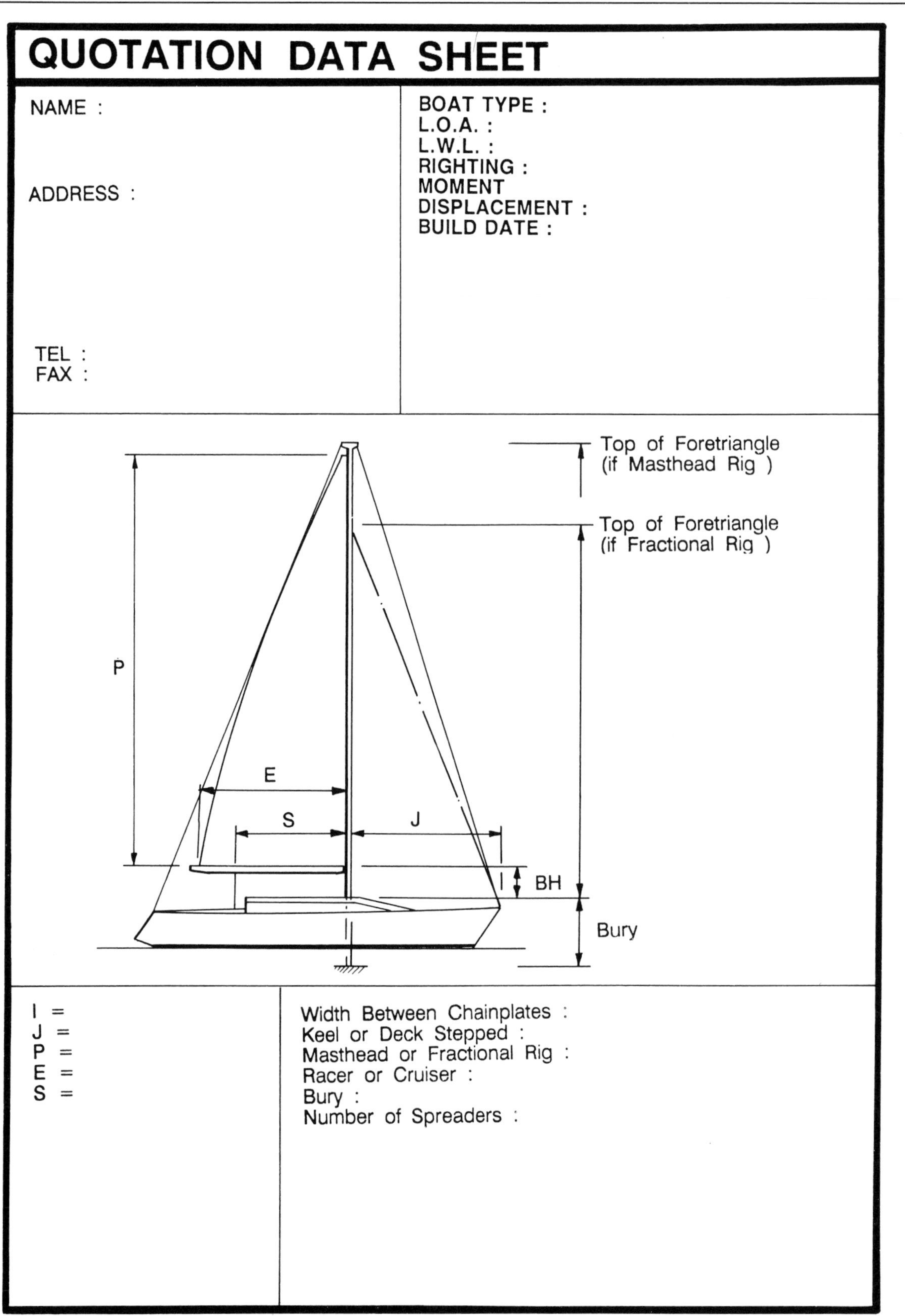

QUOTATION DATA SHEET

NAME :

ADDRESS :

TEL :
FAX :

BOAT TYPE :
L.O.A. :
L.W.L. :
RIGHTING :
MOMENT
DISPLACEMENT :
BUILD DATE :

I =
J =
P =
E =
S =

Width Between Chainplates :
Keel or Deck Stepped :
Masthead or Fractional Rig :
Racer or Cruiser :
Bury :
Number of Spreaders :

Required data for spar selection

spreaders is often used when confronted with the problem of sheeting angles as described above. Whilst increasing the number of spreaders helps the problem of shroud angles, it causes other problems such as the fore and aft support of the spar.

If one considers a mast that has fore and aft lowers, the attachment point for these stays is lower down the spar which reduces the amount of fore and aft support. The more spreaders involved the greater the problem. In order to support the spar, additional stays such as running backstays and check-stays may be required thus complicating the rig. This set up is often seen on modern racing craft where there is usually an abundance of experienced crew members, but is a distinct disadvantage to ease of handling when sailing short-handed. There is therefore a balance to be met which relies not only on the technicalities of the rig, but the application for which it is being designed.

e) Righting moment. This is one of the most important pieces of data for the mast manufacturer. Because this figure is fairly difficult to calculate it is often the most difficult to obtain.

The righting moment is an expression for the force required to heel the yacht over to a particular angle. For a keel boat it results from two factors:

i) The righting moment generated by the shift in the centre of buoyancy of the hull.

ii) The righting lever of the keel when at an angle of heel.

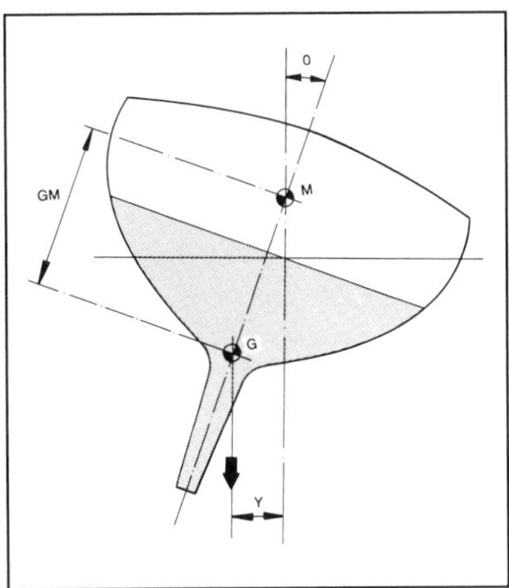

Development of righting moment

As the boat is heeled over so the value of the righting moment changes. The value of the righting moment generally increases to a peak then decreasing to neutral. At this point the boat has no stability. Further heel angle causes negative stability where the relative positions of the centre of buoyancy and centre of gravity switch to provide a negative heeling arm which continues to heel the boat until it reaches its maximum at 180 degrees. This data when plotted as a graph is known as the righting moment curve.

For the purposes of mast design we are normally only concerned with the righting moment between 1 to 30 degrees as this is usually the area of highest values (ie the graph is steepest in this range). In the case of a boat with an IOR or IMS rating this can be read straight from the certificate.

As a result of the rigging, the opposing righting moment is then transferred down the mast in the form of compression. Having calculated the amount of compression in the mast for a given angle of heel, the size of section to withstand this load can be calculated by using a form of Euler strut theory. (See scantling section for further details on methods of calculation.)

Righting moment summary:

1) Wind load causes yacht to heel
2) Righting moment develops
3) Righting moment opposes wind load
4) Rigging connects righting moment and wind load
5) Tension in rigging causes compression in mast

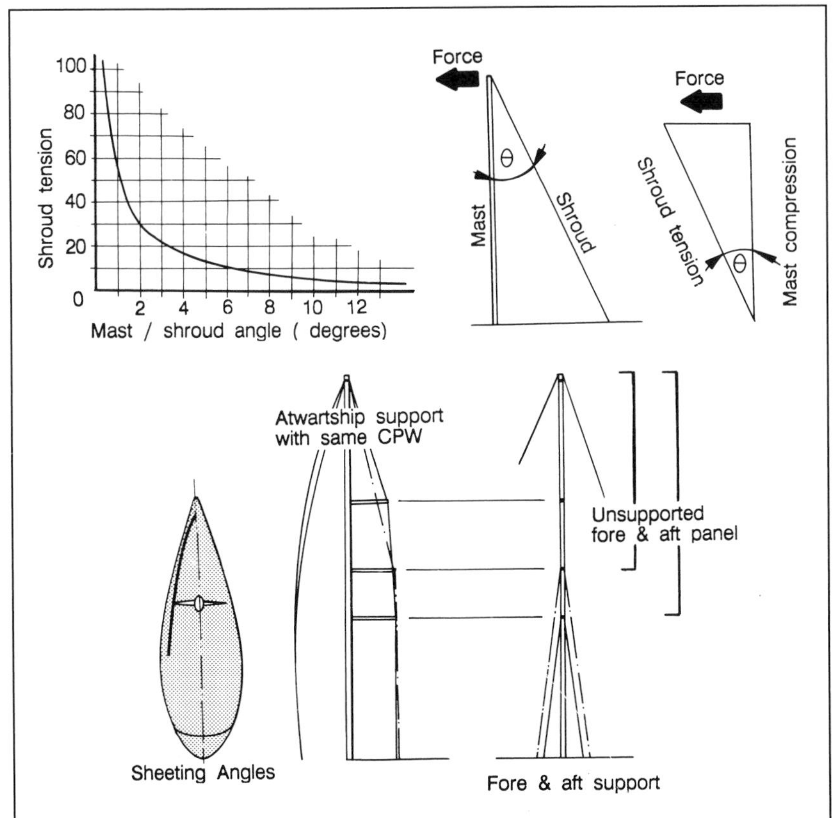

Effect of varying shroud angles

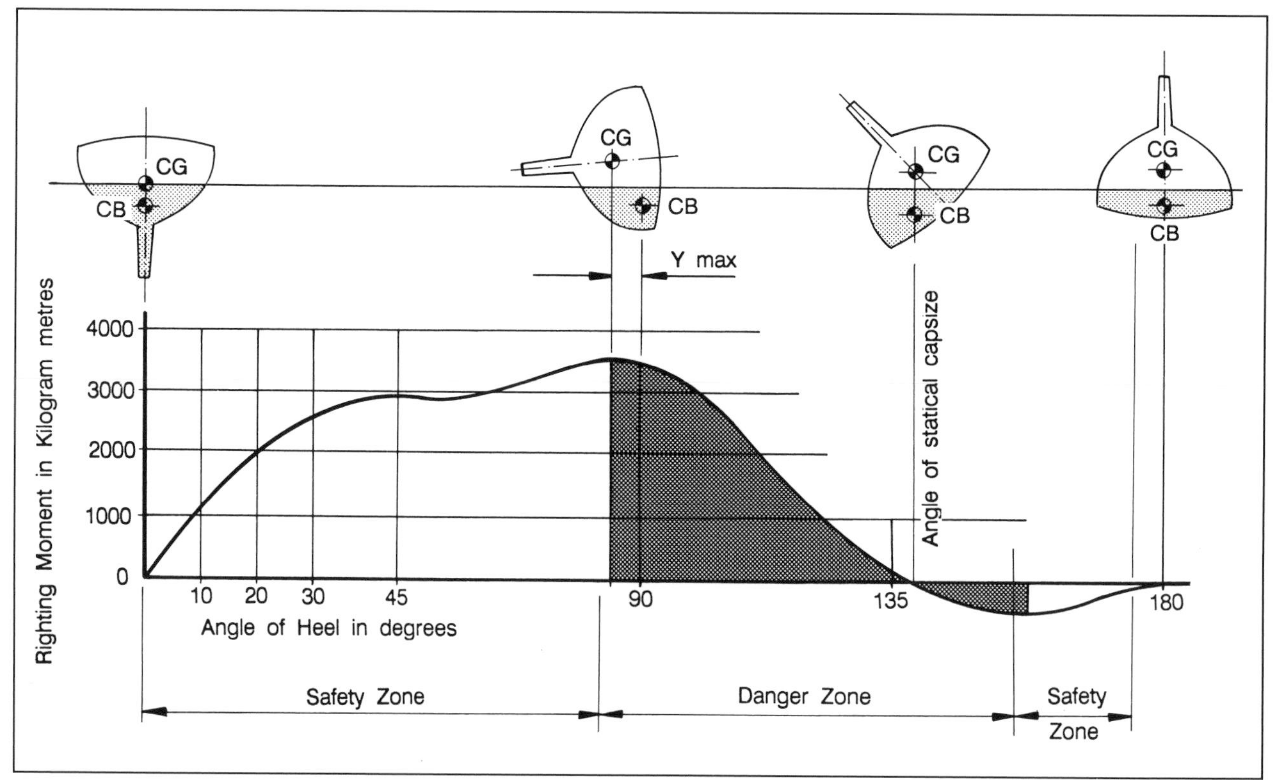

Above: Righting moment curve

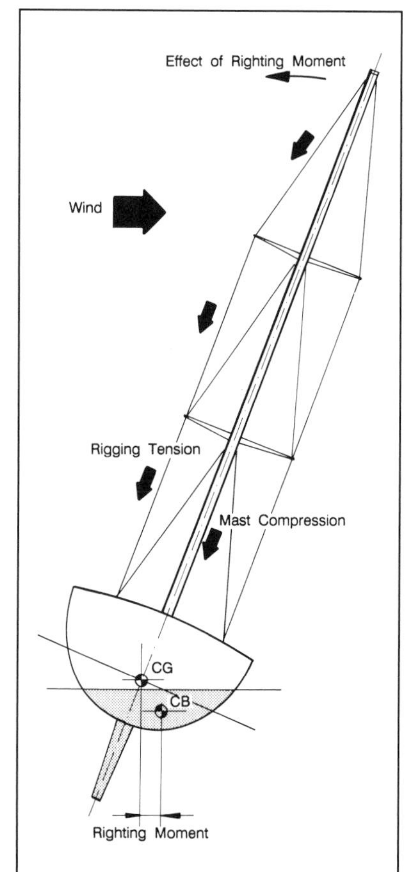

Shroud tension due to righting moment

6) Compression increases further down mast
7) Maximum compression at heel
8) Calculate necessary section size to accommodate compression loads

Calculating the righting moment is usually a complicated process normally only undertaken by the yacht designer as it involves calculating the distribution of the underwater volume of the boat for given angles of heel. If the righting moment for an existing yacht is not readily available it is possible to carry out an experiment on the boat to obtain a reasonable approximation.

The simplest method of approximating the righting moment is to:
1) Set the main boom at right angles to the centreline of the boat and fasten fore and aft.
2) Suspend a weight such as a jerry can of water from the end of the boom sufficient to heel the boat over to an angle of 5 degrees.
3) The angle of heel should be measured with a clinometer on the boat.
4) Weigh the jerry can and water that was necessary to heel the boat.
5) Measure the distance along the boom that the jerry can was suspended from the centreline of the boat.
6) Multiply the weight by the distance from the centreline to obtain the righting moment.
7) Divide this number by 5 to obtain the righting moment at 1 degree.

eg: Jerry can & water = 500 kg
Distance from centre line = 2.0m
Righting moment @ 1 degree = $\frac{500 \times 2}{5}$

= 200 kg.m

The righting moment for most boats can be considered to be linear to at least 5° and a larger heel angle is easier to measure than 1° thus increasing the accuracy.

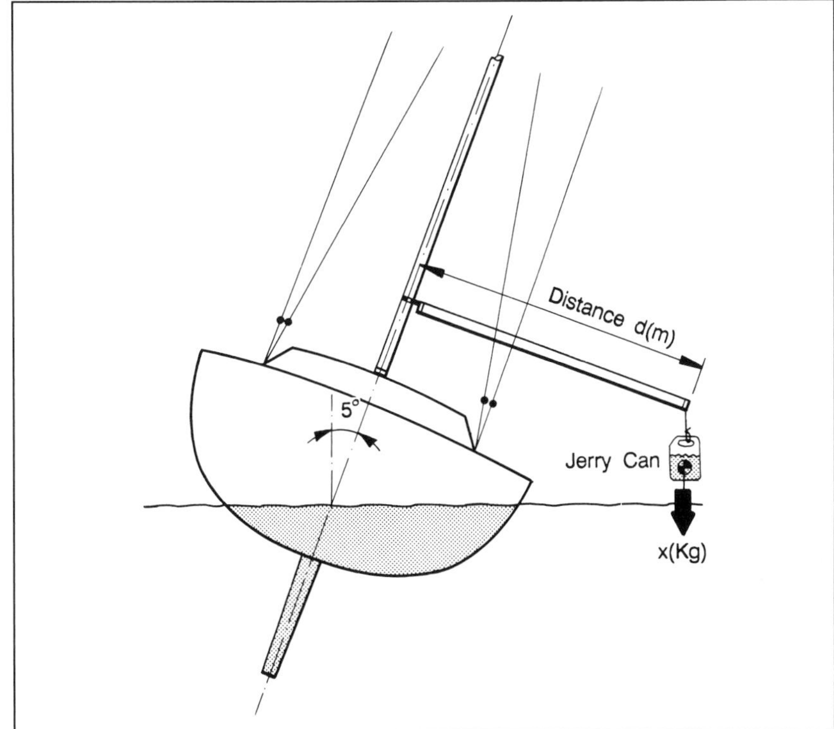

Righting moment experiment

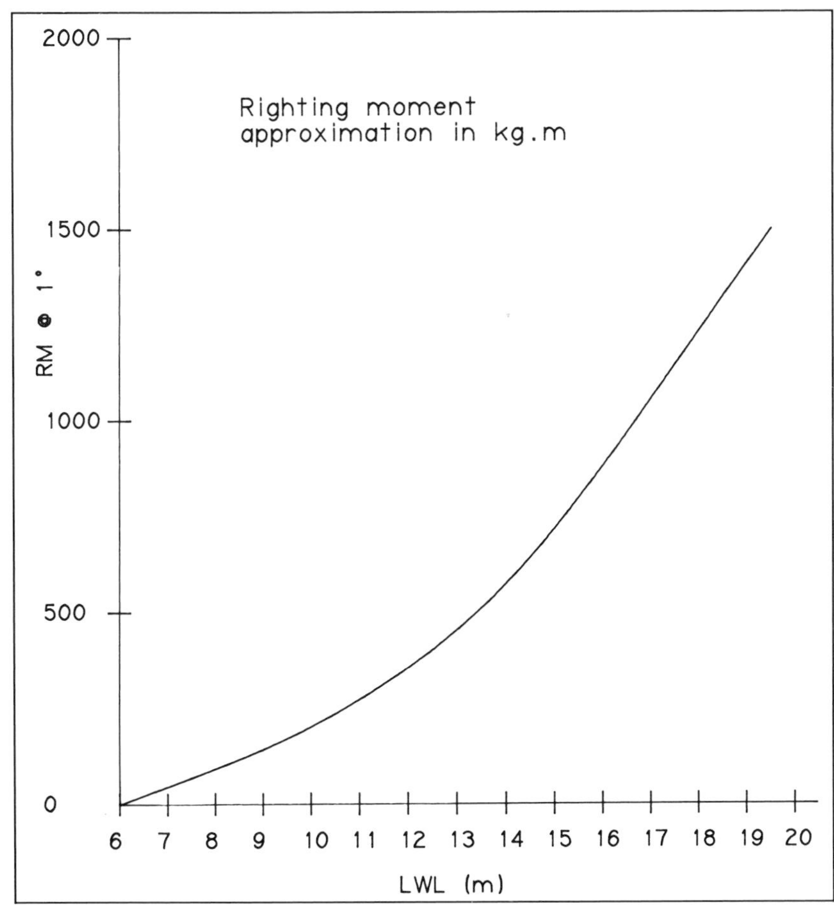

Approximating righting moment for LWL

In the event of not being able to calculate the righting moment by either method an approximation can be made from the righting moment graph. (page 12). This graph is based on the waterline length of the yacht. This data must be treated as approximate as it is based on conventional cruising yachts and as a result extreme forms such as yachts with long overhangs, ULDB'S (ultra light displacement boats) etc. cannot be considered for this method.

f) Deck/keel stepped. This is based on an engineering principle concerned with beam theory which classifies the two conditions as follows:

i) Deck stepped – 'pin jointed' at each end.
point of maximum deflection at mid height.

ii) Keel stepped – built in beam.
point of maximum deflection at a higher point than for the pin jointed beam.

Each of the above cases is

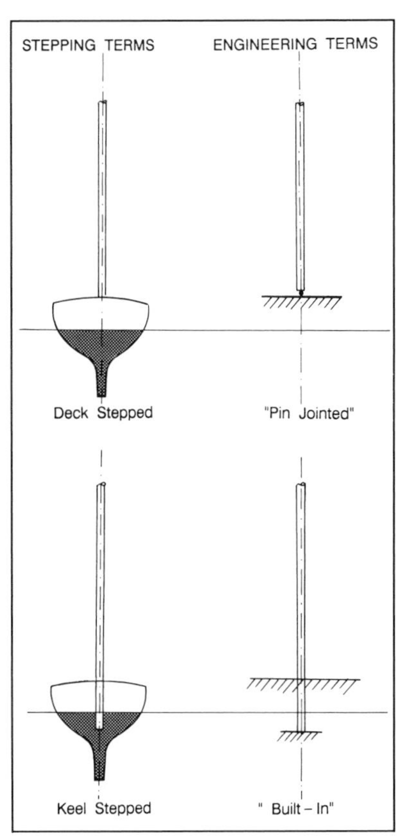

Deck stepped vs keel stepped

considered to be of uniform section over its length and is subjected to a compression load at one end.

As a result the section required for the keel stepped mast for an identical boat can be less in terms of required stiffness as some of the support is gained from the deck. There are however a number of other factors that influence whether the boat should have a deck or keel stepped mast. Accommodation space down below is often the most important criteria for designers of small cruising craft. If the mast can be stepped on deck there is more space down below and a larger section mast may be considered as a small price to pay for the increased accommodation volume.

g) Application. The purpose of the boat is very important in establishing the factors of safety that will be employed. A racing yacht will generally be fully crewed with experienced personnel who will push the yacht to its limits to obtain the very best performance. The reduction of everything to the bare minimum can improve the performance of the boat as weight is reduced. For many racing yachts it is often more of a nuisance to lose the mast than a matter of life and death. For the long distance cruising yacht the consequences of losing the mast several hundred miles from the shore are much more serious. As a result the factors of safety are generally much higher for the cruising yacht rig.

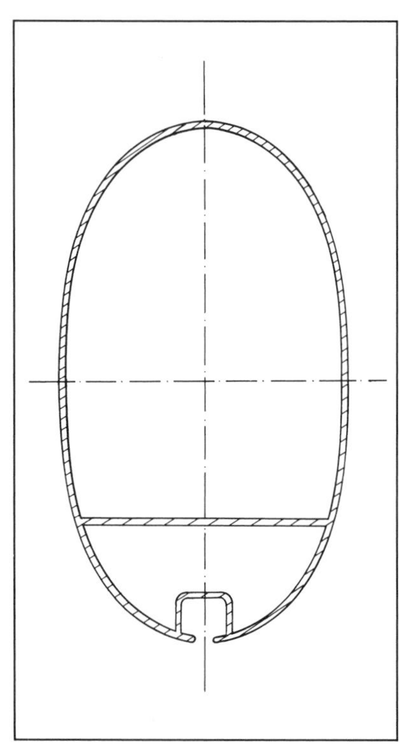

Moment of inertia of a section

From all of the above points the required stiffness of the spar in both the fore and aft and athwartships planes can be established. This is known as the required inertias of the spar and expressed as cm^4.

These requirements can now be compared against a spar manufacturer's section list which will show details of the inertias for each section.

Satisfying the requirements.
Having established the required inertias it is now necessary to set about achieving these requirements in the form of a mast section.

We have mentioned that the inertia values are a measure of the stiffness, the higher the value the stiffer the spar, but how are they derived?

The inertia values are a function of the amount of material and its position from the neutral axis for a given section. The neutral axis of a section is the centreline in terms of area in a particular plane. The two planes are, fore & aft known as Iyy, and athwartships known as Ixx. Mast sections are symmetrical about their fore and aft centreline and therefore the fore & aft neutral axis is on the centreline. However the athwartships neutral axis need not be in the centre of the section as the section may have more area towards the front.

Because the inertia is a function of the amount of area multiplied by its distance from the neutral axis, there are a number of ways of achieving a given inertia value by varying the overall size and wall thickness.

However it can be seen that with a different distribution in area and hence overall size, one is approximately half the weight of the other. So from this it is

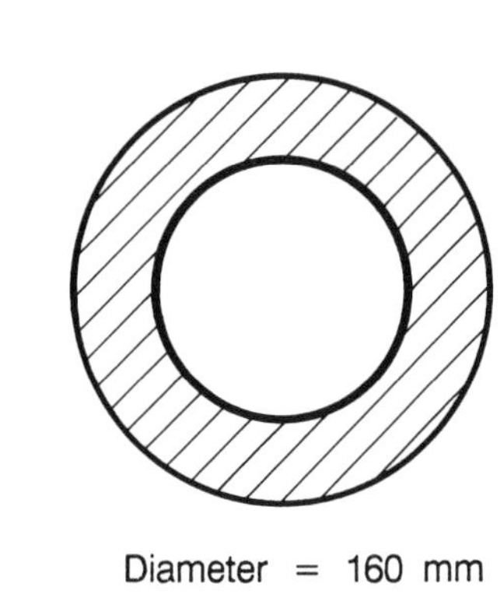

Diameter = 160 mm

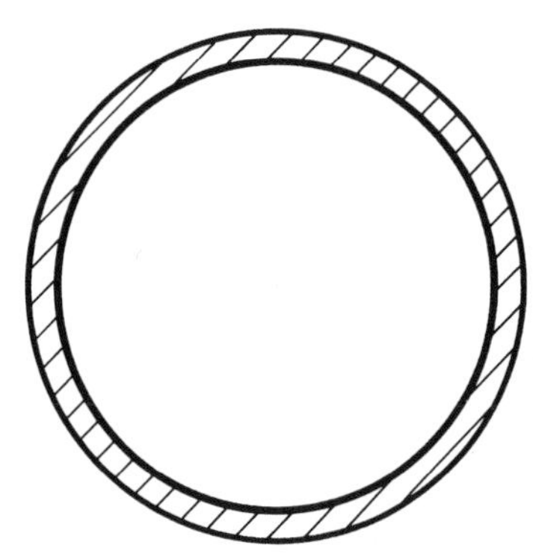

Diameter = 200 mm

Identical inertias, different sections

Outside dia. (mm)	Wall thickness (mm)	Inertia (cm^4)	Area (cm^2)	Weight (Kg/m)
200	10.0	2700	59.7	0.16
160	29.5	2706	120.9	0.32

clear that the larger section with a thin wall is more desirable from a weight point of view.

However the larger the diameter and hence the smaller the wall thickness the greater the possibility of buckling under load. In addition to this the tube now has a greater surface area and hence higher aerodynamic drag. Therefore there is an optimum set of values for a given mast.

Establishing the precise effect of drag and trying to predict the maximum loads and their directions is part of the art in mast design and means that the optimum mast is not simple to define.

We have in this case isolated a set of inertias and varied the weight. The equation does of course work the other way round and the graph shows how diameter and inertia varies for a given weight of circular tube.

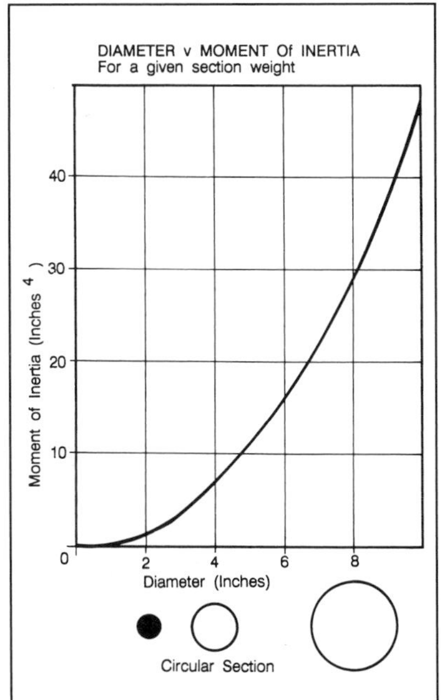

Diameter vs inertia for a given weight

Much time has been spent in research and development assessing the effect of various yacht's motion in a seaway for which the weight and centre of gravity of the mast and its rigging play a very important part.

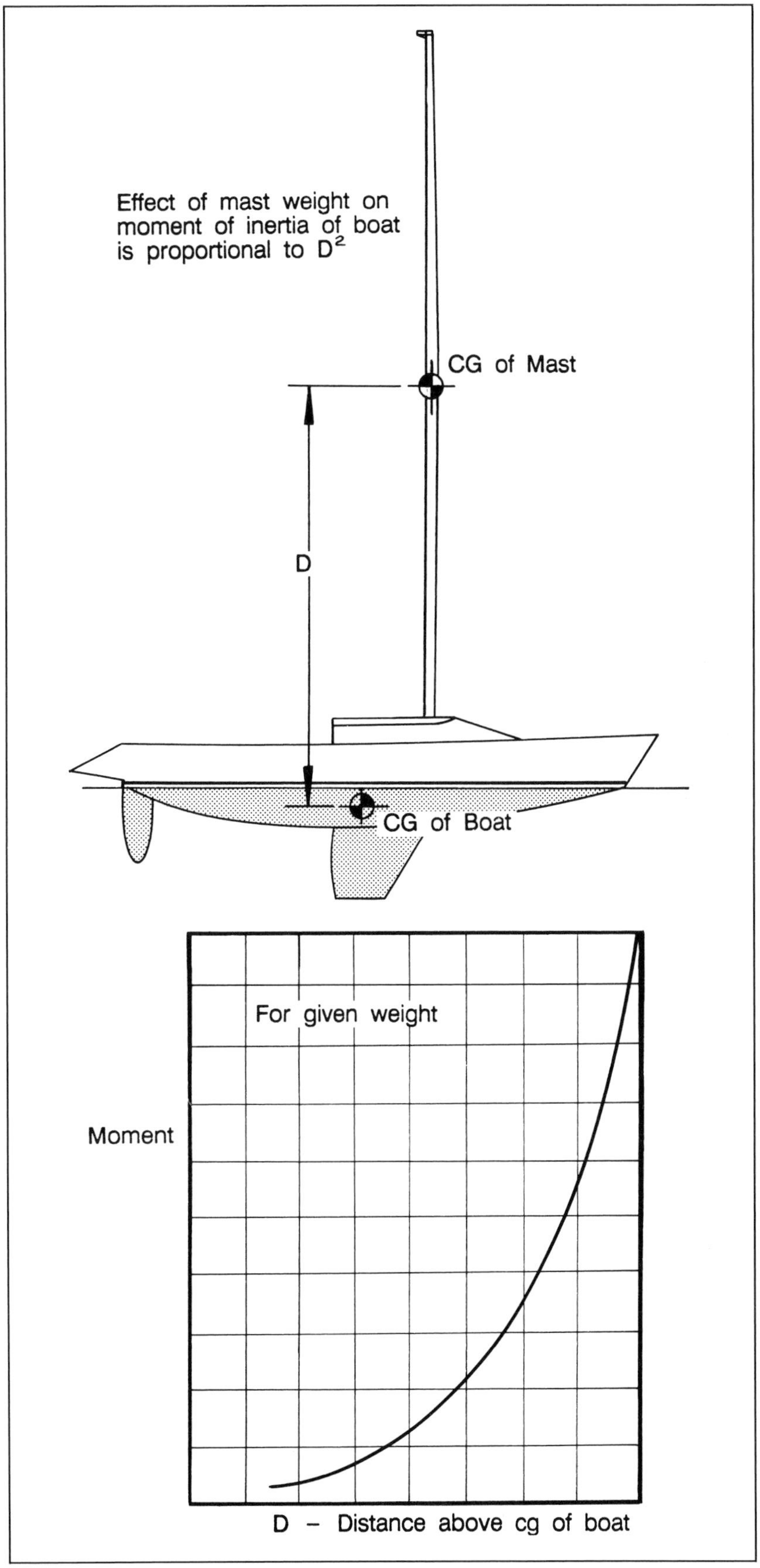

Effect of mast weight on moment of inertia of boat is proportional to D^2

CG of Mast

D

CG of Boat

For given weight

Moment

D – Distance above cg of boat

Effect of weight from C of G

It is generally accepted that in all but flat sea conditions, light masts with low centres of gravity are an advantage. The primary reason for the rig affecting the motion of the boat is that whilst the weight of the rig is relatively small compared to that of the boat, the further the weight is away from the centre of gravity of the boat the greater its effect. To be more precise, Moment of Inertia of complete rig = Weight x (distance from C of G)^2 (this should not be confused with the moment of inertia (Iyy or Ixx) of the section).

As the moment of inertia of the complete system is the main factor when considering the motion of the boat in all directions it is not difficult to see why weight and C of G have been treated so seriously for racing craft.

When a manufacturer is presented with the data for a given boat be it racing or cruising, it may be that the section requirements lie in between two existing sections making neither one an ideal solution. It is however possible to vary the number of spreaders on a rig to adjust the amount of lateral stiffening that is required. This is not always the way in which decisions are made to go for multiple spreader rigs nor should it be, but it is an option when faced, say, with a re-rig for a yacht whose present section is no longer available or for the case where a lighter rig needs to be produced. The compression figure can be reduced by altering the shroud angle. This can be achieved by either increasing the spreader length or raising the position of the spreader for the same length. (As discussed in the previous section.)

Methods of calculation and scantlings.

There are a number of approaches to deriving the correct size of a mast for a particular yacht. The most popular method is the "Euler Strut" formula with a few modifiers.

The Euler formula may be found in most engineering books and takes the form:

$$P \text{ (total compression)} = \frac{Pi^2 \times I \times E}{L^2} \times X$$

Where: Pi = 22/7 (a constant)
I = Moment of inertia (cm^4)
E = Youngs modulus of elasticity (60 MPa for aluminium)
L = length (m)

There are standard factors for X which relate to the 'end' condition of a strut. An unloaded strut which is pin jointed at both ends (X in this case is 1) when loaded sufficiently to distort it, takes an approximate form as in (a) & (b). If the strut is fixed at the base and pin jointed at the top, (c) (X in this case is 2), then it will assume a distorted form as in (d) and the formula becomes:

$$P = \frac{Pi^2 \times I \times E}{L^2} \times 2$$

Another condition known as the 'fixed/fixed' condition (e) & (f). The formula for this is:

$$P = \frac{Pi^2 \times I \times E}{L^2} \times 4$$

The moment of inertia 'I' is a function of the stiffness of the strut. Technically speaking it is described as the area of an element of the plane area multiplied by the squared distance from the neutral axis of the area to a common axis.

As has been seen earlier, the wall thickness and hence weight of a section can be varied for the same inertia value. There are further considerations. A thin walled tube has a higher stress in its material than a thick one as there is less material to take the load. Thus the thin walled section will be more prone to failure through tension or buckling. The effect of buckling can easily be observed by taking an empty toilet roll tube, placing it on its end and progressively pressing downwards. It will carry the compression loads to a certain point and then suddenly buckle near the centre. The centre of the tube is the worst supported area and hence there is failure at this point.

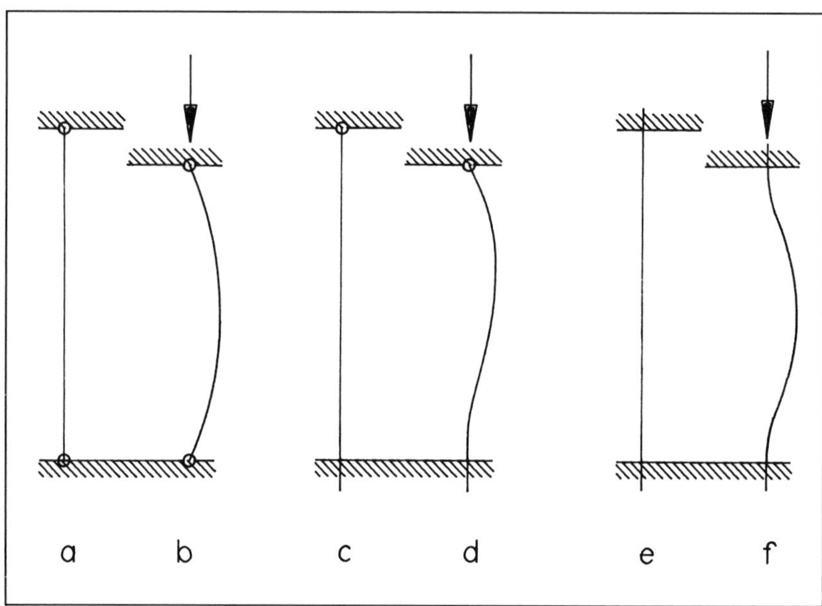

Spars under load for different conditions

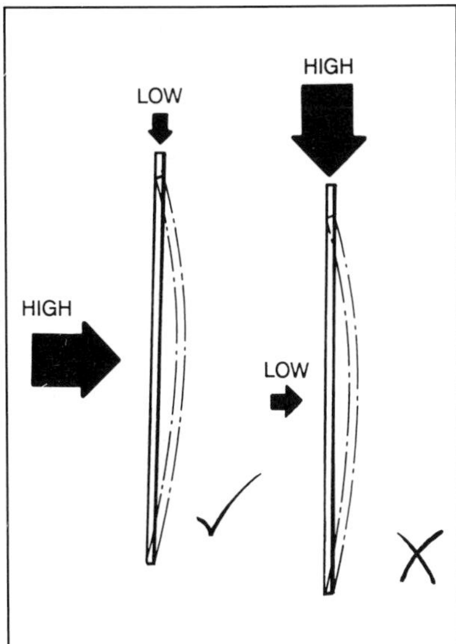

Over compression causes buckling

Calculating the required moment of inertia for a mast
Consider a cruising yacht with the following data:

LOA	= 9.00 m
RM @30°	= 2335 Kg.m
No. spdrs	= 1 pair
Lower shrouds	= 4
Chain plate width	= 1.9 m
Height above deck	= 12.8 m
Panel length 1	= 6.8 m
Panel length 2	= 6.0 m
Keel stepped	

So using the Euler formula:

$$I = \frac{P \times L^2}{Pi^2 \times E} \times 3.5$$

(Where 3.5 is a factor found to be appropriate for mast design for fore and aft moments of inertias)

The calculation process for the required inertia of the mast and strength of the rigging can begin.

Firstly we need to find the mast compression (P). This is a result of the righting moment of the boat (RM). Most yachts sail at a maximum of 30° heel and the righting moment at this angle is the figure usually used (written as RM30). The units are Kg.m. However the maximum righting moment of the average yacht is at around 45° of heel. So to ensure all parts of the rig end up at the correct size we should take this into account. This is achieved by multiplying RM30 by 1.5. This factor will allow for the mast compression induced by the stiffness of the boat transferred by the side shrouds.

There is also the support from the fore and aft rigging such as the forestay and backstay to be taken into account. It is difficult to evaluate the loads in these stays. The load is at its highest in the backstay when running and at its highest in the forestay when beating. The athwartships righting moment induces no fore and aft loads. There is however a force acting in the fore and aft plane that opposes the pitching action of the boat. This figure is difficult to calculate and while it is high it is generally assumed that the sails would blow out before excessively high loads could be transferred to the rig. As a result the general rule is to consider the fore and aft load to be an additional 80 per cent of that from the athwartships load due to the righting moment. This may not be considered to be a very scientific approach but from experience it has been found to be relatively accurate.
Using simple lever theory:

$$P = RM30 \times 1.5 \times 2 \times 1.75/CPW$$

Therefore for our example,

$$P = 2335 \times 1.5 \times 2 \times 1.75/1.9$$

$$= 6452 \text{ Kg}$$

which gives a figure for the mast compression.

This figure can also be derived by other means such as taking the load in the sails at a certain wind strength and resolving this into a series of loads. However it becomes a complex problem in deciding what actual wind load to use, how is the load distributed and how much load is carried by the sheets.

Having established the maximum compression in the mast we can now apply this to the Euler formula. Firstly it is necessary to decide which panel is under consideration. For calculating the inertias the panel length will be as follows:

Fore and aft inertias:
Single panel = 12.8 m

Athwartships inertias:
Panel 1 = 6.8 m
Panel 2 = 6.0 m

Therefore;

$$I\ f/a = \frac{6452 \times 12.8^2}{Pi^2 \times 69 \times 3.5}$$

$$= 444 \text{ cm}^4$$

The required inertias reduce in the upper area of the panel as there are less shrouds to induce compression. This can be calculated but a good approximation can be obtained by using 75% of the required inertia at the top and tapering the inertia to the point at which the maximum value is required. (see page 18) Hence the required moments of inertia for the fore and aft panel will be,

75% 444 = 333 cm^4

To calculate the required inertias for the lower panel in the athwartships plane for our keel stepped example,

$$I = \frac{P \times L^2}{Pi^2 \times 69 \times 1.63}$$

(where 1.63 is the approximate end condition factor for athwartships inertias in the lower panel of keel stepped masts.)

$$= \frac{6636 \times 6.8^2}{Pi^2 \times 69 \times 1.63}$$

$$= 269 \text{ cm}^4$$

Again the required inertias can be reduced in the upper athwartships panel. An approximation would be for the inertias to be 92% of the maximum ie;

92% 269 = 247 cm^4

So to summarise:

Fore and aft inertias	top	= 333 cm^4
	bottom	= 444 cm^4
Athwartships inertias	top	= 247 cm^4
	bottom	= 269 cm^4

The nearest equivalent mast section can be selected from a mast manufacturer's catalogue.

Section selection graph
Another method by which the required inertias can be estimated is by using the graph.
Method:
1) Add together the waterline length of the boat and the 'I' dimension. ('I' = The vertical height of the foretriangle.)
2) Find this position on the horizontal scale of the graph and follow up vertically until you intersect the line that corresponds to the number of spreaders and mast configuration that you require.
3) Move horizontally from this point to find the required minimum athwartships inertias.
4) Now repeat the process on graph No.2 to find the minimum required fore and aft inertias.
5) You now will have a set of required inertias to which you can match against a spar makers section data sheet to establish the correct section.
IMPORTANT: This method should be considered as an approximation and a mast manufacturer should be consulted for more detailed advice in ALL cases.

Section shapes
The simplest shape of extrusion for a yacht mast would be a round tube. This would be both simple to calculate the properties and relatively simple to obtain. This was indeed the way in which early aluminium masts were introduced but as with most developments we are now presented with an enormous range of section shapes from which to choose. In a book of this size it would be impossible to cover every size and style of section, giving an individual assessment. Instead we will look at some of the most common types and discuss the points that influence their design.

We have already seen some of the main factors that influence the inertia requirements for a particular yacht. We must now look at the way in which the two sets of required inertias are matched. For example, a typical mast calculation for a 10m fractional sloop rigged yacht may result in the following required inertias:

Iyy (bottom) = 25.0 cm^4
Ixx (bottom) = 13.3 cm^4
Iyy (top) = 21.0 cm^4
Ixx (top) = 8.7 cm^4

If we look at the relationship between Iyy & Ixx it can be seen that Iyy/Ixx = 1.87. This value is the ratio between fore and aft inertias and athwartships inertias and is related to the aspect ratio of the rig.

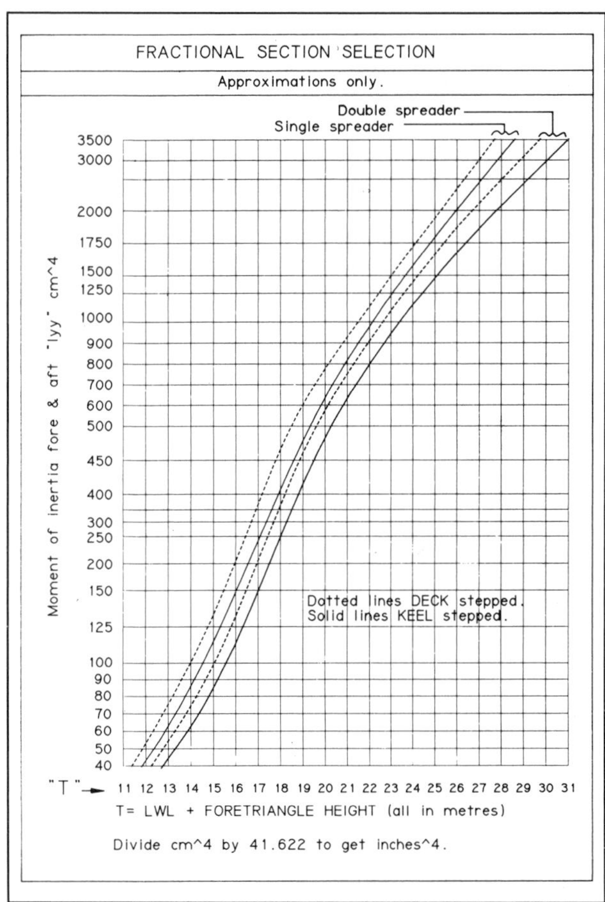

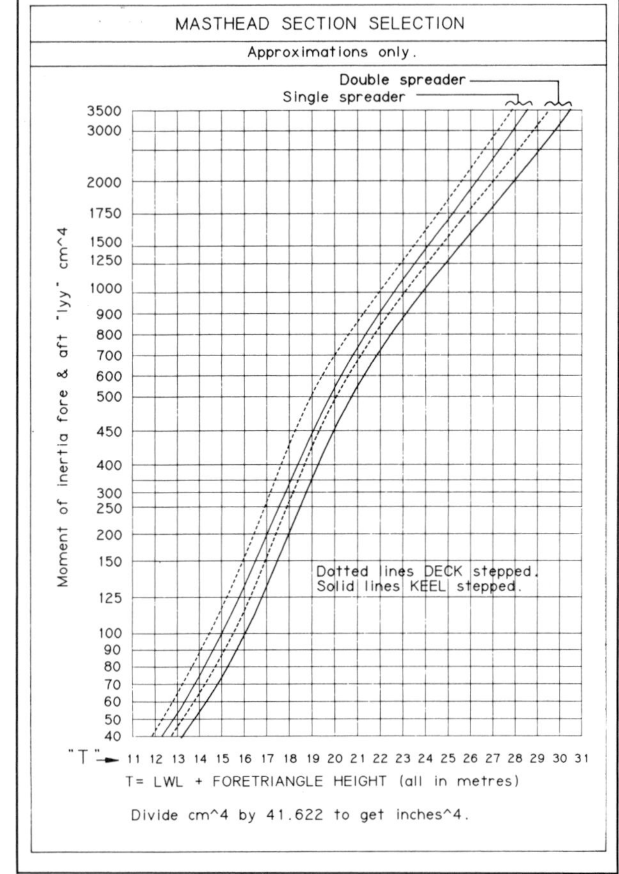

Above left and right: Required inertia guide for mast

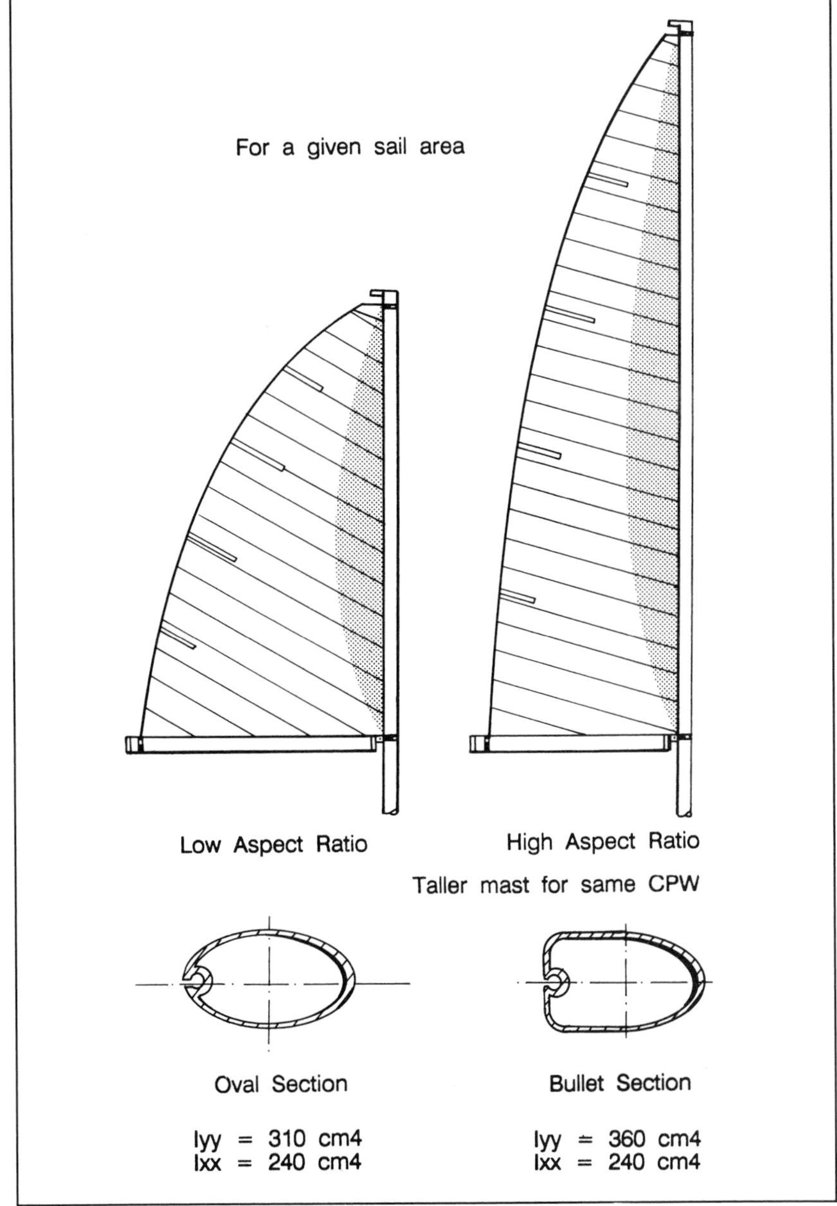

The aspect ratio of a rig can affect the section shape

As yacht design has developed over the years rigs have generally become of higher aspect ratio mainly for performance reasons. That is to say that for the same chain plate width the rigs have become taller. This means that the required fore and aft inertias will be relatively higher than the increase in athwartships inertias. As a result mast sections shapes have moved from the oval type with a constant wall thickness to the 'bullet' shape sections with their varying wall thickness and relatively high Iyy values and high inertia ratios.

The example inertias above show a separate set of values for the mast at the top of its section. The compression forces on a mast are at their greatest at the bottom of the mast and at their smallest at the top. As one moves from the top of the mast down the compression is increased as a result of the additional loads imposed by the attachment of additional spans of rigging.

When a mast manufacturer selects a mast section it must not only match the inertia requirements for the bottom section but also be capable of being tapered sufficiently to achieve the required inertias at the top. This must be done in order to reduce the topmast weight as far as is reasonably possible, even on a cruising boat.

As was mentioned earlier, section shape is important from a windage point of view especially on craft that operate at high apparent wind speeds such as multi-hulls. Often these types of boats use wing masts, but many use conventional mast sections but rotate them to reduce the windage. It is interesting to note that the modern bullet sections are aerodynamically inferior to the more traditional type oval sections.

For a static non-rotating mast however one must look carefully

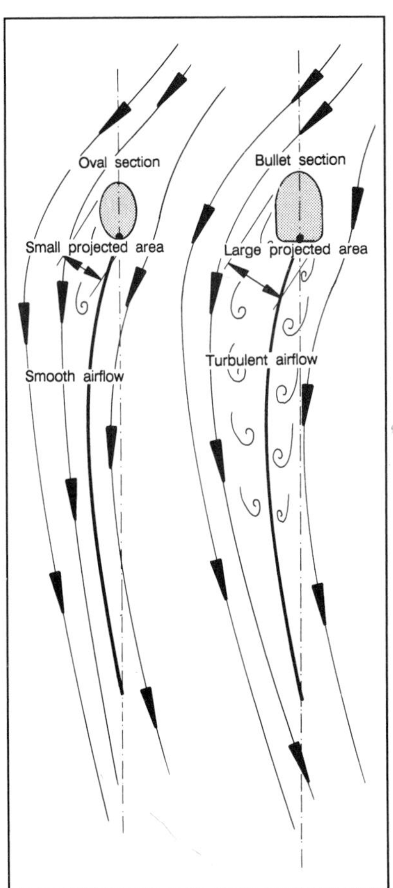

Aerodynamic effect of oval and bullet sections

at the section profile as it is the section through a diagonal plane that is most important from a windage point of view.

Another consideration when selecting a mast extrusion is that of a mode of attaching the luff of the mainsail (or mizzen or foresail) track. Most popular sections have integral tracks or bolt rope grooves each having its particular advantages. The merits fall into two groups:

a) Bolt Rope

Good aerodynamic seal between mast and sail.

Quick to bend on, so long as there is a pre-feeder.

Easier to slab reef.

This type is generally the only sensible option for the racing yachtsman.

b) Sail slide

Good control over mainsail when lowered.

Easy to stow on boom.

This system is virtually a must for the short handed sailor.

types of slides it is better to have an integral system.

It is usually possible to change from one system to another by fitting external track over the existing, but this is time consuming and often costly.

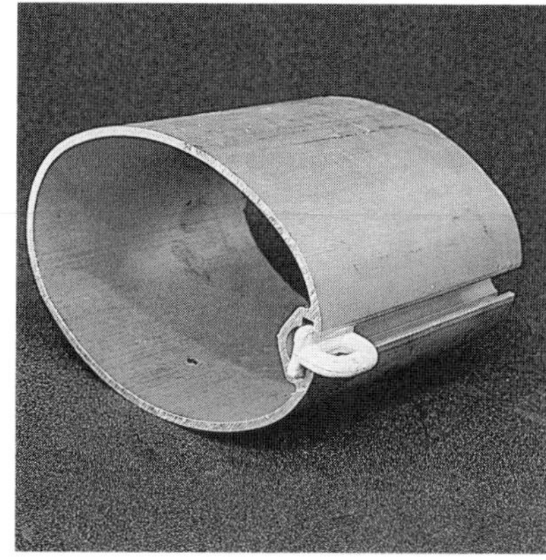

Some mast sections incorporate sail slide tracks

Track and car systems

Modern slab reefing systems for fully battened mainsails sometimes use externally mounted tracks with cars in order to reduce the friction involved as a result of the compression from the battens. This type of system makes for easier reefing on large mainsails. If this type of system is to be employed it is important to check that the mast section is suitable for fastening such a track.

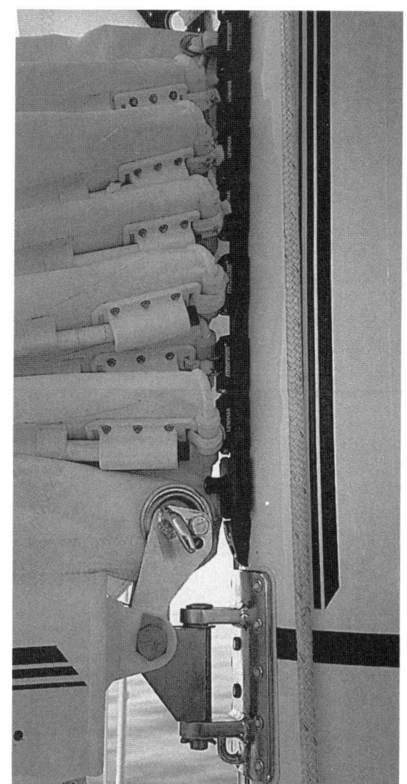

A track and car systems for mainsail luff

Popular sail sliders

A great deal of sections will in fact take both systems where the sail slides are slug type slides which run in a bolt rope type groove. One example of such a slide is the slug slide. These type of slider are generally suitable for boats of up to about 12m (39ft) LOA. Above this size or with high power rigs it may be necessary to use flat sliders such as the 23mm (0.9 in). For this type of system it is important to find an extrusion that has this type of track as an integral part of the section. Again whilst tracks can be fitted to the aft face of the mast to take these

Trysail tracks

Often a separate externally mounted track, running down to deck level, is fitted for the trysail alongside the main track. This allows the trysail to be bent on at deck level and easily ready to hoist without having to

Trysail track

remove the mainsail. It should be checked that the mast section can accommodate the fastening of such a track if required.

Fittings design and specification

So far we have looked at the design considerations of the section and how to match it to the boat to achieve the optimum solution. There is more to mast design and selection than purely the type and shape of the section. The design of the fittings and method of manufacture varies from one application to another and one must be aware of the processes and options available in order to establish the complete correct specification for a particular yacht.

Mast materials

The most fundamental difference between mast manufacturers and often the most overlooked is the material from which the masts are produced. Assuming that we are considering aluminium masts there are a number of different aluminiums used in mast extrusions.

While there are always bound to be exceptions to the rule it is generally the case that 6061 is used for most high quality spars, as it is a relatively easy material to extrude with high mechanical properties. 6082 is used on advanced extrusions, typically Grand Prix racing spars or thin walled sections where the higher mechanical properties need to be exploited with minimum increase in weight. This grade alloy is more difficult to extrude (especially on large sections) and requires water quenching to achieve the higher mechanical properties which in itself can cause problems. As a result spars produced from 6082 grade alloy are usually only available from the more established mast manufacturers. In addition to the 6000 series alloys, 7000 and 2000 series materials are sometimes used in extreme cases such as America's Cup yachts. These materials possess even higher mechanical properties than 6082 alloy, but they also possess problems such as low corrosion resistance and stress corrosion. Along with their high price this generally prohibits their use on all but the most extreme yachts.

The material used in the construction of fittings is often also overlooked. A great number of the production mast manufacturers for example use cast aluminium spreader brackets as they are both relatively cheap to produce in large numbers and easy to fit whereas the custom manufacturers will often use stainless steel or internal mountings both of which are customized fittings. The object of producing these types of fittings can be either for reasons of servicing or aesthetics. The case of aluminium spreader brackets is a case in point, as they are not aesthetically pleasing, nor are they easy to service or repair without a complete new fitting or specialized tools. We shall look into the question of specific items later, but for the moment it is important to appreciate the need for detailed examination of the specification for a particular project.

Popular aluminium specifications for spars

Material	(Old spec)		UTS (MPa)
6063	(HE9TF)	185	Low quality spars
6061	(HE20TF)	280	High quality spars
6082	(HE30TF)	295	High quality spars

Where: UTS = Ultimate tensile strength
TF = Hard condition

Mastheads

All rigged masts (as opposed to unstayed masts) do however require masthead units, be they simple backstay cranes on a fractional rigged boat or large ocean going mastheads on a masthead rigged boat. There are two main types of masthead assembly:

a) Welded-in type

These units are the best structurally fitted as they become virtually an integral part of the mast. They are mainly found on long distance cruising yachts where reliability and longevity are prime factors, and racing yachts where there is a need to maximize the mechanical properties in order to minimize the overall weight.

Welded masthead

b) Bolt-in type

These units are incorporated where either cost prohibits the use of a welded masthead or where due to the internal workings of the mast it is not possible to weld a mast head unit and assemble the mast. Such a case as the latter is for 'In-mast' furling systems where the furling equipment needs to be

'Bolt-in' masthead

inserted into the mast before the masthead unit is fitted. The need to be able to disassemble the complete unit means again that a welded masthead cannot be incorporated.

The mechanics for both systems are the same in that they are both subject to almost solely compressive forces and therefore the method of fastening be it welding or bolting is not usually (in the case of masthead rigs) the main structural link. In order for this to be the case the masthead must be designed so that the interaction of forces lies directly over the centreline of the mast so that no bending moments are set up.

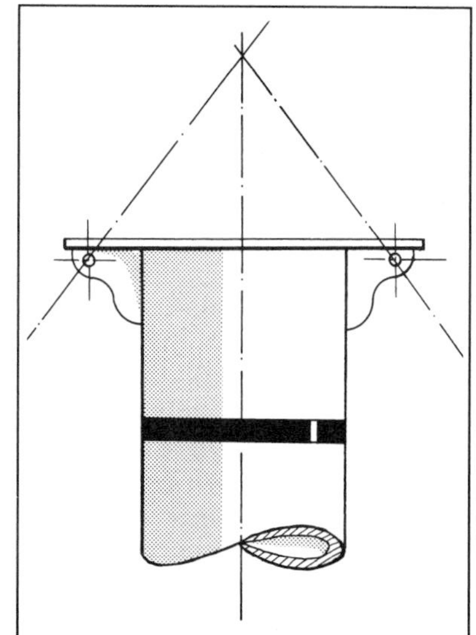

Interaction of forestay and backstay loads

Material fatigue is always a concern with yacht masts and the rigging attachments on any mast are particularly susceptible to this. Rigging toggles or similar devices should always be fitted to allow freedom of articulation in all directions. If the fitting is restrained areas of it will become stressed and fatigue may occur. On racing mastheads where heavy rigging toggles need to be eliminated from a weight point of view, shaped pins known as barrel pins are used which allow the eye fitting to rock whilst under load. This reduces the chances of fatigue.

Fatigue can result from poor articulation

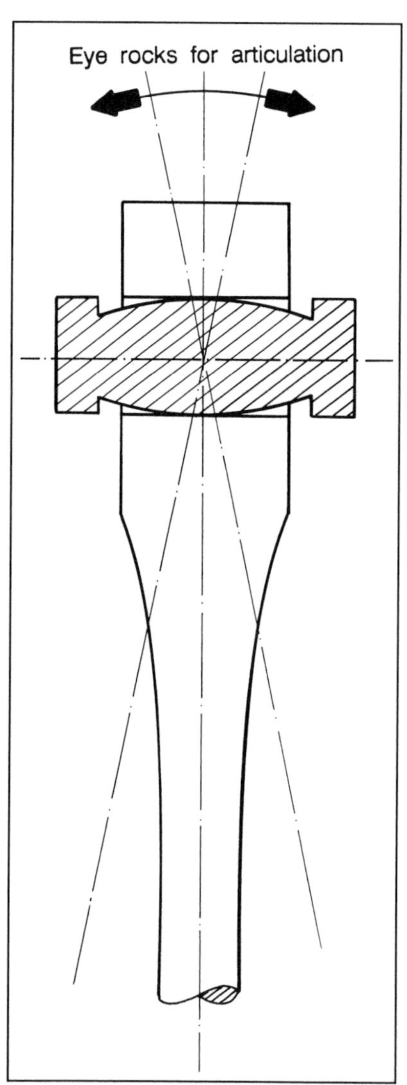

'Barrel Pin' allows limited articulation

Chafe protection is a very important feature of the masthead not least because it is so difficult to see without climbing the mast or having it lifted out of the boat. Sheave boxes should have chafe protection around them which normally takes the form of stainless steel bars. This protection is important for a number of reasons:

a) Halyard wear. Halyards running over a metal edge can deteriorate very quickly.

b) Mast structure. Halyards that are continually allowed to cut into the mast or masthead wall will seriously weaken the whole structure and may cause failure.

c) Ease of handling. Indentations and grooves at the masthead can be very dangerous if a halyard or splice should get caught in them. This could prevent sails from being lowered with potentially disastrous consequences.

d) The main halyard can also be a problem especially if a large headboard is fitted. On yachts with large roach mainsails this will become more of a point to watch for in terms of masthead design and should be considered carefully.

Genoa halyards are relatively simple to protect as the halyard rarely moves far away from the sheave cage. This is not the case for main halyards and in particular spinnaker halyards. The latter, by their very nature, are constantly changing their alignment with the masthead creating the potential for chafe on most faces of the masthead sheave cage. It is for this reason that there is such a large number of different designs for spinnaker halyard exit sheaves.

Sheaves and cages

Poor sheave cage design is very often responsible for halyard chafe and in the worst case, failure of the masthead. A harsh deflection around a sheave box reduces the life of both the halyard and the mast fitting as well as making halyards very difficult to hoist and lower.

The sheaves fitted in the sheave cages are also an important part of the design. Aluminium alloy sheaves have been very popular, but are being superseded by plastic sheaves which are usually manufactured from either Delrin or Ertalyte (a high load plastic). The advantage of these non-metallic sheaves is primarily that they do not suffer from corrosion problems and therefore are less likely to seize in the sheave cage and damage the halyards. An added advantage for racing yachts is that the Ertalyte type sheaves are approximately half the weight of the aluminium.

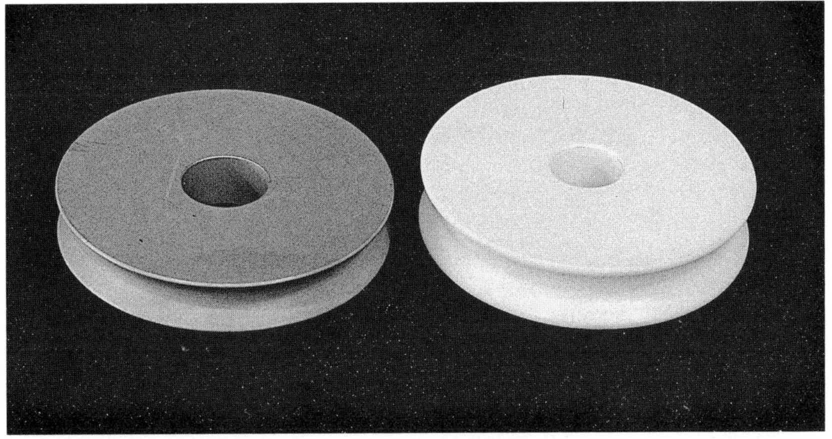

Aluminium (left) and 'Ertalyte' (right) sheaves

With the increasing uses of kevlar for halyards and the fatigue problem of the material, special kevlar sheaves have been developed.

Because of the wear and corrosion problems between the steel halyards and the aluminium mast most sheave cages are fitted with wear strips that are manufactured from stainless steel. These can be used quite satisfactorily in areas where there is only a small deflection of the halyard around the cage. More severe deflections will require a larger radius in order to minimize the effects of chafe. This often means the use of deflector sheaves which consist of externally mounted sheave cages which are allowed to rotate freely. This type of system can be used on items such as topping lifts which need

Standard wire and Kevlar carrying sheaves

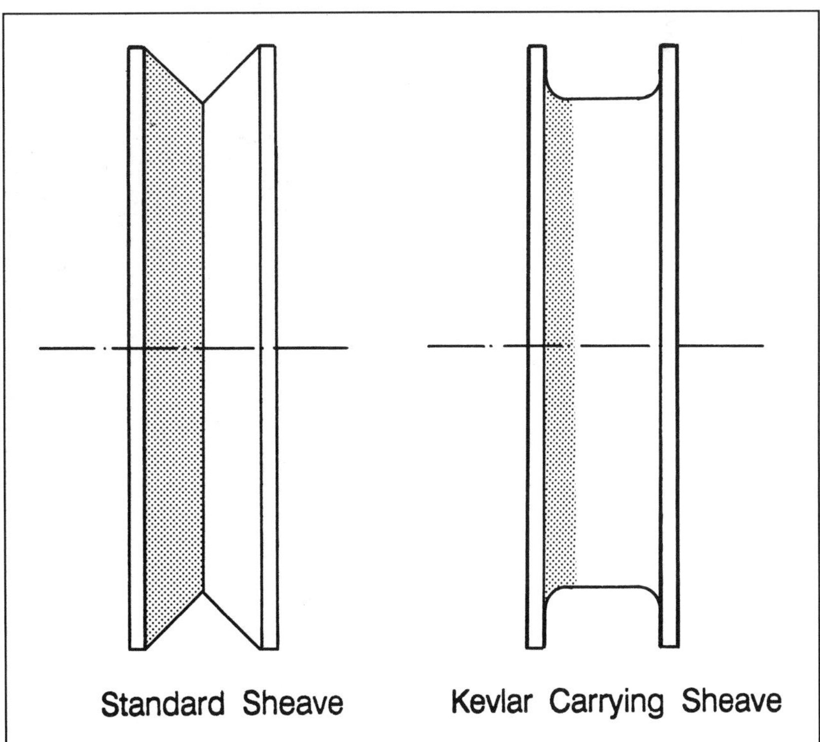

to operate through a wide range of angles. They may also be found on genoa halyards where a furling headstay system is being used in order to deflect the halyard away from the rotating part of the forestay and hence prevent the halyard from wrapping around the furling rod.

A large degree of movement is required for some halyards

Where spinnaker halyards are concerned there are three main types of deflection systems which are as follows:

a) Bulls eyes are the simplest version of static deflector and are machined such that a large internal radius is provided for the spinnaker halyard to run over. This system is generally suitable for boats of up to approximately 40ft (12.2m) loa.

b) Blocks on rail. This system is used for yachts of generally above 40ft (12.2m) loa and consists of a rail mounted on the forward face of the mast at the hounds area. On this are mounted one or two blocks free to articulate in all directions. The sheaves on these blocks provide a much larger radius for the halyard to travel around and therefore reduce the chances of chafe especially over a version such as the bulls eye system.

Above, below and right: Spinnaker halyard chafe protection methods

c) Rollers. This system is mainly found on masthead racing yacht masts and consists of two vertically mounted rollers again providing a relatively large radius onto which the spinnaker halyard can bear. This system is used where weight and windage are critical factors. On cruising yachts, this system is not normally used and a set of blocks suspended from 'U' bolts mounted on the under-side of the masthead fitting is favoured.

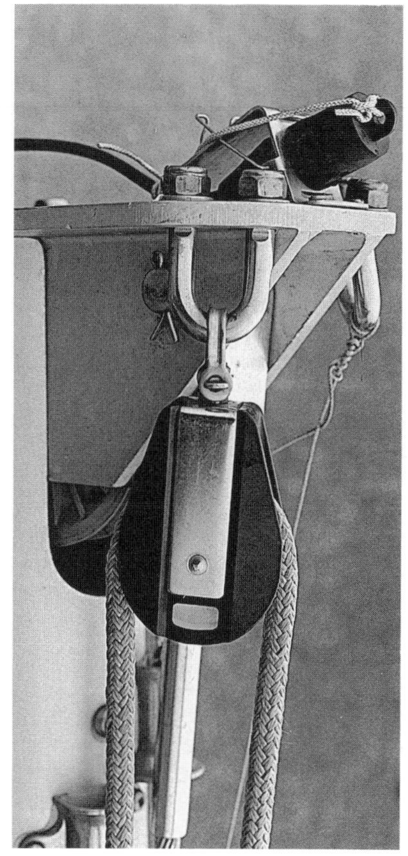

Turning at deck

Unless the halyards exit from the mast and then go directly onto winches mounted on the side of the spar, some form of turning arrangement will be necessary to lead the halyards back to the cockpit. Swivel leads are often fitted around the base of the mast through which the halyards pass and are then led back to the cockpit. Whilst this system is quite popular it is generally undesirable as it a) imposes high loads at an area of the mast which is already highly loaded and b) requires a number of fastening holes in the mast wall which reduces the overall strength of the spar at a highly

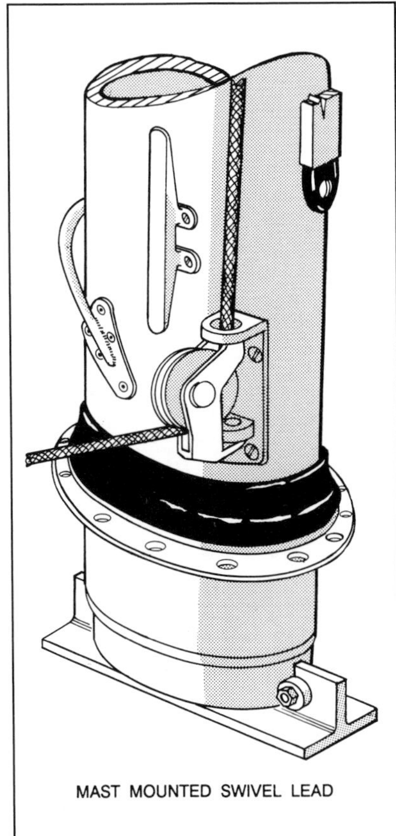

Mast mounted swivel lead

loaded point.

A much better system is to fit a deck ring onto the boat which has a number of take-offs onto which blocks can be attached. This not only reduces the load on the mast but also allows the mast section to remain intact. However care must be taken to make sure that the positions of the blocks are such that the halyards lead out of the exits on the side of the mast without chafing against the mast wall.

Fastenings

We have already discussed one form of fastening, welding, but there are a number of other methods the most popular of which include:

a) Rivets. These can be monel, aluminium or stainless steel. They are selected on the basis of both their strength in a certain plane and their gripping action. Attention has to be paid to their individual corrosive tendency, which is discussed later. The table shows the properties of some of the most common rivets and their use.

b) Machine screws. These are stainless steel and again particular care has to be taken to prevent excessive corrosion between them and the alloy mast wall. They are often used for areas such as mast joins and fittings fixtures.

c) Bonding. This is becoming more popular with the advent of higher strength easy to apply glues. In particular it is used for bonding doublers or sleeving material to the mast wall to either replace the rivets or relieve them of some of the sheer loads and thus reduce the tendency for the rivet hole to elongate. Some of the popular types are shown below.

Popular rivet types & mechanical properties

Type	Mtl	Size (in)	Size (mm)	Max Shear load (KN)	Max Shear load (lbf)	Max Tension load (KN)	Max Tension load (lbf)
'Monobolt'	Al	3/16	4.76	550	2.45	490	2.18
'Monobolt'	Al	1/4	6.35	1300	5.78	930	4.14
'Monobolt'	St	3/16	4.76	1575	7.00	1300	5.78
'Monobolt'	St	1/4	6.35	2400	10.67	2172	9.67
'Pop'	Al	3/16	4.76	455	2.02	630	2.80
'Pop'	Al	1/4	6.35	720	3.20	1150	5.11
'Pop'	St	3/16	4.76	967	4.30	989	4.40
'Pop'	Mon	3/16	4.76	742	3.30	843	3.75
'Pop'	Mon	1/4	6.35	1214	5.40	1517	6.75
Large fl	Al	3/16	4.76	454	2.02	629	2.80
Large fl	Mon	3/16	4.76	699	3.11	800	3.56

Large fl = large flange type
Al = aluminium alloy
St = stainless steel
Mon = monel

Holes

The cutting of holes in a mast should be treated with the utmost care and precision as each hole, no matter how small, is removing material from the mast and thus weakening it. Holes can develop areas of stress concentration, which can in turn lead to mast failure. These effects can be limited by correct design and implementation. As a rule of thumb there are a few simple guidelines that should always be considered when contemplating cutting the mast wall in any way.

a) Holes should always have rounded corners.

b) No two holes should be in the same horizontal plane.

c) Holes should be kept as far away as possible from the deck area where the loading is highest.

Shroud tangs

The shroud tangs are very important, as between them they offer the greatest proportion of support to the rig. There are many different types of shroud tang for many different applications and it is very important that the correct type of tang is specified for the particular task to be carried out. There are however two requirements that are common to all types:

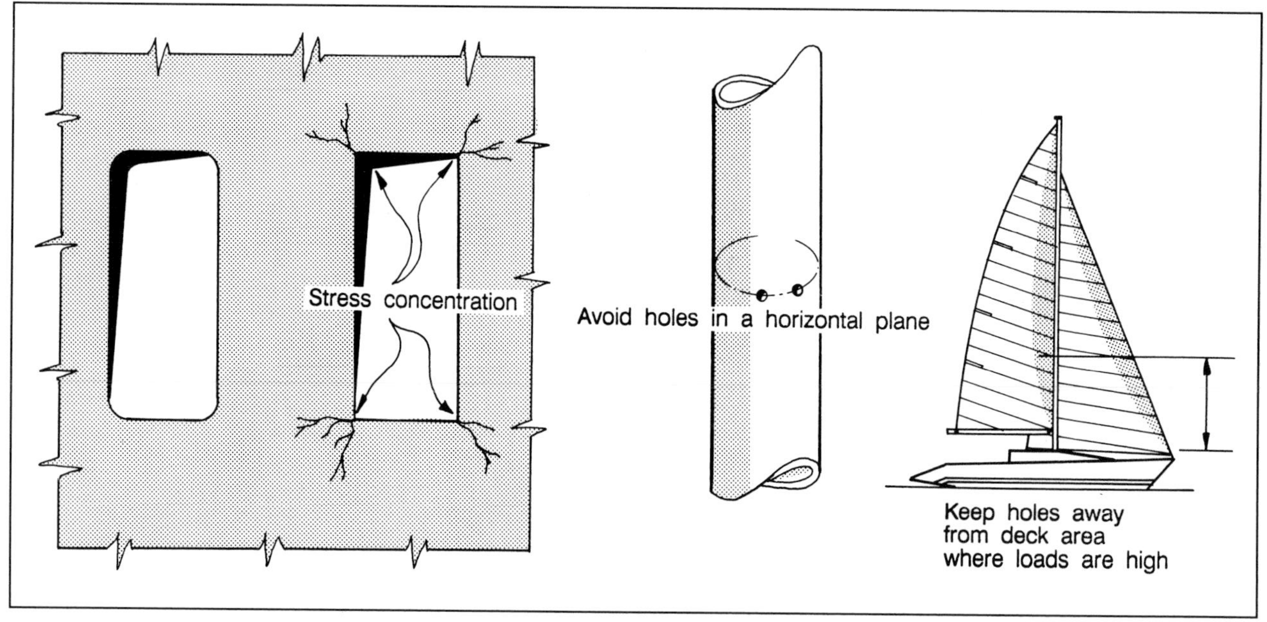

Hole cutting guide lines

a) The tang should be capable of taking the maximum load carried by the wire.
b) The design of the tang should be such that there is sufficient articulation to reduce the chances of fatigue.

From the two main types of rigging (ie rod or wire, see Chapter 3), wire tends to be the more forgiving in the sense that it is more flexible. Rod rigging is stiff and must be treated with extreme care as it can fatigue very quickly if there is insufficient articulation at the rigging joints. It is for this reason that a number of tangs have been developed to allow high loads to be carried but with ease of articulation. One of the most common types of tang is the ball and socket type but this is in fact a poor type of fastening, from the point of view of high load articulation, especially for rod rigging. It is however commonly used on modern racing craft where the limited life span of the mast is outweighed by the advantages of the low weight fittings. The problem is that as the load in the terminal increases so does the friction between the ball and socket and therefore the less likely the chance of articulation but the greater the likelihood of fatigue. One answer is to use barrel pins as on the tangs (shown on page 22) manufactured by Proctor Masts. This system relies on the fact that when a high load is applied, the eye can still rock to give some degree of articulation and hence reduce the tendency to fatigue. The following is a guide chart for the type of tangs and their applications. The rigging itself is discussed in more detail in Chapter 5.

Standard shroud tangs

Tang type	Rigging	Use
St.st 'Dog Bone'	Rod and wire	Most rigging terminations Mainly cruisers
Internal pin type	Rod and wire	Mainly racers Mainly rod
T-terminal	Wire	Small cruisers
Coquille type	Mainly rod some wire systems	Mainly Racers

Common shroud tangs types

Tang type	Rigging	Use
St.st 'Dog Bone'	Rod & wire	Most rigging terminals Mainly cruisers
'Proctang'	Rod & wire	Mainly racers Mainly rod
T-terminal	Wire	Small cruisers
Coquille type	Mainly rod	Racers

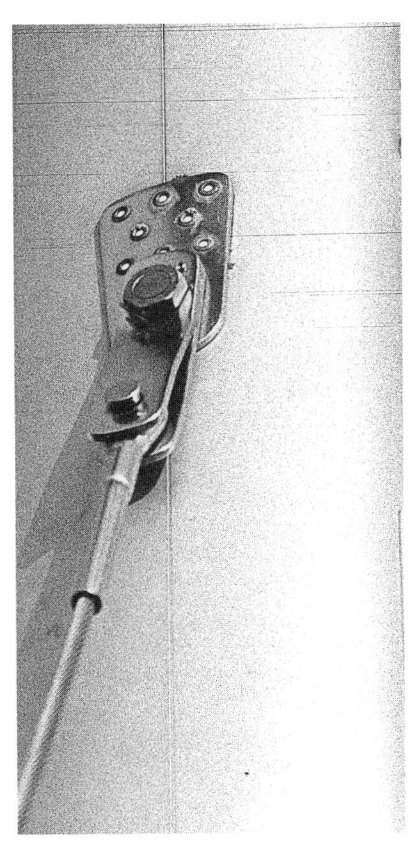

Above: Standard shroud tangs

Spreaders

Other highly loaded parts of the rig are the spreaders and their fixings. A high percentage of yachts loosing their rigs do so as a result of spreader (or its associated fittings), failure. Whilst the mast is in column on an 'In-Line' rig the spreaders are in compression only. The problems begin when the mast begins to bend and the spreaders start to take fore and aft load. This in turn tries to twist the mast imposing high loads on the spreader roots. The twisting problem is there right from the start on an aft-swept spreader system and therefore care must be taken in the design process with all types of spreader.

There are two basic types:

a) Round tube
b) Aerofoil section.

Nowadays there are relatively few boats with the former type. Due to the high loads that can be imposed in the fore and aft direction the spreader generally requires greater stiffness in this plane than in the vertical plane. As a result and also for windage considerations the spreaders are aerofoil shape in section. There are two main types of mounting for both types of spreaders, the cup and the spigot. The cup system tends to be used more by the cruising boats for which longevity and ease of maintenance are the overriding factors.

The spigot system however offers a light, simple and low windage system for the more racing orientated yachts. (The outboard end system is described later in Chapter 3.)

The most important detail that must be remembered when designing or setting up spreaders is that the outboard end must bisect the angle of the shroud. Failure to do this will mean that the spreader will be subject to a vertical load for

Photographs below left to right: 'RT', 'Proctang' and 'NP' tangs

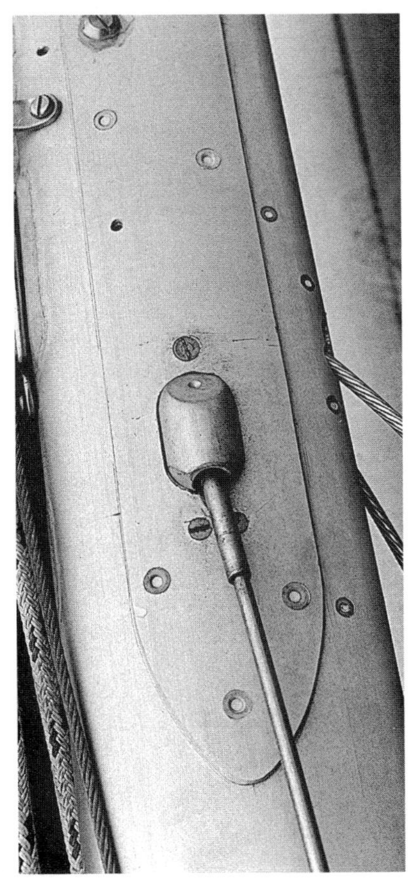

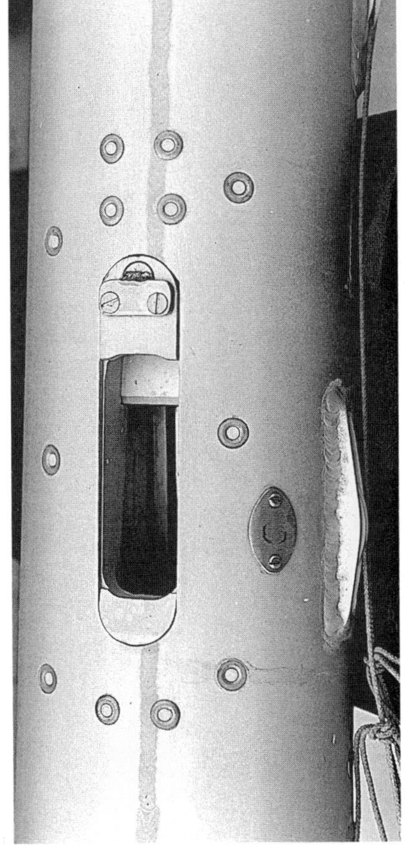

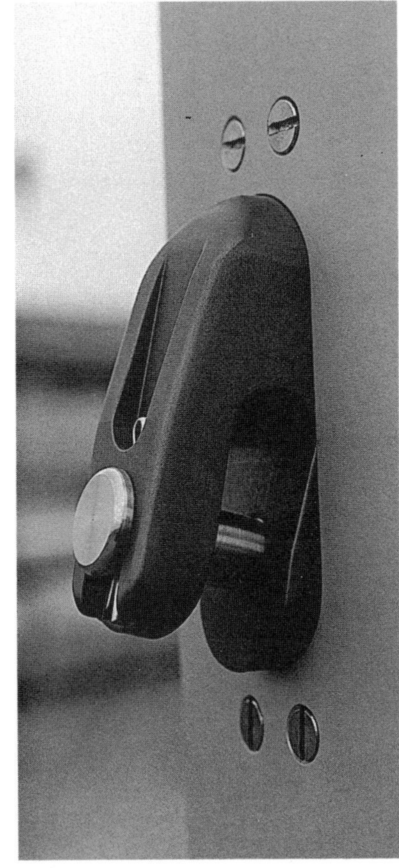

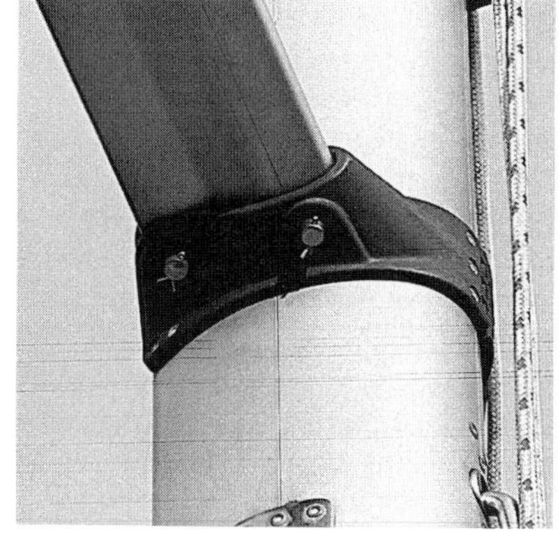

(a)

(d)

Spreader mountings -
Cast bracket (a)
Spigot (b)
Stainless steel bracket (c)
'Tadpole' type (d)

which the spreader and mounting have not been designed. This is a common cause of mast failure as the spreader folds up and the mast is left with little or no support. Once the spreaders have been set up correctly it is also important to make sure that they are bound in some way in order to prevent them from altering their angle to the shrouds. As a result you should check that there is a facility for holding the spreader tips to the rigging.

(b)

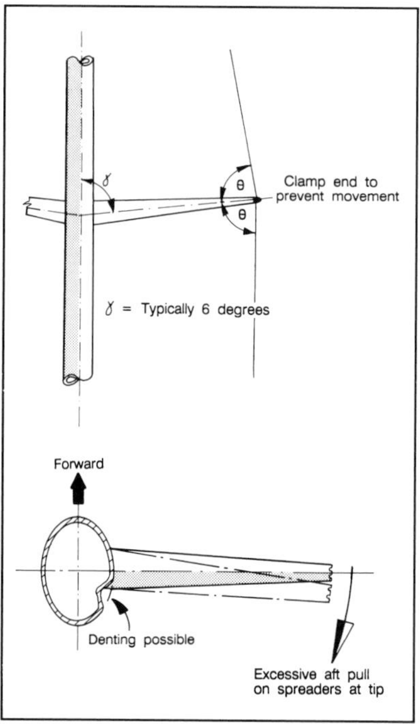

Spreaders are badly set up and risk mast failure

(c)

Left: Spreader angle must bisect shroud angle

An aspect of spar design which does not normally cause mast failure, but is a very common fault and contributory factor, is mast wall denting. This denting of the mast wall, usually at the point of the aft edge of the spreader on the mast, is caused by the trailing edge of the spreader pressing into the mast wall. This can occur as a result of excessive mast bend and/or poor spreader fitting.

If the yacht is to be sailed over long distances it may be necessary to consider the leading and trailing edges of the spreaders for chafe protection. This usually takes the form of stainless steel wear bars that prevent the halyards from rubbing on the spreaders.

Corrosion
Dissimilar metals and salt water are the worst enemy of a spar. The electrolytic action between dissimilar metals can cause severe corroding if they are not correctly insulated. The degree by which corrosion takes place is largely due to the relative positions of the two metals in the galvanic series. The further apart, the greater the chance for corrosion. The most commonly found dissimilar metal is stainless steel in the form of items such as spreader brackets, gooseneck brackets, machine screw fixings etc. All of these fittings need to be insulated against the aluminium usually with zinc chromate paste. In some cases plastic insulating pads are used for large areas as on mast mounted winch pads.

Another common area for corrosion to take place is at the mast heel where salt water can gather and lie for long periods of time. This, if left long enough can cause the mast wall to swell as the corrosion develops between the heel insert and the mast wall. This is a potentially dangerous situation as the mast wall may split and with the high compression loads force itself over the outside of the heel plug. The height of the mast is then lowered reducing the rigging tension with disastrous consequences. In order to prevent this the mast heel should have a drain hole in the very bottom to allow the water to escape.

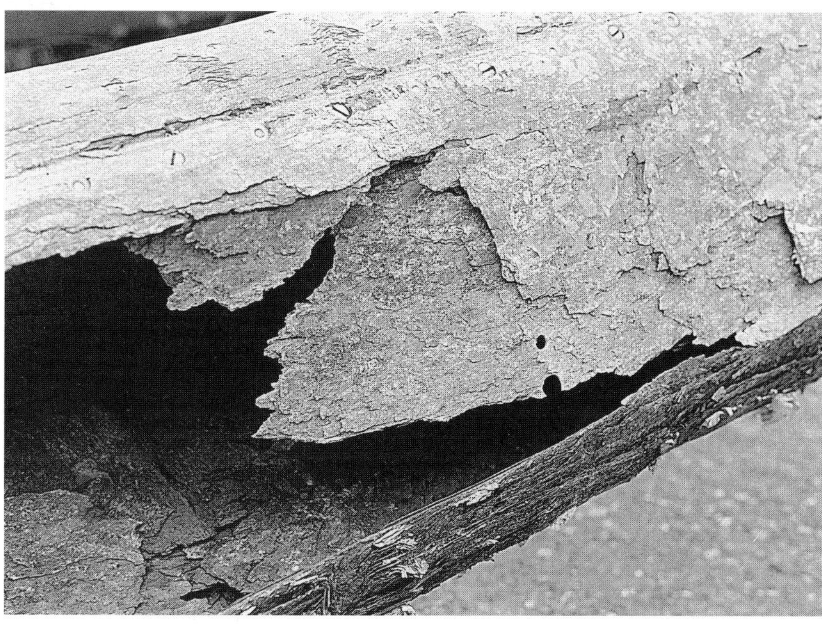

Some alloys are more susceptible to corrosion!

Finish
The most common type of finish is anodizing (further described in Chapter 9). This is usually silver in colour, but other colours are viable though they do have a tendency to fade. Silver, because it is the same colour as the mast, does not tend to show up so severely when fading or scratched. The anodizing process relies on the aluminium being fairly porous and allows a a protective film to be deposited in the outer layer of the material. An absolute minimum thickness for protection is 15 microns but is typically 20-25 microns for most spars. This type of finish offers the best protection for aluminium. One distinct advantage of anodizing over other finishes is that the inside of the spar can also be protected. It is sometimes not possible to anodize large spars due to their overall length and weight (or sometimes from a cosmetic point of view) and in these cases the spars have a painted finish.

Paint finishes are usually a two-part polyurethane or in some special cases powder coated. The disadvantage of such protective coatings is that they are susceptible to chipping, leaving the aluminium exposed and allowing corrosion to take place. In addition to this the mast tube cannot be protected inside. Having said that, aluminium develops an oxide layer on its surface which if left untouched does inhibit further corrosion.

Galvanic series table

Corroded end	**Approx voltage**
Magnesium alloy	-1.60
Galvanised iron	-1.05
Zinc	-1.03
Aluminium 3003	-0.94
Cadmium	-0.80
Aluminium	-0.75
Carbon steel	-0.61
Grey iron	-0.61
Lead	-0.55
Stainless steel 304 (active)	-0.53
Copper	-0.36
Admiralty brass	-0.29
Manganese bronze	-0.27
70/30 Copper nickel	-0.25
Copper	-0.24
Nickel 200	-0.20
Silicon bronze	-0.18
Stainless steel	-0.18
Titanium	-0.15
Silver	-0.13
Stainless steel 304 (passive)	-0.08
Monel	-0.08
Stainless steel 316 (passive)	-0.05
Protected end	

Applications and specification requirements
This section of the chapter deals with some of the main reasons for the need for different specifications and why it is important to acknowledge and identify them. When purchasing a car for example, a wide range of criteria need to be considered before a decision can be reached. Such criteria may include:
a) Purpose
b) Load carrying ability
c) Price
d) Performance
e) Economy
f) Life span etc.

For example the required specification for a family of four with the car being the only form of transport will differ enormously from that of a single person wanting a high performance 'fun car'. Because most people deal with this type of decision frequently, the decision process is usually well understood. However in the case of a yacht this is not always such a straightforward decision.

The process is however the same in that a number of criteria have to be met in order that the yacht is capable for the purpose intended. Typically the broad outline of purposes can be said to include the following groups:
a) Day sailing
b) Short cruising
c) Passage making
d) Racing
e) Advanced racing ie. rotating and wing masts.

Each of the above classifications will require a different specification to obtain the best results in terms of both performance and cost effectiveness. We will now consider some of the differences.

Cruising craft
The *day sailing* specification can be considered to be the simplest and assumes that the boat will be sailed close to land and in relatively flat water conditions. The specification of the spar can be simple without the need for specialist tapers or fittings. The *short cruising* specification will require the spars to be capable of overnight passages in exposed conditions and hence the rig will need to be equipped with navigation lights, reefing systems etc.

Passage making yachts require the highest specification of the cruising craft where one of the most important factors is that of reliability. The rig package needs to be correctly designed in order that fatigue loads are reduced to the absolute minimum. Long distance cruising will mean that the yacht will be sailing in waves for long periods of time which set up load oscillations which can often be more harmful than a static load. As a result, the fatigue considerations are very important and the design of the spar must be such that all parts of the rig that may move, such as shroud tangs, are allowed to do so freely in order to prevent fatigue and failure.

Another important consideration is that of ease of maintenance. Long distance cruising may take the yacht to places where there is very little, if anything, in the way of specialist equipment for carrying out repairs. Therefore it is very important that the spars are capable of being stripped down and repaired with the minimum of tools. This generally means that the fittings such as shroud tangs, spreader attachments etc. should be external. The rigging should be wire so that replacement terminals can be fitted if required.

Racing yachts
Generally speaking racing yacht spars are designed with the knowledge that the spars will not have the same life-span as those for a cruising yacht and will need to be replaced on a more frequent basis. All spars need to be checked over frequently if problems are to be minimized, but in the case of a racing yacht this will need to be carried out on a much more frequent basis with the mast being un-stepped perhaps a number of times throughout a single season. The design of the spars will also vary dramatically, particularly in areas such as taper details, fittings design, spreader attachments and section shape.

Weight and the position of the centre of gravity are usually the factors that influence the design of the spars. The mast section and each fitting need to be as small as possible in order to reduce the overall weight of the spar. The further away from the deck of the boat the more important this is as the weight has a more significant effect.

For example, a racing yacht will often use rod rigging to support the mast. This type of rigging may require different shroud fittings which may make the rigging difficult to remove from the mast. The section of the mast will usually be as small as possible which means that it is even more important to keep any cut-outs in the mast wall as small as possible in order to maintain the strength of the rig.

The rules for a particular class of racing yacht may also require the spars to be of a particular size and weight with a certain minimum centre of gravity.

3: Standing rigging

By tradition, the wires used to support masts are known as standing rigging while the term running rigging applies to control lines such as halyards, sheets and tackles.

The requirements of each category are quite separate and as a result the specification of the rigging reflects this. For example most running rigging will need to be flexible in order to travel over sheaves to provide purchases. This would not be the case for standing rigging which normally consists of single spans, whose greatest deflections are around spreader ends. The requirement for flexibility is not as important as that for the low stretch properties.

There are two ways in which the standing rigging can be described and they are, shrouds and stays. The term shroud is used for rigging in the athwartships plane and stays for that in the fore and aft plane,

eg Cap shroud	– Athwartships
Lower shroud	– Athwartships
Forestay	– Fore and aft
Backstay	– Fore and aft
Babystay	– Fore and aft

When considering the way in which the rigging is fitted to the mast and spars, there are again two methods, continuous and discontinuous. Continuous type rigging consists of full length spans, each of which is attached

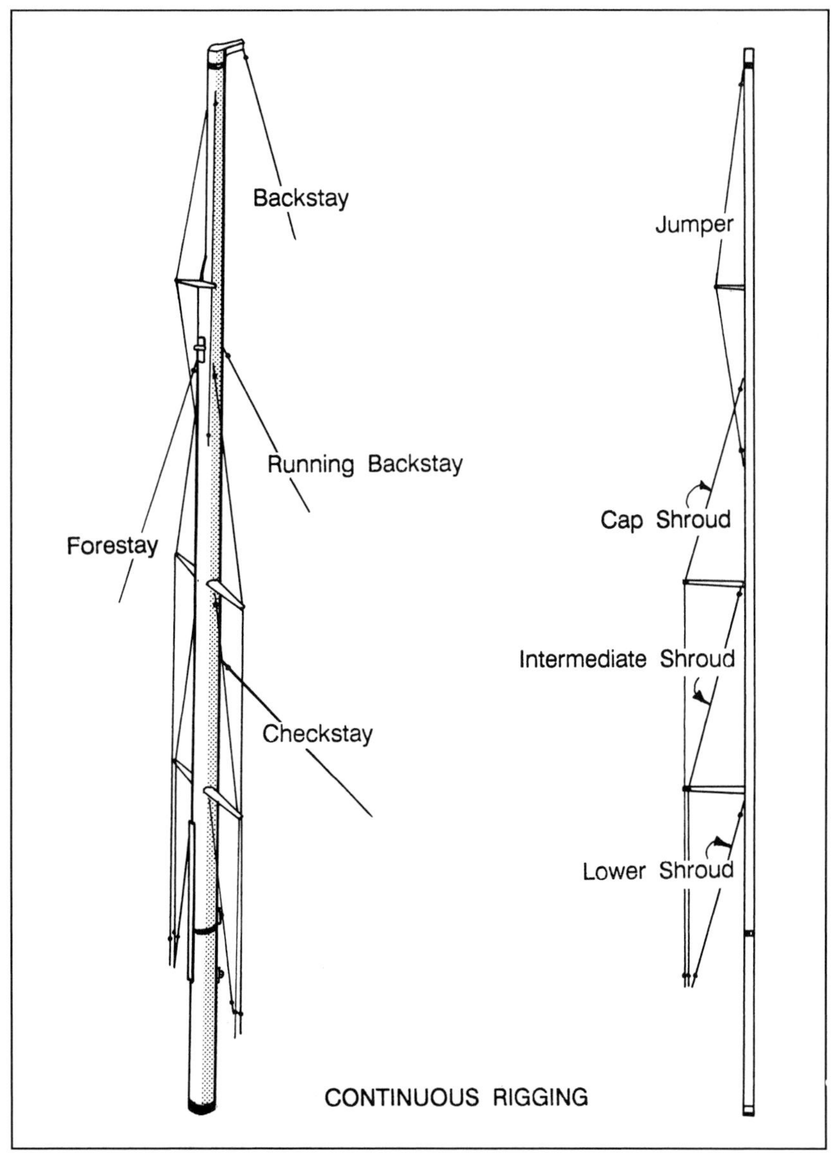

Staying arrangement – continuous rigging

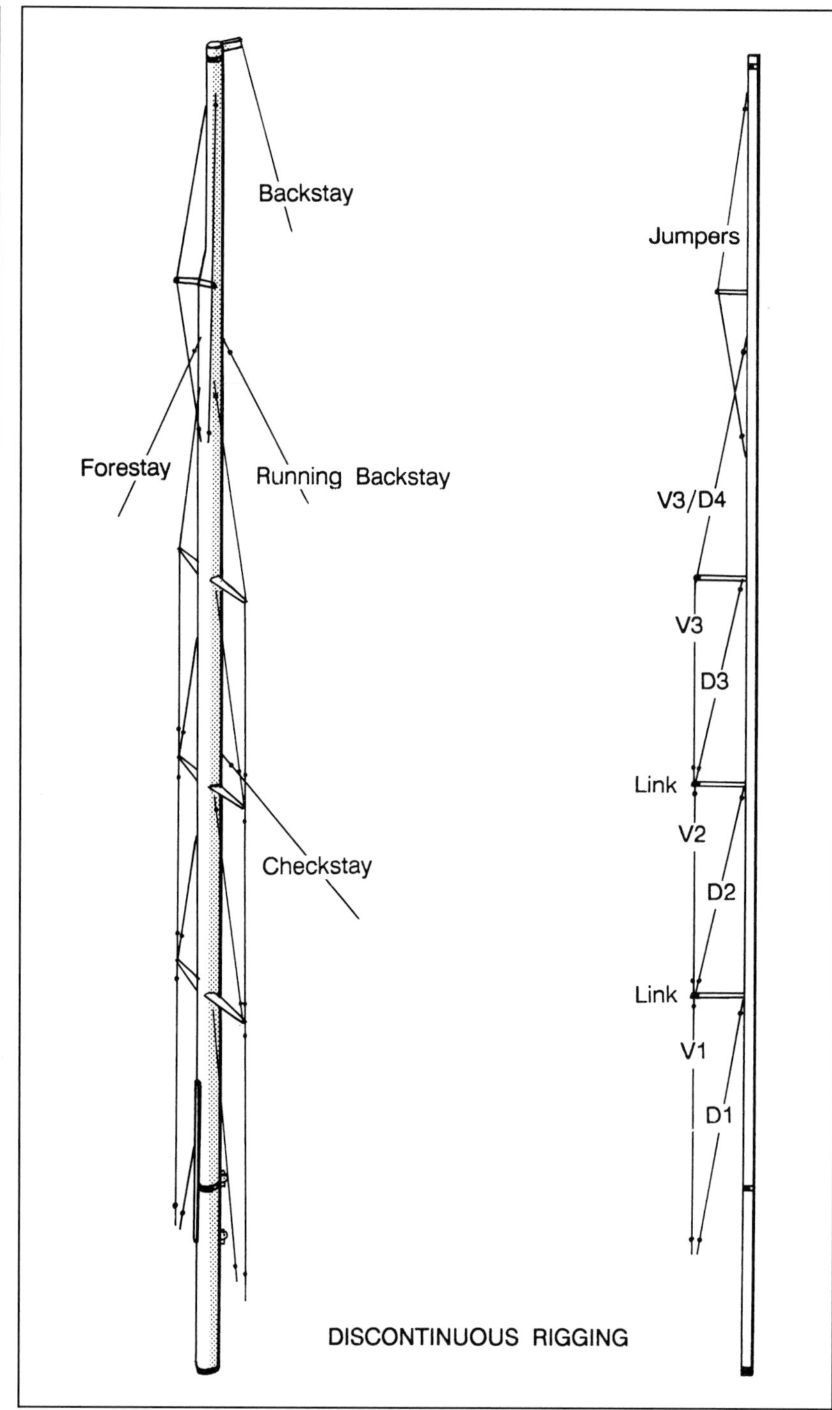

Staying arrangement – discontinuous rigging

to the mast and is continuous down to the chain plates. Discontinuous rigging consists of individual spans which are terminated and linked at spreader ends. Very often the rigging diameters will change at these link ends. The terminology used for describing the individual spans for each type of rigging system is slightly different to that used to itemize a continuous rigging system. The merits and drawbacks of the two systems are discussed later.

The way that a mast is stayed is the definition of the type of rig. The uses of such stays have, to a certain degree, already been covered in the chapter on rig types. However, whilst considering staying arrangements there are a number of important points that should be considered.

Since the advent of simple single spreader masthead rigs, running backstays have been avoided on all but racing yachts. Over the years there has been a trend back towards fractionally rigged boats. Most people have again tried to avoid the use of running backstays from a simplicity point of view and have opted for aft swept spreaders in order to try to achieve the required fore and aft support. This system whilst appealing on paper is in practice a difficult one to set up, as can been seen in Chapter 6.

The need for running backstays however cannot be stressed too highly on cutter or most fractionally rigged boats, especially if they are to be sailed long distances. A masthead cutter rig without a set of running backstays will have no support in the forward direction and will impose high loads on the mast in this area. In addition to this it is often not sensible to support a mast, that is to travel long distances, with only one stay in the fore and aft plane.

Mizzen masts can sometimes also have running backstays, usually when there is no deck area aft of the end of the boom on which to attach a backstay.

Wire rope

By far the most popular type of standing rigging is produced in wire. It benefits from being relatively cheap and simple to use especially since the advent of swageless terminals where no specialist tools are required to terminate the wire. Most standing rigging is constructed from 1x19 stainless steel wire.

The type of wire is described by its construction in the way that the strands are laid. For example 1x19 wire consists of 19

Wire construction examples

	Wire type	Properties	Use
a)	1x19 Stainless steel	Low stretch, high strength. Good finish	Standing rigging
b)	1x19 Stainless steel Dyform	Very low stretch, high strength reasonable finish	Standing rigging
c)	7x19 Stainless steel	Flexible wire, good resistance to crushing.	Running rigging
d)	7x19 Galvanised	More flexible, good resistance to crushing.	Running rigging
e)	7x7 Stainless steel	Good strength, good resistance to crushing. Reasonable flexibility	Standing rigging & guy ropes
f)	7x7 Galvanised	Good strength, good resistance to crushing. Better flexibility.	Standing rigging & guy ropes

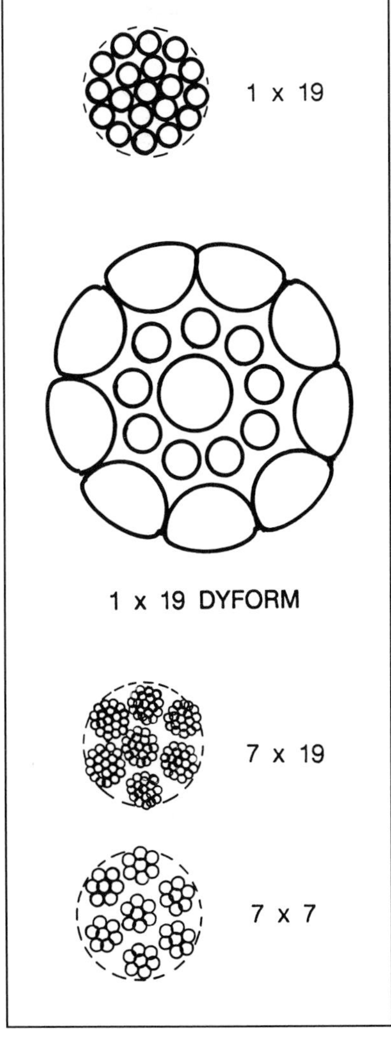

Wire construction examples

Stainless steel wire break load table

Wire diam. (mm)	Wire diam. (in)	Pin size (mm)	Pin size (in)	Min. brk. 1 x 19 (kg)	Min. brk. 1 x 19 Dyform (kg)
2.50		4.8	$\frac{3}{16}$	500	–
3.00	$\frac{1}{8}$	6.3	$\frac{1}{4}$	720	–
4.00	$\frac{5}{32}$	8.0	$\frac{5}{16}$	1280	–
4.76	$\frac{3}{16}$	–	–	1800	2240
5.00	–	9.5	$\frac{3}{8}$	2000	2440
5.50	$\frac{7}{32}$	9.5	$\frac{3}{8}$	2470	–
6.00	–	11.1	$\frac{7}{16}$	2880	3550
6.35	$\frac{1}{4}$	–	–	3220	4020
7.00	$\frac{9}{32}$	12.7	$\frac{1}{2}$	3550	4910
8.00	$\frac{5}{16}$	12.7	$\frac{1}{2}$	4640	6150
9.00	–	16.0	$\frac{5}{8}$	5870	–
9.50	$\frac{3}{8}$			6580	8760
10.00	–	16.0	$\frac{5}{8}$	7250	9770
11.00	$\frac{7}{16}$	19.0	$\frac{3}{4}$	8770	12100
12.00	–	19.0	$\frac{3}{4}$	10400	14400
12.70	$\frac{1}{2}$	–	–	11650	15800
14.00	$\frac{9}{16}$	22.2	$\frac{7}{8}$	14180	19300
16.00	$\frac{5}{8}$	25.4	1	18560	25600
19.00	$\frac{3}{4}$	28.6	$1\frac{1}{8}$	21620	32000
22.00	$\frac{7}{8}$	35.0	$1\frac{3}{8}$	29070	–
26.00	1	35.0	$1\frac{3}{8}$	40600	–

(Courtesy Norseman Gibb Ltd.)

single strands. 7X19 however consists of 7 core strands each made up from 19 single strands. The properties of a given wire are directly related to the method of construction and the amount of material for a given cross-sectional area. The higher this ratio is (for the same material) the higher the tensile strength and lower stretch will be achieved. Whilst this is usually the main requirement for standing rigging, running rigging needs to be flexible in order to travel over sheaves and a specification such as 7x19 would be considered. This type of wire has many more strands, less material for a given cross-sectional area and hence greater flexibility.

The table below shows the breaking loads of the various options on wire construction.

Dyform wire, developed by British Ropes Ltd., is constructed from specially shaped strands which fill a greater proportion of the overall cross-section. This means that there is more material in the cross-sectional area for a given wire diameter which therefore means a higher breaking load and more resistance to stretch.

The problem of stretch is one that mainly concerns the racing yachtsman who is trying to get the very best performance out of the rig. The rigging that has the highest resistance to stretch, and ideal for the racing application, is rod rigging (see page 47) but this can be very costly compared to conventional wire rigging. Dyform rigging offers a good compromise in terms of cost and its more suitable mechanical properties and mean that this Dyform is used more on cruiser/racers where good performance is required at a lower cost than rod rigging.

In addition to this, rod rigging often requires expensive specialized mast fittings. Whilst this is essential on the all out racer, it is yet another prohibitive cost on the cruiser/racer or club racer type boat. Dyform however uses the same end terminations as conventional wire (in most cases), and therefore it can be fitted as replacement rigging without the need to change the mast fittings. This is a distinct advantage as existing rigs can be re-rigged with Dyform in order to improve the performance at a relatively low cost.

Care must be taken when measuring wire sizes to ensure that the correct diameter is being measured. There are exact ways to measure the diameter of a multi-stranded wire.

Terminations

In the early days of wire rigging, splicing with or without a thimble, was the only way in which a wire could be terminated. Nowadays there are many more ways to terminate wires the most common of which are as follows:

a) Swaging

The swaging process squeezes a hollow fitting onto the wire under very high pressure to the extent that the fitting material 'flows' in between the strands of the wire. Specialist equipment is required to carry out this operation in view of the high pressures required. There are two types of machine that are used for swaging:

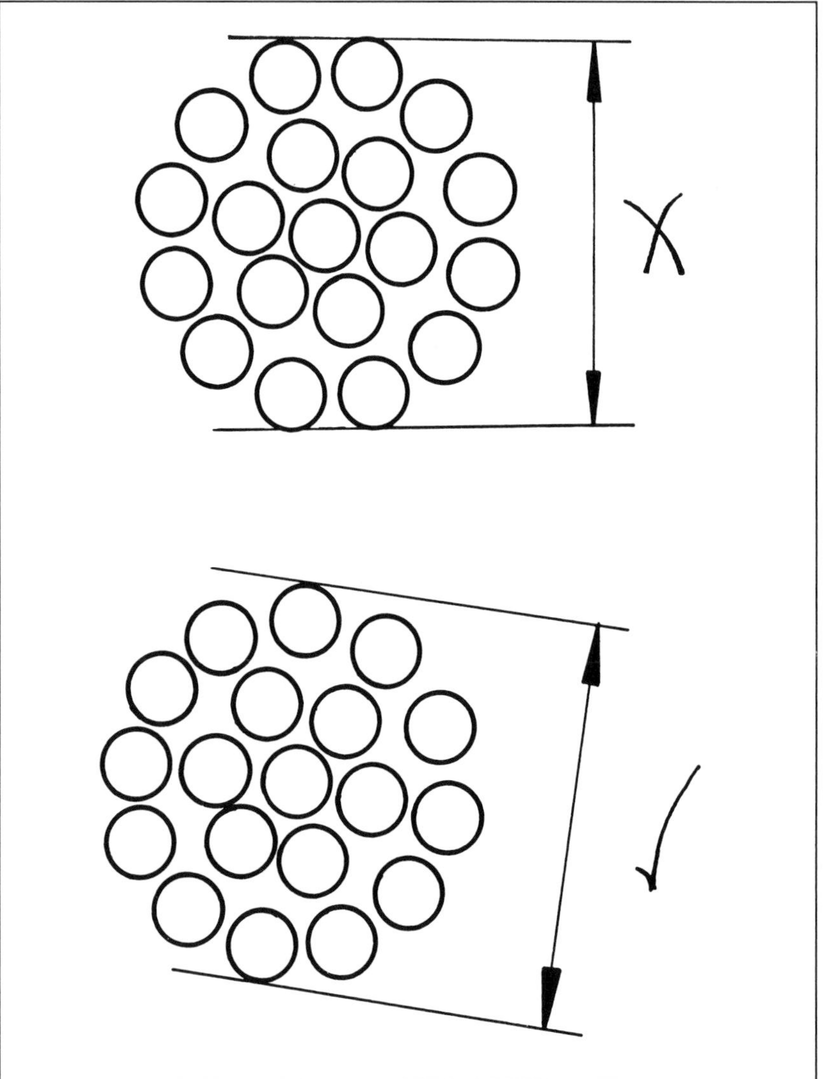

Measuring wire diameters correctly

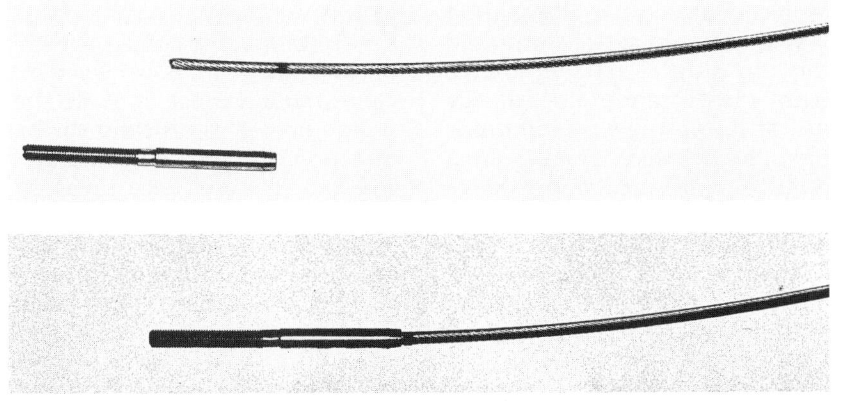

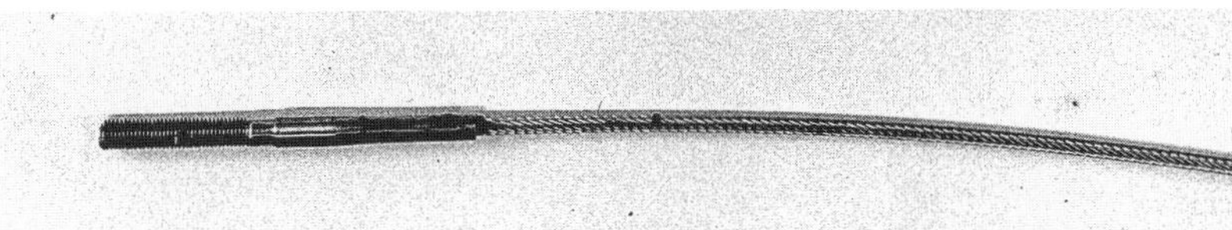

Roll swaging procedure

Whilst swage terminals are amongst the simplest and neatest of end fittings they can suffer from a number of problems. Fortunately this type of wire terminal is very popular and most riggers are familiar with the system making the chances of assembly fault relatively small. It is however important that these types of fittings are checked thoroughly as manufacturing and assembly flaws can usually be visibly identified. Some of the most common faults to look for are as follows.

Residual stresses can be set up in the material of the swage if the fitting has been badly or over-swaged and this can cause cracking either at the time of swaging, afterwards or whilst the fitting is in use. This will eventually lead to the complete failure of the fitting. Overswaging can often be spotted as the terminal will be bent along its length often with cracks at the end of the swage. In section the swage should be nearly round. If however it is oval in shape or has a distinct flat side on it, it should be viewed with caution.

Under-swaging can also occur where the fitting has less pressure applied than is required to keep the fitting on the end of

i) Roll swaging. The fitting and wire are passed through a set of dies that are specially formed for the particular size of rigging. This is usually achieved by drawing the fitting and wire through with a hydraulic ram twice.
ii) Rotary hammer. This system holds the end fitting and wire firmly in place in a set of specially formed dies which are then subjected to hammer blows which squeeze the swage onto the wire.

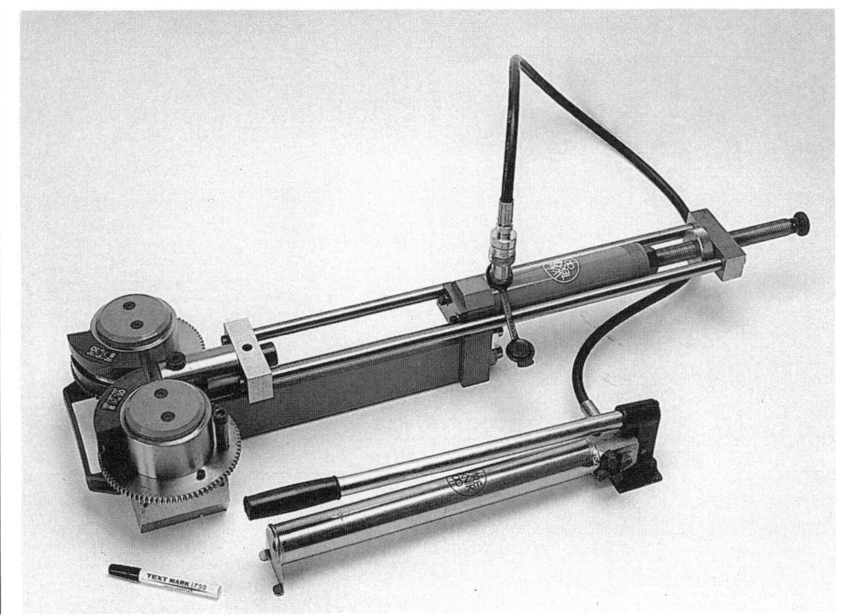

Norseman Wireteknik Roller Swager (Courtesy Norseman Gibb Ltd)

the wire whilst under load.

Corrosion is often talked about as being a big problem with swaged fittings. This need not be the case so long as the fittings and wire are manufactured from 316 grade stainless steel. Some of the earlier equipment and indeed some present day overseas equipment is manufactured from 304 grade stainless steel. This grade does not possess the high corrosion resistance of 316 and there have been some problems. Having said that, precautions should still be taken with 316 fittings and wire, especially on the lower ends which are frequently submerged in salt water.

This type of corrosion starts with the water running down the strands and into the swage where it can corrode the wire unseen. Whilst this is not necessarily a problem for yachts that have their rigging checked or replaced at regular intervals it may be a more serious problem for long distance cruising yachts. Such yachts cannot afford the risk of losing their rig hundreds of miles offshore or even in a remote harbour many miles from a specialist rigging service. As a result mechanical swageless fittings such as 'Norseman' or 'Stalok' are often used on the bottom ends. The top of the rigging spans are not such a problem for swaging as they do not (one hopes) get submerged in salt water.

Wire fatigue can be a problem on swaged fittings as the wire cannot move once it is in the swage part of the fitting. If the direction of the loading changes the line that the wire takes up must also change. If the end terminal is restricted in its movement the wire will tend to bend around the end of the swage which will fatigue the wire. This can often be seen on a broken stay where the break is at the end of the swage.

Poor rigging alignment can cause fatigue

Photographs above and overleaf: Talurit/Nicropress procedure

b) Talurit / Nicropress

This system is similar to the swaging process in that a ferrule is squeezed onto the wire under high pressure between two dies. The ferrule is usually a copper alloy and is used mainly for halyards although it is sometimes used for standing rigging terminations on smaller boats. This system normally employs a thimble, either hollow or solid for the wire to wrap around and it is from the friction caused by this eye that the fitting is given some of its strength.

Because the wire needs to wrap around the thimble there are some sizes of 1x19 wire

A correctly made Talurit

which will be difficult to form as they are not flexible so care must be taken to ensure that the wire is seated correctly. In order that the fitting should achieve its full strength it is essential that the tail end of the wire protrudes through the collar at least $\frac{1}{2}$ the diam of the wire.

c) Norseman / Sta-lok
These are the two most popular manufacturer's swageless end fittings and they require very little in the way of tools to fit them. As a result they have become very popular especially for long distance cruising boats which need to rely (as little as possible) on specialist equipment for repairs. They are also used a great deal on rigs that have not been spanned (see Spanning the mast) as the rigging can be supplied over-length and cut to suit on site when the mast is stepped. They consist of a split cone that compresses and holds the wire inside a tapered body. This tapered body forms part of the end termination onto which a range of fittings such as eyes and forks can be attached.

Not only are there advantages in the ease of assembly of these end fittings, but the wire inside the terminal can be protected from corrosion to a greater degree than the swaged alternatives. Whilst the fitting is being assembled silicone rubber can be squeezed into the body which will prevent any salt water penetration.

Another advantage of these types of fitting is that so long as replacement cone inserts are used, these fittings can often be used repeatedly.

The following fitting instructions are an example of those supplied with most swageless fittings and show how easy they are to assemble. (See Norseman instructions.)

Norseman fitting instructions
(Courtesy Norseman Gibb Ltd.)

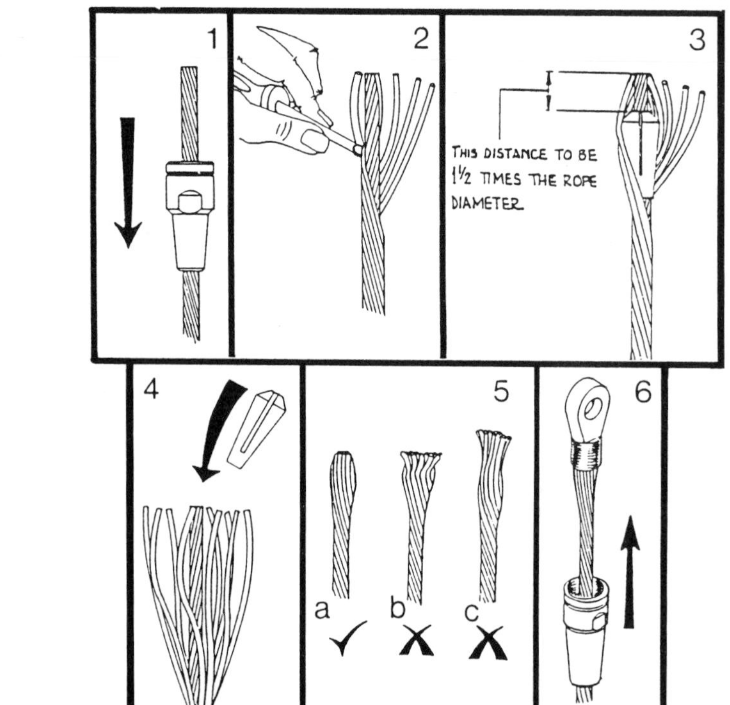

Note: Use **Non-Corrosive** Marine Sealant

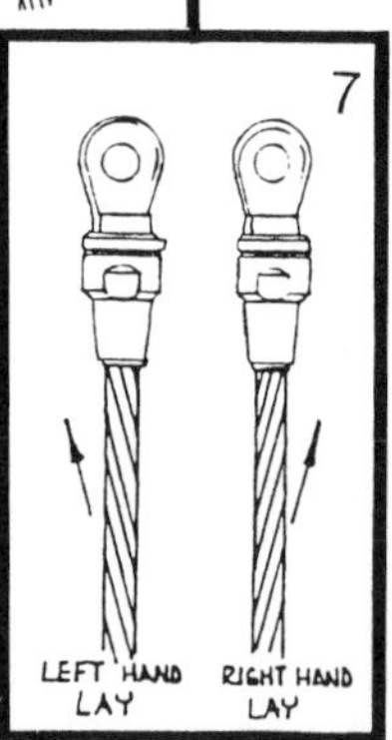

MK 6 Terminal fitting instructions

1. Unscrew the end fitting from the body and remove the cone. Slide the body over the rope as shown in fig 1.
2. Unlay the outer wires from the centre strand. A screwdriver is useful for this. See fig 2.
3. Fit the cone over the centre strand with the long taper facing the body. See fig 3.
4. Position the cone on the centre strand with 1½ times the rope diameter protruding. See fig 4. Reform the outer wires around the cone, one at a time. Ensure that the cone remains in its correct position.
5. The cone/rope assembly should now resemble fig 5a. If there is too little protrusion of the centre strand, then the assembly will look similar to fig 5b. Too much protrusion and the assembly will look similar to fig 5c.
6. Push the blind hole in the end fitting over the end of the cable. Bring the body up the rope and start to screw the two pieces together. If using a left hand lay rope then turn only the end fitting. If they rope is right hand lay then turn only the terminal body. See fig 7 for definition of lay directions.
7. Once the two pieces have been screwed together 2 or 3 turns, the terminal can be completely tightened by turning the end fitting. DO NOT OVERTIGHTEN, this will not improve the performance of the fitting and may result in damage to the screw threads. The fitting is sufficiently tight when the cone is fully seated in the taper inside the body. Until this occurs there will be minimal resistance to turning the end fitting. As soon as the resistance increases the fitting is tight enough and should not be tightened further.
8. Unscrew the end fitting and inspect the internal assembly. The outer wires should be evenly spaced around the cone.
9. Apply a non-corrosive marine sealant* to the blind hole in the end fitting and to the inside of the body. Screw up the assembly hand tight. Repeat if necessary until sealant oozes from the body and wipe away excess sealant.
10. Apply the thread locking adhesive to the screw threads and re-tighten the terminal as described in 7) above.

*Use only non-corrosive marine sealant. DO NOT use domestic 'bath' sealant as this contains acetic acid, which is harmful to stainless steel. (These sealants may be identified by their strong 'vinegary' smell.).

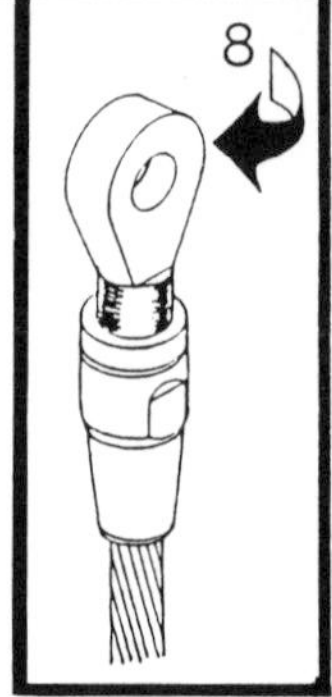

d) Splicing
This method is still very popular but mainly for running rigging and less so for standing rigging. One of the reasons is that end terminations are now very cheap for standing rigging compared to the time it takes to produce even a simple splice in addition to which, 1x19 is not a very flexible wire and does not tend to splice easily.

As with all types of termination splicing is not without its problems. Care must be taken that no particles of dissimilar metal enter the splice where they can be inadvertently covered in. If this does happen the wire may corrode when immersed in salt water and go unnoticed until it fails. This can happen when the splice has been made by using a cheap Marlin spike from a material other than stainless steel.

e) Bulldog clips
These fittings are used mainly as a temporary repair and achieve about 80% efficiency of the breaking strength of the wire. They consist of a threaded U-bolt with a shaped backplate known as the saddle. In order to achieve a secure fastening at least two should be used and aligned with the saddle side on the standing part of the wire.

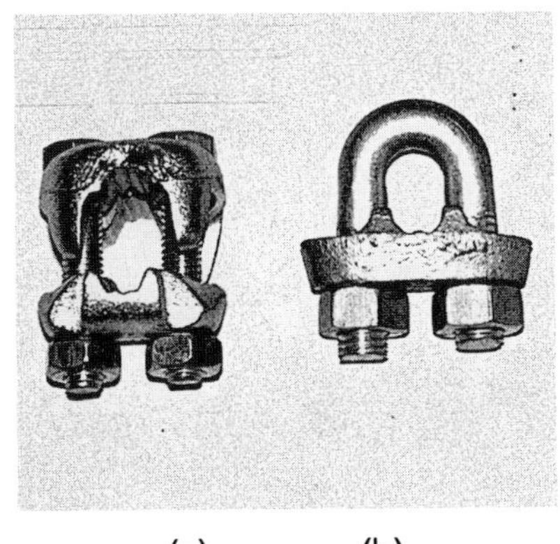

(a) (b)

A 'Fist Grip' (a) and 'Bulldog clip' (b)

f) Fist grips
These are similar to the Bulldog clip but are symmetrical. They are also ideal for emergency repairs and are fitted in a similar fashion.

End Fittings
So far we have looked at the method of attachment of end terminals, the following are some of the most popular types of end fitting. These end fittings can come as an integral part of the termination, such as the case of a swaged eye, or a range of end fittings can be fitted onto the wire fastening as in the case of Norseman fittings. Nowadays most of the fittings are produced in 316 stainless steel which has very good resistance to corrosion coupled with good strength properties.

However, 316 stainless steel is a relatively expensive material and there is often a temptation to cut costs by using a fitting manufactured from a lower grade material. With high load critical items such as are found on the rigging, it is highly advisable to always use 316 grade as the consequences of losing a rig as a result of a fitting failure are often serious.

a) Eyes
For rigging terminations eye fittings are preferred as they are not as susceptible to fatigue as fork fittings and should be used wherever possible. So long as the mast fitting allows sufficient articulation, fatigue stresses can be kept to a minimum as the eye fitting will move more readily and take up a desired line than a fork fitting.
There are four main types of eye fitting which are:
i) Hard eye. This is a solid fitting that terminates in an eye. The size of the fitting is defined by the wire diameter that it suits.
ii) Soft eye. This fitting is a loop of wire that has no insert. The loop can be held together by either a talurit or a splice. (Mainly used for running rigging)
iii) Thimble eye. This is also a loop of wire but has an insert known as a thimble which prevents the wire from collapsing under load. The size of the thimble is expressed as the wire size to which it is suited.
iv) Solid thimble eye. This is similar to a standard thimble eye but the thimble is solid apart from the hole that the rigging pin passes through.

Eye and fork fittings must be free to articulate

b) Fork fittings
i) Swaged forks. The fork is an integral part of the swage fitting and may also incorporate a toggle for better articulation.
ii) Screwed forks.These are found on the Norseman / Sta-lok fittings where the end fittings are interchangeable.

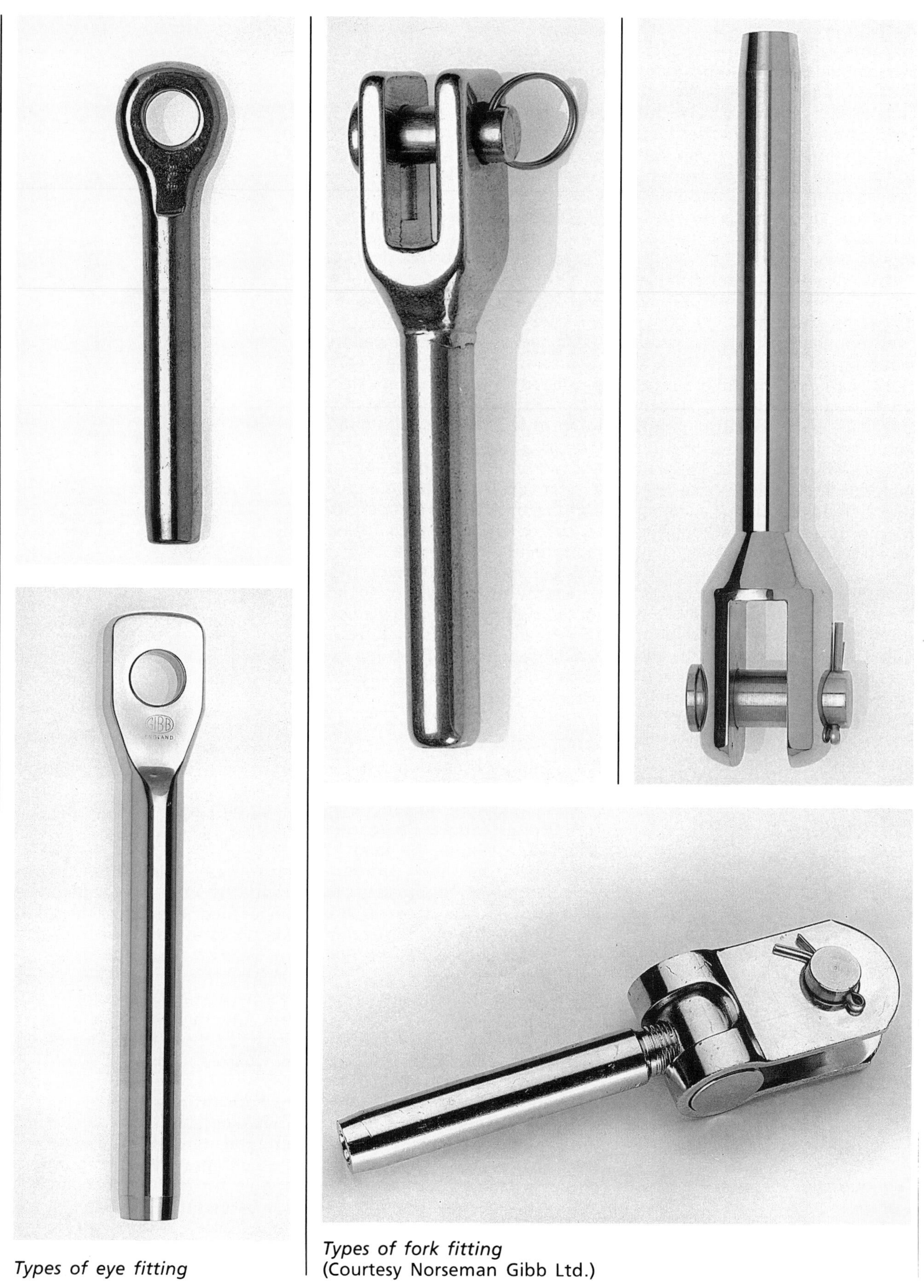

Types of eye fitting

Types of fork fitting
(Courtesy Norseman Gibb Ltd.)

c) Stud fitting
This type of fitting is as it suggests, a length of studding that usually forms part of the rigging screw assembly. It is available in two forms:
i) Swaged stud. This component is an integral part of the swage fitting.
ii) Screwed stud. This fitting links onto the Norseman / Stay-lok type fitting with a female thread at one end.

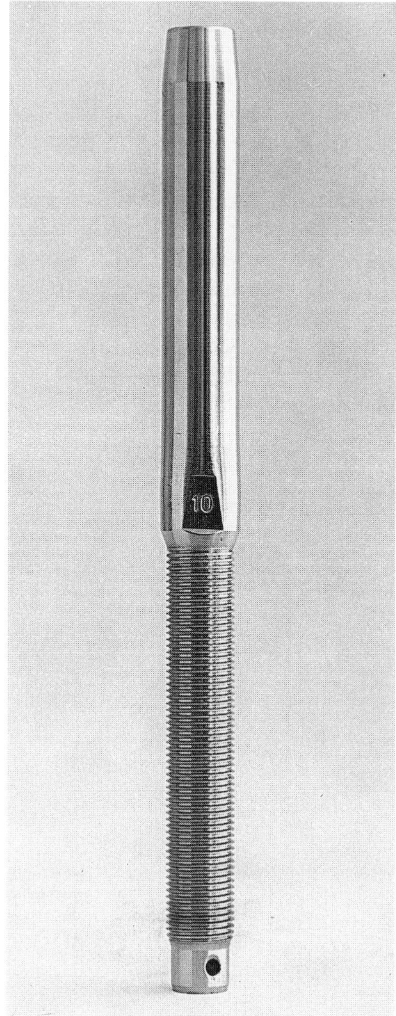

Swage stud fitting
(Courtesy Norseman Gibb Ltd.)

d) T-terminals
These are possibly the simplest form of rigging attachment as they consist of a rectangular hole in a stainless steel backplate into which a 'T' shaped fitting is inserted at 90' and

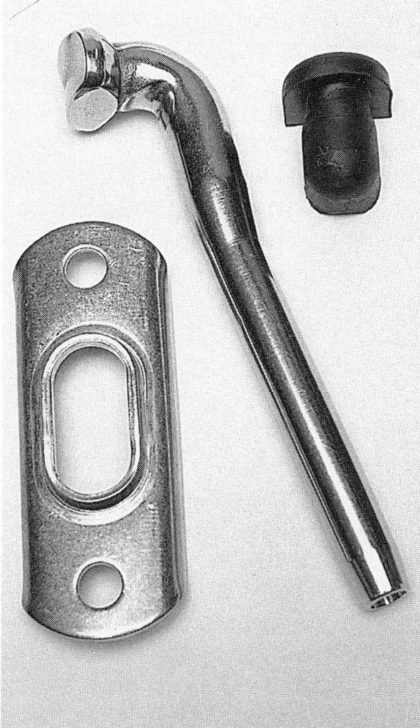

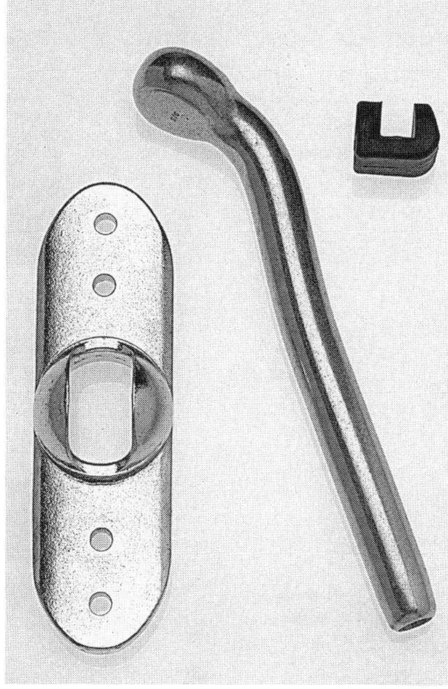

'T' type terminal with backplate and retaining plug (top), and 'T - ball' shroud terminal

then aligned.

There are two versions of this type of fitting available:
i) The conventional T-terminal – as described above.
ii) The T-ball terminal. This version uses a ball type fitting on the upper end as opposed to the above T shape in order to improve the articulation. In addition to this the angle at the head of the fitting is reduced to increase the strength of the fitting by reducing the fatigue problem.

Both of the above type fittings are available to suit either a swage or a screw end fitting. (ie. Norseman / Stalok)
The advantages of T-terminals are that they are:
a) Light weight
b) Easy to both fit and remove
c) Cheap
The disadvantages are, however, that:
a) They do not allow much articulation and therefore there is a risk that they can set up fatigue loads in the rigging which can lead to failure.
b) Due to their shape the fitting itself is susceptible to fatigue as it tries to straighten out under load.
As a result, whilst they are cheap effective rigging terminations, they should not normally be used for the main staying supports for long distance cruising yachts.

It is quite common to see these terminals being used for running backstay and checkstay attachments but this use should be avoided if at all possible. The terminal should always be fitted with a rubber plug that should prevent the T-terminal from locking in the wrong direction. However there have been many cases of the T-terminal becoming forced in the wrong direction by the mainsail headboard when hoisting in some cases even bending the terminal. When the stay is tensioned it can pull on the terminal in an un-natural direction and cause fatigue which could eventually lead to the failure of the fitting.

Another limitation of such fittings is on rod rigging. Rod rigging is particularly susceptible to fatigue if there is not sufficient articulation in the end fittings. As already mentioned T-terminals do not offer much in the way of free articulation and therefore T-terminals should only be used on stays that have relatively low loadings and that do not need much articulation such as jumper stays.

Quick release

This type of fitting is used for stays that need to be disconnected from time to time such as Babystays or inner forestays. The most popular type is the Pelican hook which is similar to a snap shackle but with a longer clip. The long arm provides a means of pre-tensioning the wire where only a limited degree of travel is available.

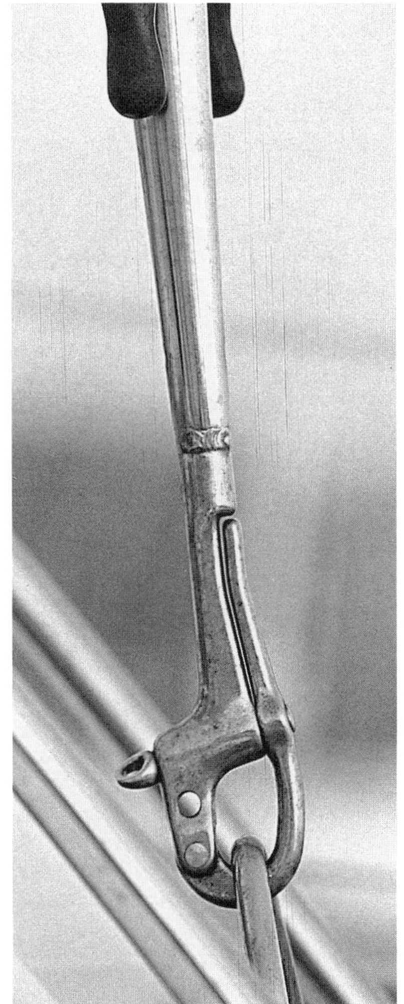

'Pelican' hook

Links

The link between the stay and the boat or mast fitting is very important and the need for free articulation is paramount. These are often used where the rigging is too short or where a number of positions are required such as on the tack end of a forestay. Fatigue is one of the biggest causes of rigging failure as the rigging is restrained in unnatural positions whilst the load is applied. Areas where it is particularly important are sail carrying stays such as forestays. The upper and lower ends of this stay must be free to move transversely as well as in the fore and aft direction due to the inevitable sag in the luff of the sail. Failure of the forestay can cause catastrophic damage to the boat and its crew as the mast falls aft and must be avoided at all costs. Therefore toggles or links must be incorporated in each end of a stay to allow for movement and the following are a number of ways in which this can be achieved.

Toggles

These are the most common way of achieving articulation and are available in a variety of configurations;

a) Fork to eye
b) Fork to fork
c) Fork to stud

As with all types of rigging link the hole sizes should match to avoid point loading and to maintain the breaking load specifications throughout the stay. The jaw width of the toggle must also match the eye or chain plate fitting to which it is attached. There are two ways in which toggles are manufactured being either machined from solid or cast. The latter should be avoided if at all possible as they can suffer from flaws in the casting which may not be immediately visible to the naked eye. The machined variety should be in stainless steel preferably 316 grade to avoid corrosion problems.

A forestay link plate

Toggle types

Shackles
These are of course used in many areas on a boat but should not generally be used for primary standing rigging. There are however some cases where they are suitable such as the lower ends of running backstays or checkstays. Where used they should always be wired up to prevent them shaking loose. The size of the shackle must always match the load carrying ability of the stay and therefore the breaking load of a shackle should be considered before fitting.

Discontinuous rigging links
This type of link differs from the above types in that it is positioned in the span of the shrouds at the tip of a spreader. The rigging system that incorporates these types of links is known as discontinuous rigging. Its main advantages and the way in which this system is set up is described in more detail in the setting up section. (Chapter 6)

This system is usually only found on multiple spreader rigs and typically on racing yachts where the rigging sizes reduce towards the top of the mast in order to reduce the weight of the rigging. The changes in rigging size occur at the spreader tips and the links need to accommodate 3 rigging terminations. Two vertical attachments for the vertical stays and an attachment for the diagonal stay.

There are two types of spreader link:

i) The external link which is usually a link plate mounted vertically on a horizontal mounting pin which fits into the end of the spreader tip. This type is mainly found on multiple spreader cruising rigs for large cruising yachts and can be a combination of eye and fork

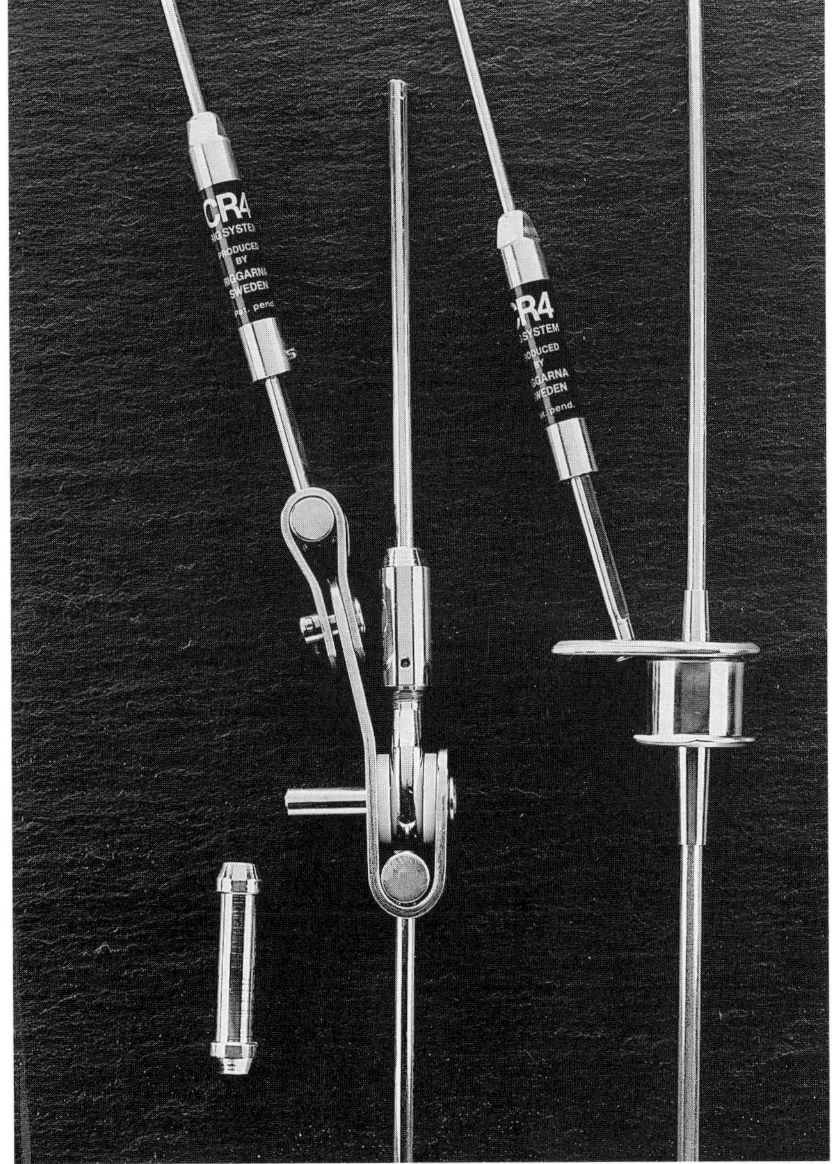

Spreader link ends for discontinuous rigging
(Courtesy Riggarna UK Ltd.)

terminals. The system can be used for both wire and rod rigging. The advantage of this link is that individual spans of rigging can usually be removed without dismantling the spreader, an important consideration for long distance yachts.
ii) The integral spreader link which is fitted as an integral part of the spreader tip and is often referred to as a tip cup. It is found mainly on racing yachts where the weight and windage needs to be kept to an absolute minimum. Due to the way in which the rigging spans are seated, this type of end can only be used in conjunction with rod rigging.

Tensioning
Modern materials and production methods now mean that the need for 'Dead eyes' and lashing on the bottom end of the rigging spans has now been superseded by the use of rigging screws on all but the most traditional types of yachts. There are two main types of adjustment that may need to be carried out on a rig.
i) The tensioning of shrouds in order to balance the rigging tensions. Once these positions have been established they are usually left for long periods of time without alteration.
ii) The adjustment on the fore and aft stays of the rig such as the backstay, running backstays, checkstays etc. require regular adjustment of generally much larger range.

The requirements of the two conditions are completely different and so are the methods by which they are achieved. Firstly we shall look at the transverse rigging and the way in which it is tensioned.

Rigging screws, bottlescrews and turnbuckles
All of the terms above are often considered to be the same type of fitting, (turnbuckle being the American term). In general terms this is so but there are variations. Most types of screw offer a range of end fittings such as fork, eye, stud or toggle.
a) Rigging screws – Open bodied. This type of rigging screw has most of the thread in each end exposed through the open body. They are usually manufactured from either stainless steel, chromed bronze, galvanised steel or Superston (an ultra strong alloy). The use of bronze reduces the chances of the threads binding and thus locking the screw.

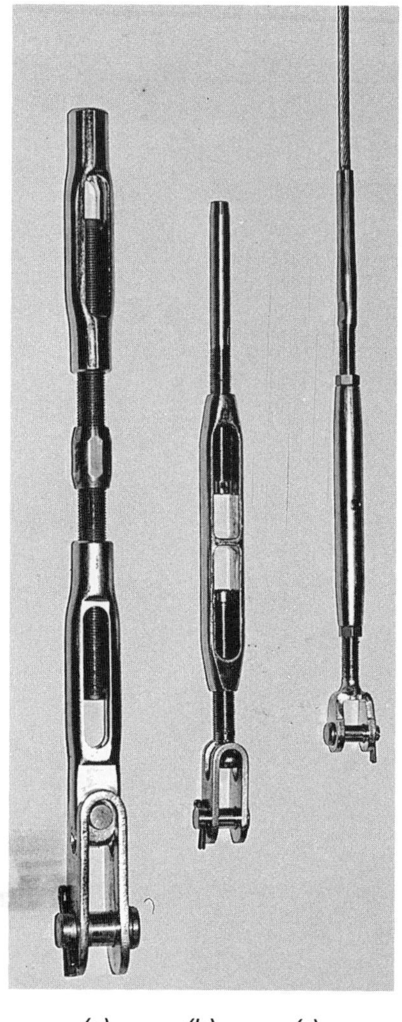

(a) (b) (c)

Centre screw (a), Open bodied rigging screw (b), Bottle screw (c)

Open bodied screws are generally the preferred type for most applications as they can easily be inspected for corrosion or damaged threads. It is also easy to see at a glance how much travel is left. Locking off such screws is a simple task involving only two split pins per screw. Adjustment is easy although care must be taken when using a screwdriver or similar through the open body to turn the rigging screw. Excessive pressure caused by too long a lever can force open the body and cause serious damage.
b) Rigging screws – centre screw. These are the opposite arrangement to the above screws in that there is one central stud and a body at each end. These bodies are restrained from turning and the adjustment is made by turning the centre stud. Again these are easy to adjust and maintain as most of the parts can be easily checked for corrosion or damage.
c) Bottle screws – closed body. The layout and operation for these screws is the same as the open bodied rigging screw with the exception that the body is closed with only a small hole in the centre. They are usually manufactured completely from stainless steel which does make them susceptible to binding. (The hole can also be used to turn the body.) The threads at each end cannot be seen and therefore the screw cannot easily be checked whilst in situ for corrosion or damage. In addition to this they are difficult to adjust as it is not easy to see how many threads are left inside. The locking device is usually a lock nut at each end which, in most cases, is acceptable but they do run the risk of vibrating loose unless some action is taken to prevent this from happening. (If the screw stretches slightly the nuts can again become loose.)

In essence they are a reasonable screw adjuster for simple applications, but should be avoided for long distance cruising yacht rigging.
d) Rigging screws CR4 type.

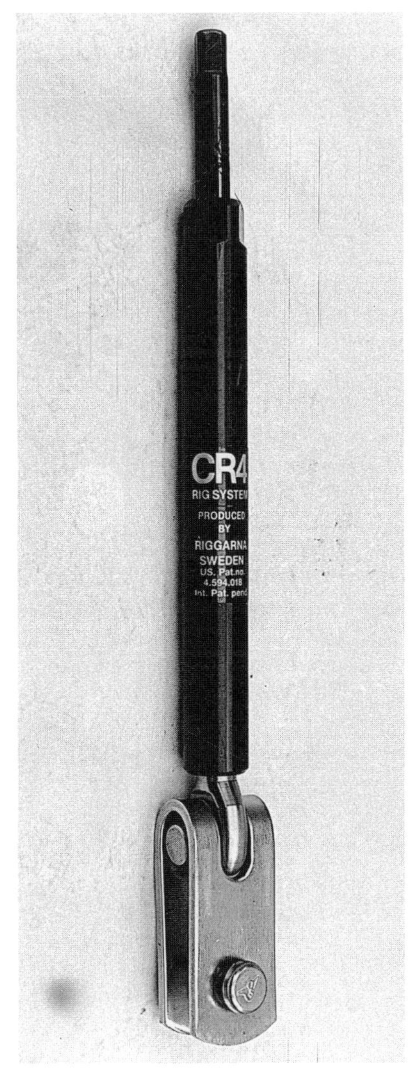

'CR4' turnbuckle

These screws have an aluminium bronze enclosed body and therefore make inspection of the screw for corrosion and thread damage difficult. They are however quick to adjust and are often calibrated. These features make them a desirable proposition for the racing yachtsman for whom ease of adjustment is of primary importance. There are a range of end fittings available for both rod and wire rigging. A locking screw at the lower end of the body ensures that the rigging screw cannot vibrate loose.

(a)

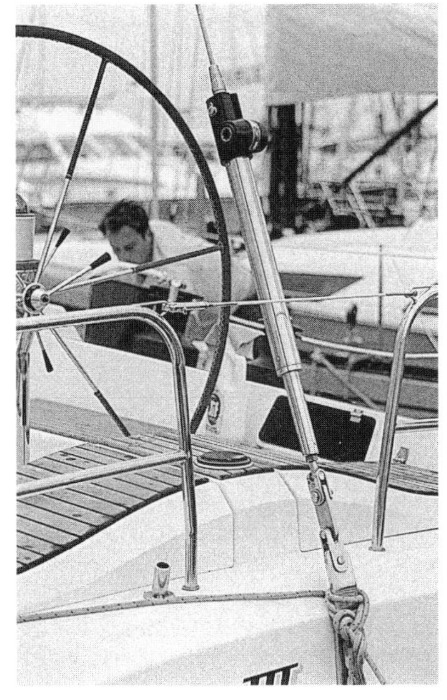

(b)

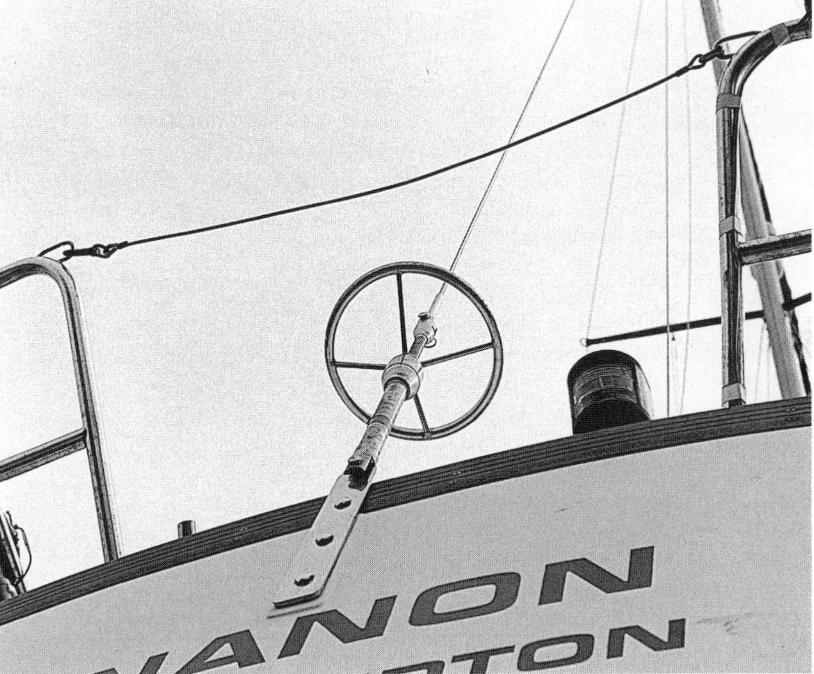

(c)

Backstay adjuster examples – rack and pinion (a), integral hydraulic (b) wheel and screw (c)

Adjustment

The adjustment of the fore and aft rigging generally requires much more travel and is varied more often than for the shrouds. Rigging screws can of course be used for items such as the permanent backstay but in practice fittings that are easier and quicker to adjust are more common. The following is a brief list of the most popular types of rigging adjustment. The order in which they appear bears no significance as each application must be judged individually as to its suitability.

a) Block and tackle. Possibly the simplest form of adjustment is that of the block and tackle. Photographs here show some of the possibilities for backstay adjustments.
b) Ratchet and worm / Rack and pinion. This system is based on a rack and pinion type system similar to that found on the steering of most cars. The moving part is provided by the rack and the adjustment is made normally with a winch handle which operates the pinion drive. This is a powerful means of adjustment but does suffer from being a relatively slow operation and one which has a limited travel. It is therefore suitable for items such as the permanent backstay.
c) Wheel and screw. This system also has a large purchase but also suffers from its relatively slow operation. It is probably best described as operating in a similar way to a single thread rigging screw. Adjustment is made by turning a large wheel which is part of the fitting. This wheel is sometimes substituted by a set of fold down handles.
d) Lever. The lever system can also be a very powerful method of adjustment and can also be a very quick way of making an adjustment. The restriction with this system is that it only has a limited travel. Whilst this can be improved with reverse purchases it should only be considered for adjustments which require a relatively small amount of travel. Such an application could be the backstay which requires a high power purchase, small degree of travel with as little friction as possible.

The simplest way of increasing the power of this type of system is to make the lever longer but there are usually restrictions in terms of the space available for such levers. As a result blocks and tackles are often used to improve the power of the system.
e) Hydraulic. A very powerful means of adjustment can be achieved with the use of hydraulic rams. In fact so much so that extreme care must be taken when specifying hydraulic equipment to make sure that it will not damage the boat or its fittings.

Lever backstay adjustment

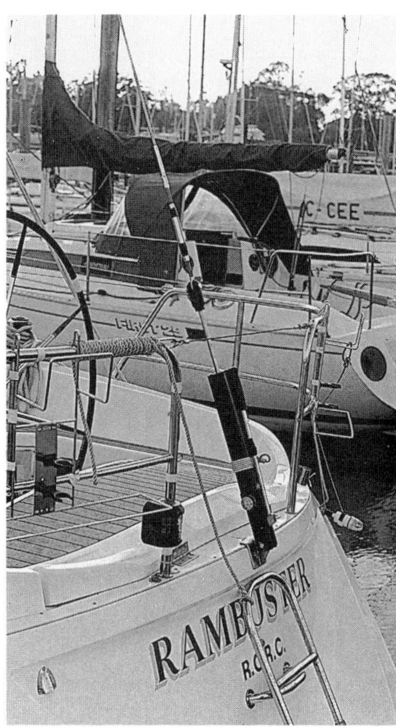

Hydraulic tensioning for backstay

Because hydraulic systems can be made to generate such high power they can in fact achieve quite long throws by the use of reverse purchases and as a result can be used for items such as: flattening reefs, cunninghams, outhauls and even mainsheet tensioning systems. Hydraulic rams are often used as the final tensioning part of the running backstay on some large cruising yachts.

Their main uses on a rig are for:
a) Backstays
b) Checkstays
c) Inner forestays
d) Kicking straps

f) Highfield lever. The highfield lever is based on an over centre lock system which allows final tensioning of a stay. This system is most commonly found on dinghy halyards but can quite easily be adapted for yacht tensioning systems. Such applications could include cunningham and outhaul adjustments.

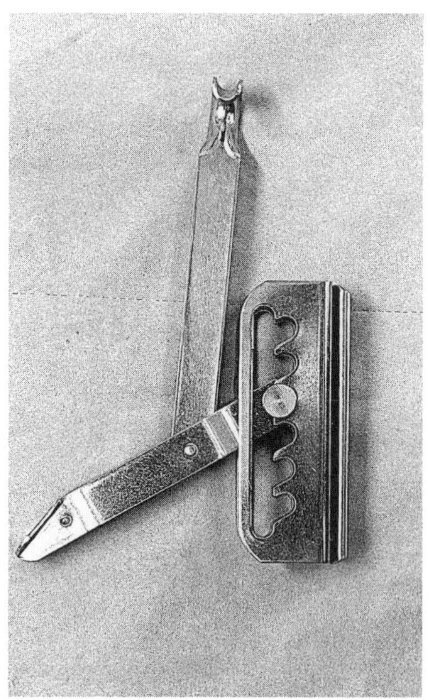

Highfield lever

g) Winch. This is the most common form of adjustment aboard most yachts and can be used for most applications. Its advantages include: ease of operation, high power ratios available and fast operation. However a winch should not be used in cases where the stay is a primary support such as the backstay on a masthead rigged boat. Whichever the system that is used it must not disconnect completely should the tensioning device be released completely.

Rod rigging types
Rod rigging consists of solid bars in a range of diameters and materials. There are a number of advantages to this type rigging system which include:
a) Low stretch
b) Reduced weight
c) Lower windage

The reduction in stretch for a given diameter of rigging is achieved with rod rigging as there is more material for a given cross sectional area. In addition to this, the stretch properties of the rigging can be improved by using higher grade materials such as Cobalt and carbon fibre.

Because there is more material for a given cross section area the ultimate tensile strength of rod rigging is higher than that for conventional 1x19 stainless steel wire for the same diameter. Therefore, the weight of the rigging can often be reduced as smaller diameter rods, compared to the equivalent wire sizes, can be used. Weight saved in the rigging has a more significant effect the further it is positioned away from centre of gravity of the yacht (see mast design section). It is therefore very important for most boats to reduce the weight of the rigging as far as is practically possible in order to improve the performance and motion of the boat. It has been argued that the weight of the rigging is not a significant consideration during the design of a boat. This may have been the case for older cruising yachts but nowadays yacht designers are very aware of the effect of weight aloft on performance and this is now a consideration for most sailing craft.

The advantages of rod rigging are not without their problems and one of the most important factors that prohibit the use of this type of rigging on cruising yachts is that of cost. In addition to this, fatigue of the rod as already mentioned is a potential problem. As a result the mast fittings need to be specifically designed for this type of rigging and allow a sufficient degree of articulation in order to minimize the effect of fatigue. The net result of this is that the attachment fittings can often be more expensive than conventional shroud tangs.

Standing rigging comparison for 38ft (11.6m) fractional cruiser/racer

Item	1x19 St.St (mm)	Dyform 1x19 St.St (mm)	Rod Nit.50 (mm)
Forestay	8.00	8.00	7.50
Backstay	5.00	5.00	4.50
Cap shrouds	8.00	8.00	7.50
Int. shrouds	6.00	6.00	5.50
Lower shrouds	8.00	8.00	7.50
Babystay	6.00	6.00	5.50
Jumpers	4.00	4.00	3.50
Weight (Kg)	19.16	23.95	27.20
Stretch (mm)	42.96	34.37	29.38

(Courtesy Riggarna UK Ltd.)

Whilst weight is a very important consideration for the choice of rigging, the factor that is probably most noticeable when sailing is that of stretch. It is possible to specify a set of rigging that is well within the breaking loads required but is underspecified in terms of stretch. This is a very important consideration for racing yachts, even cruiser racers. Rigging sizes that allow a great deal of stretch in the shrouds will cause the mast to 'fall off' to leeward and make tuning very difficult. Not only can the mast not be tuned correctly but the performance of the boat will be well below its best. The effects of 'fall off' are discussed in Chapter 6; at this stage we should accept that excessive rigging stretch is undesirable.

The reason for mentioning the stretch problem is that it is a common mistake for rigs to be specified with sizes matching the minimum breaking loads shown on a rigging table with no consideration of stretch.

A third consideration that may be used to justify the use of rod rigging is that of windage. With smaller diameter rigging less area is presented reducing the drag. This type of consideration is usually only found on multihulls that have very high apparent wind speeds and therefore wind resistance is an important factor. Sometimes rod rigging is profiled to reduce further the windage. This type of rigging is known as lenticular.

There are four main types of material used in rod rigging manufacture which are as follows.

a) Nitronic 50. This is the standard material used and is a nickel chromium molybdenum alloy. For a given diameter its advantages over stainless steel wire rigging is that it has a

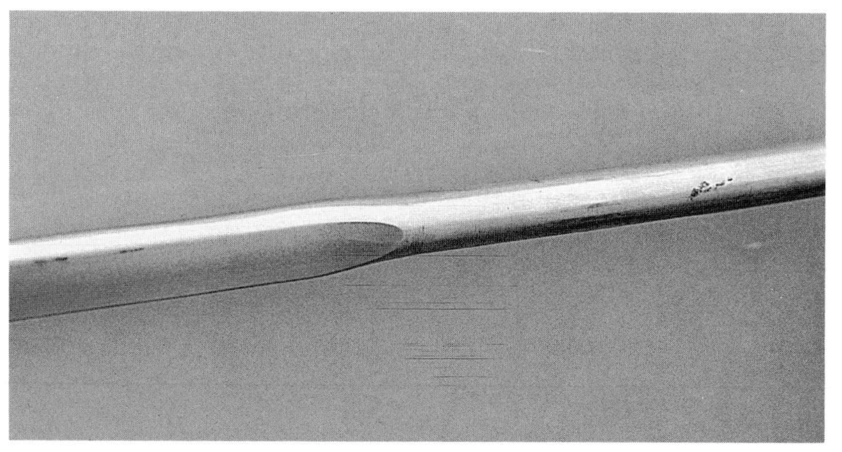

Lenticular rigging

higher breaking strength and a lower stretch factor. This type of rod has a high resistance to corrosion, an essential quality for yacht equipment.
b) Cobalt. These type of rods are made of MP35N, a nickel cobalt alloy with characteristics exceeding those of standard Nitronic 50 rod with regard to strength, low stretch and corrosion resistance. This type of rigging is almost exclusively found on racing yachts where the very best weight or stretch properties need to be achieved. (Its high price means that it is rarely found on cruising yachts.) The advantages of cobalt rigging can be exploited in a number of ways.
i) Weight – As Cobalt rigging has a higher modulus of elasticity an advantage in weight can be gained by using a smaller size without necessarily an increase in stretch.
ii) Stretch – By retaining the same diameter as for the standard rod the stretch of the rigging can be reduced without a large increase in weight.
iii) Size – Due to the higher breaking load of Cobalt rod, a smaller diameter of rigging may be used thus reducing the windage. However care must be taken that the pin sizes match the rod sizes in terms of their

Minimum breaking load – Nitronic 50 rod

Rod diam. (mm)	– Size	Pin size (mm)	Pin size (ins)	Min. brk. (kg)
3.50		8.0	5/16	1452
4.00		8.0	5/16	1860
4.50	-4	9.5	3/8	2270
5.00	-6	9.5	3/8	2720
5.50		11.1	7/16	3220
6.00	-8	11.1	7/16	3900
6.50	-10	12.7	1/2	4500
7.00	-12	12.7	1/2	5350
7.50		15.8	5/8	6400
8.00		15.8	5/8	7350
8.50	-17	15.8	5/8	8000
9.00		19.0	3/4	9000
9.50	-22	19.0	3/4	9750
11.10	-30	22.2	7/8	13600
12.70	-40	25.4	1	16300
14.30	-48	28.6	1 1/8	20900
16.75	-60	31.8	1 1/4	26800
18.03	-66	31.8	1 1/4	29500
20.60	-75	31.8	1 1/4	34000
22.23	-90	34.9	1 3/8	40800
25.40	-110	38.1	1 1/2	49900

Loads based on Riggarana rod rigging.

Minimum breaking load – cobalt MP35N rod

Rod diam. (mm)	Pin size (mm)	Pin size (ins)	Min. brk. (Kg)
3.50	8.0	5/16	1627
4.00	8.0	5/16	2125
4.50	9.5	3/8	2689
5.20	9.5	3/8	3591
5.70	11.1	7/16	4337
6.00	11.1	7/16	4781
6.35	12.7	1/2	5355
7.20	15.8	5/8	6862
7.92	15.8	5/8	8340
8.35	15.8	5/8	8994
8.71	15.8	5/8	10080
9.50	19.0	3/4	12049
10.30	22.2	7/8	14091
11.10	22.2	7/8	16364
11.58	22.2	7/8	18182
12.70	25.4	1	20909
13.00	25.4	1	21818
14.30	28.6	1 1/8	24545
15.30	31.8	1 1/4	29545
16.70	31.8	1 1/4	34091

Loads based on Riggarana rod rigging.

Mechanical properties of rod and wire (for given load)
(Courtesy Riggarna UK Ltd.)

Material	Size (mm)	Min-Brk (Kg)	Stretch (mm/m)	Weight (Kg/m)
Std 1x19 st.st	11.00	9450	2.10	0.451
Dyform 1x19 st.st	10.00	9770	2.10	0.466
Nitronic 50 rod	9.50	9750	1.74	0.560
Cobalt MP35N rod	8.71	10045	1.73	0.500

Stretch calculated at 25% of break load in mm/m

load carrying ability. Consideration must also be given to the increased stretch factor as a result of reducing the rod diameter. It is all too easy to throw away the advantages of a low windage set of rigging by using such small diameter rods that the high stretch makes the rig virtually uncontrollable and very difficult to tune.

c) Titanium. This type of rod is again usually only found on racing yachts where the weigh considerations are very important. It differs dramatically from other types of rod as it has relatively poor stretch properties but is however very light. These two factors mean that it is usually only found on permanent backstays on fractional rigged masts.

Terminations
There are two ways of terminating rod rigging;

a) Swaging. This is exactly the same process as for wire swaging and utilizes the same end fittings. However, whilst it is a simple and cheap method of terminating rod rigging it is to be discouraged on all but lightly loaded stays for which there is very little movement or change of angle. The reason for this is again one of the fatigue problems. As rod rigging does not deflect as easily as its wire counterpart, there is a higher risk of fatigue loading because the swage cannot accommodate any of the deflection. The changes in angle can only be effected by either the tang moving or the rod deflecting or both. T-terminals are particularly bad on rod rigging as they do not deflect easily and therefore the rod has to accommodate any movement. The fatigue loading will normally be concentrated at the end of the swage and this is often where failure occurs.

Therefore if swage terminals are to be used they should only appear on items such as the jumper stay attachments where the loading and deflections are relatively low.

b) Cold heading. This method is by far the most common and suitable way of terminating rod rigging. Before the heading takes place the type of end fitting must be considered and the appropriate additional fitting, such as a stemball, be positioned on the rod (see page 50). The process involves clamping the end of the rod in a special die, (for a given rod diameter) and applying a high pressure to the end of the rod. This is achieved with the use of a hyraulic ram. The result is a cold formed head which can withstand the breaking load of the rod.

The equipment required to produce the cold head is specialized and cannot be readily found to the same extent as say swaging machines for wire. In addition to this it is usually a large piece of equipment and cannot be easily moved to the dockside for on site use. Both of these limitations mean that the rigging has to be made to length on the rigging company premises and cannot be made overlength in the way that wire rigging can be. Boats with rod

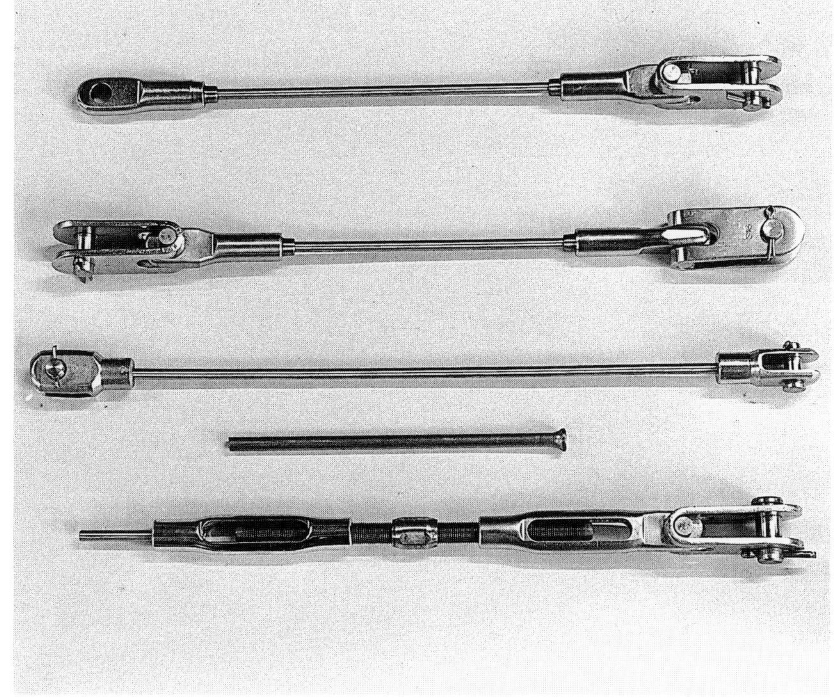

Types of eye and fork fitting for rod rigging

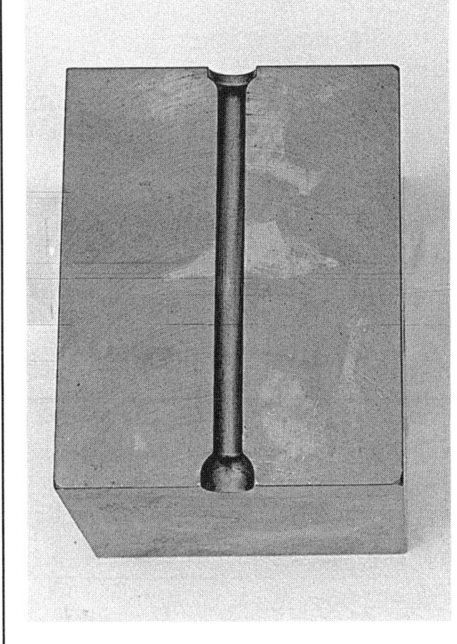

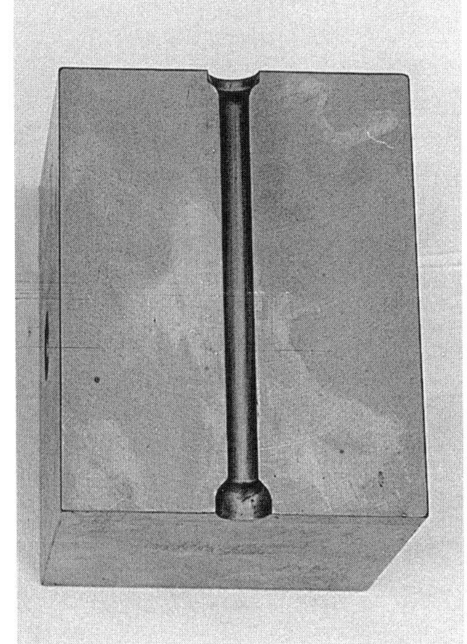

Photographs on this and the facing page top: Cold formed heads on rod rigging

rigging have to be accurately spanned before the rigging can be made (see Spanning the rig). Whilst this is not a difficult or complicated task it is worth bearing these factors in mind when ordering the rigging especially if the boat is some distance or overseas from the rigging supplier.

End fittings
With the exception of Talurit or Nicro-press type fittings, the end

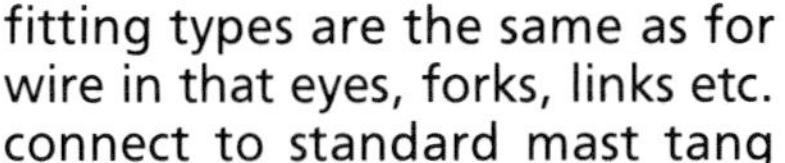

fitting types are the same as for wire in that eyes, forks, links etc. connect to standard mast tang systems. As we have already mentioned, swages can be used and therefore fittings such as studs, t-terminals, eyes etc. are generally attached in the same way as for wire rigging.

However for the cold head process the method of the attachment to the rod is different.

Photographs below: Fitting eyes and forks on rod rigging

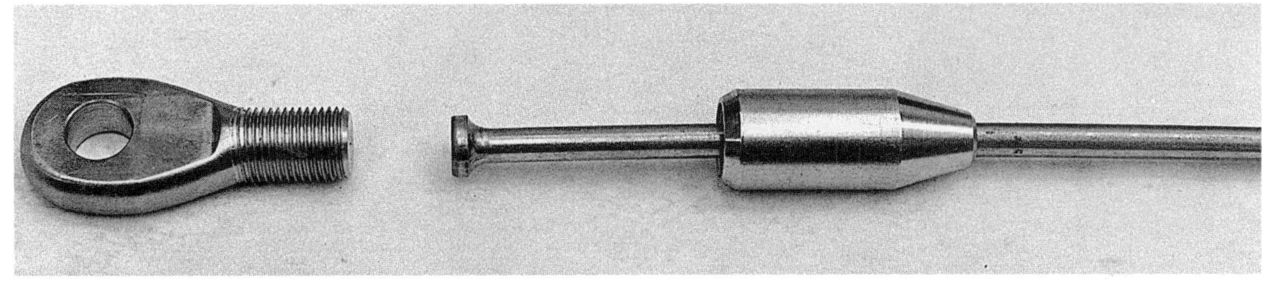

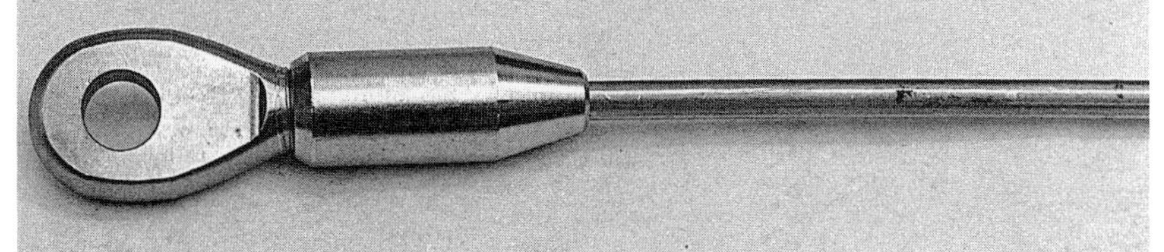

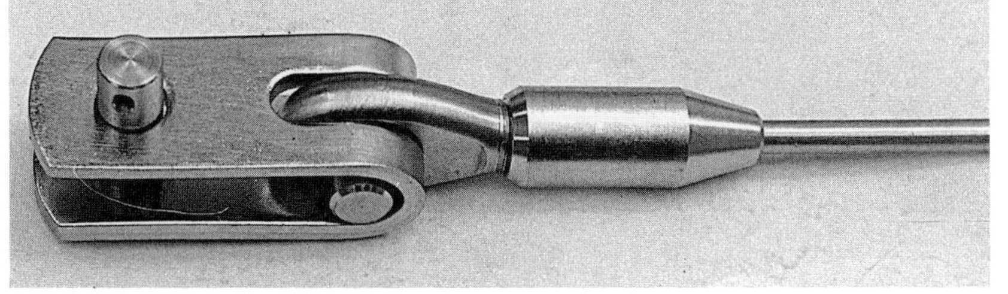

Eyes and forks

Before the rod is headed a machined collar is slid onto the rod. This collar has a cup shaped hole in which the rod is seated. The inside top surface has a thread. Once the head has been formed a machined eye or fork can be screwed into the cup fitting. The cup shaped seating allows the head of the rod to move in much the same way as a ball and socket joint which means that the rigging can move through a limited range of angles thus reducing the fatigue loading. A roll pin is then inserted in the fitting to prevent the two components from unscrewing.

This type of system can also be

used for T-terminal, stud connections and wire to rod connections. One advantage of this method of attachment is that should the fitting become damaged it can be replaced independently of the rod.

Stemballs
Another type of end fitting is the stemball type which secures into a fitting such as the Proctor 'RT tang'. This fitting consists of a seating component known as a stemball which supports the rod from under the head. The stemball is then seated in the coquille fitting. The purpose of the stemball is twofold. Firstly it provides a greater bearing surface for the end of the rod. Secondly it distributes any bending load away from the head of the rod by means of the stem. This stem is often tapered so that any bending can be spread along its length instead of merely transferring it to the end of the stem.

This type of fitting is used where weight is a critical factor and therefore it is usually only found on racing yachts.

Fitting a stemball for an 'RT' tang

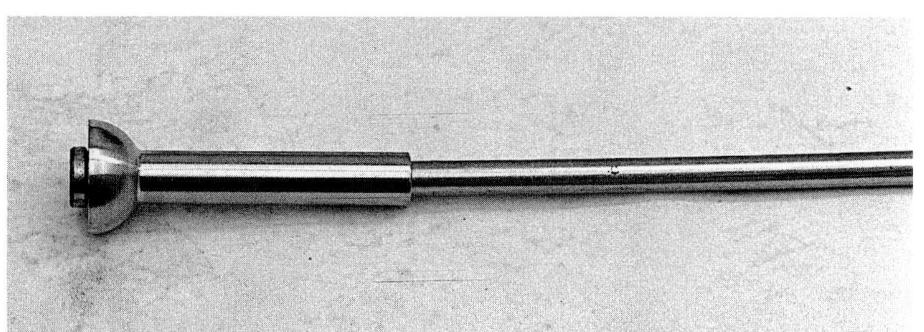

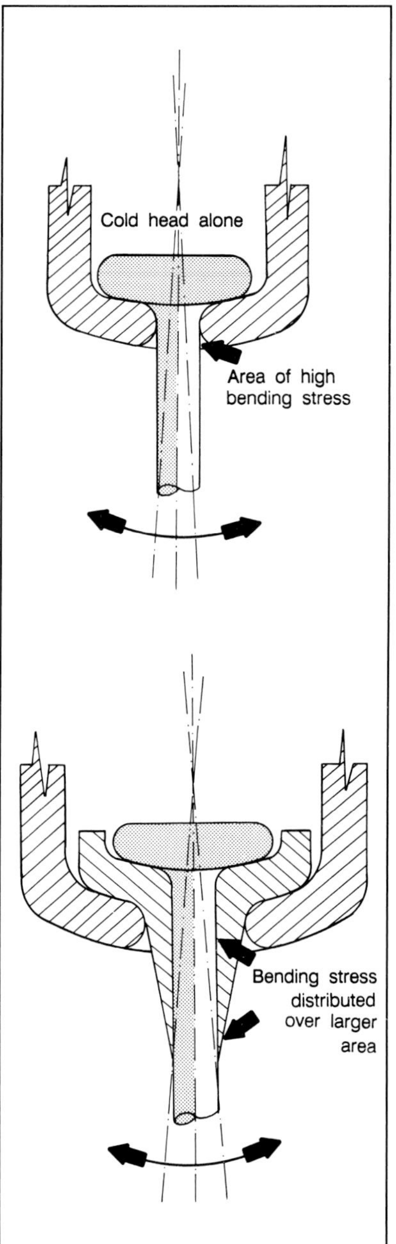

The stemball distributes bending stresses

Calculating rigging sizes
When faced with the problem of specifying a set of standing rigging sizes it is important to bear in mind that a rigging company will in most cases be best equipped to provide such information. There may however be occasions where you wish to

make some checks on the sizes of rigging where perhaps specialist knowledge is not readily available. The following is a guide to some of the methods that will help you to establish such sizes.

These approximations are intended for conventional type cruising yachts and should not be considered as a definitive method nor should they be used for racing yachts or extreme yachts either in their design or purpose.

Method 1
As a rule of thumb for cruising yachts, the cap shroud breaking load should be approximately equal to twice the weight of the ballast keel of the yacht.

eg. For a 35 ft (10.7 m) yacht with a ballast keel weight of 2200 Kg (485 lb)

Cap shroud break load = 4400 Kg

For 1x19 stainless steel wire rigging
Diameter = 8.00 mm

(see rigging size table)

Method 2
Another method of approximating the rigging sizes is to consider the vertical load on the chainplates. This is again an approximation which should only be used to check a set of rigging sizes and not for specifying a rigging package.

Vertical chainplate load =

$$\frac{\text{Righting moment @ } 30^\circ \times 1.5}{0.5 \times \text{chain plate width}} \times \text{F of S}$$

(where F of S is a factor of safety usually 2.5 - 3.0)

e.g For a 32 ft (9.75 m) yacht with;

RM @ 30 = 1300 Kg.m
CPW = 2.40 m
Single spreader
Masthead rig
Single lowers
F of S = 3.0

Vertical chain plate load = 4875.0 Kg

Assuming that the vertical load is equally split between the cap shroud and the lower shroud, the chainplate load can be divided by two to give the breaking load for the cap shroud and lower shroud (in the case of a single spreader rig).

Breaking load = 2437.5 Kg (Each wire)

For 1x19 stainless steel wire rigging:

Cap and lower shroud diameter
= 6.00 mm (0.24 in)

(see rigging size table)

Having established the cap and lower shroud diameters the forestay and backstay diameters can be established. (It is important to remember that this is an approximation based on a simple masthead rig.)

These stays should have a minimum size equal to the largest shroud size. Therefore the 32 ft (9.75 m) yacht described above should have a forestay and backstay of no less than 6.00 mm (0.24 in).

Both of these methods are based on calculating the vertical load on the chainplates for conventional sloop rigged yachts. If one is considering the rigging for a racing yacht it is interesting to note that for the same set of variables (ie RM, chainplate width etc.) the vertical load on the chainplates is the same. The factor that is varied in order to allow the rigging sizes to be smaller is the factor of safety.

Method 3
Mast compression and factors for simple rigs.

Chain plates
The strength of a complete rigging system can only be as strong as the weakest link in that system. The chain plates are of course an essential part of the rigging system and as a result need to be compatible, strength wise, to the rest of the components.

Most chain plate systems are mounted on deck at a position on, or inboard of the gunwales. The precise position is determined by the angle that the shrouds intersect the mast for which there is a minimum in order to support the mast sufficiently. Too small an angle results in high compression down the mast with little athwartships support. (Chapter 2)

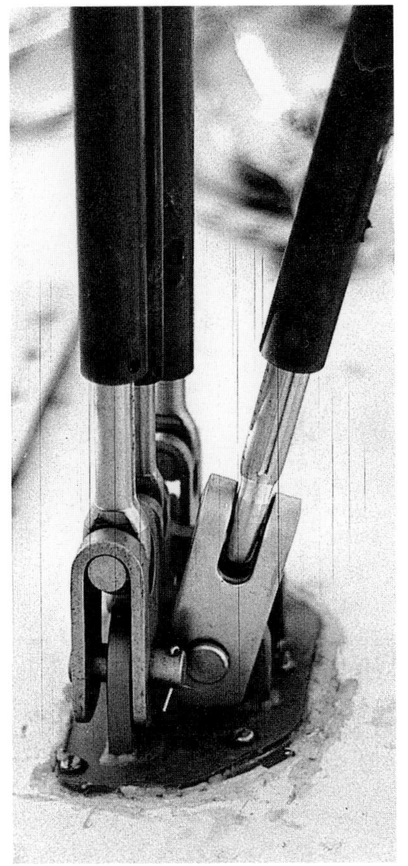

Chainplate alignment to reduce fatique

The chain plates need to carry at least one set of lower and cap shrouds and to allow sufficient articulation their orientation is important. That is to say that the chainplates must be in line with the load from the shroud or stay. The cap shroud chain plates should be mounted in the fore and aft plane in order to accommodate mast bend and rake. The chain plates for the lower shrouds should be aligned in the athwartships plane so as to allow for the angle at which the shroud connects. Each stay should also have a toggle allowing movement in the opposite direction. ie The lower shrouds should have a toggle allowing fore and aft movement and vice versa.

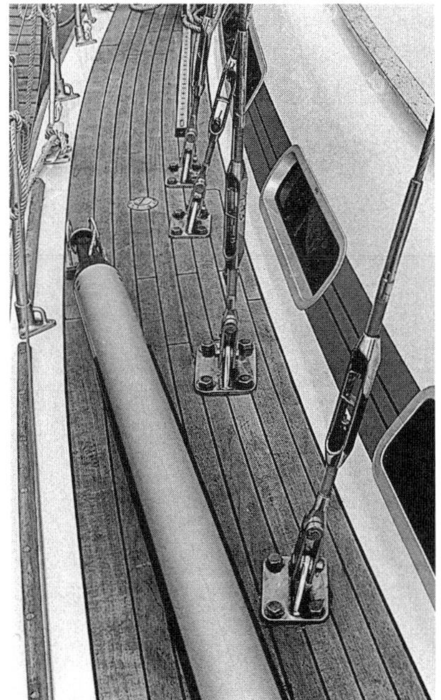

Chainplate orientation to suit individual spans

In order to prevent the deck area being lifted as a result of the rigging loads the chain plates must be connected in some way to the keel of the boat. This can be achieved either in the form of attaching the chain plates to a bulkhead or ring frame that is in way of the mast or using tie downs from the underside of the deck to the mast step (assuming a keel stepped mast).

On some racing yachts the chain plates are mounted below deck. This both reduces windage (although in practical terms the saving is minimal) and keeps the decks clear and reduces the chances of sails snagging on the rigging screws.

The requirement for free articulation in all directions is every bit as necessary as for the on-deck type chain plates. They must also be connected to the mast step by means of a bulkhead, ring frame or set of tie downs.

Whichever method is used there are dimensions that must be adhered to in order to ensure both the strength of the fitting and its compatibility with common rigging attachments. The dimensions of the chain plates will vary depending on the material that is used for their construction.

Aluminium chain plate dimensions. (H30, 20 TF)

Wire diam. (mm)	1x19 St.St Breaking load load (Kg)	Pin size (mm)	t + (mm)	w + (mm)	y + (mm)
3.0	720	6.4	2.96	16.01	7.51
4.0	1280	8.0	4.21	20.02	9.38
5.0	2000	9.5	5.54	23.77	11.14
5.5	2400	11.1	5.69	27.77	13.02
6.0	2880	11.1	6.83	27.77	13.02
7.0	3550	12.7	7.36	31.78	14.90
8.0	4640	12.7	9.61	31.78	14.90
9.0	5870	16.0	9.65	40.03	18.77
10.0	7250	16.0	11.92	40.03	18.77
11.0	9450	19.0	13.09	47.54	22.28
12.0	10400	19.0	14.40	47.54	22.28
13.0	13200	23.0	15.10	57.55	26.98
14.0	14200	23.0	16.25	57.55	26.98
16.0	18600	25.4	19.27	63.55	29.79
19.0	23200	28.6	21.35	71.56	33.54
22.0	30825	35.0	23.18	87.57	41.05

+ See diagram overleaf

Stainless steel chain plate dimensions. (EN58J)

Wire diam. (mm)	1 x 19 St.St Breaking load (Kg)	Pin size (mm)	Δ t (mm)	Δ w (mm)	Δ y (mm)
3.0	720	6.4	2.96	16.01	4.81
4.0	1280	8.0	4.21	20.02	6.01
5.0	2000	9.5	5.54	23.77	7.13
5.5	2400	11.1	5.69	27.77	8.43
6.0	2880	11.1	6.83	27.77	8.43
7.0	3550	12.7	7.36	31.78	9.54
8.0	4640	12.7	9.61	31.78	9.54
9.0	5870	16.0	9.65	40.03	12.02
10.0	7250	16.0	11.92	40.03	12.02
11.0	9450	19.0	13.09	47.54	14.27
12.0	10400	19.0	14.40	47.54	14.27
13.0	13200	23.0	15.10	57.55	17.27
14.0	14200	23.0	16.25	57.55	17.27
16.0	18600	25.4	19.27	63.55	19.08
19.0	23200	28.6	21.35	71.56	21.48
22.0	30825	35.0	23.18	87.57	26.28

Δ See diagram overleaf

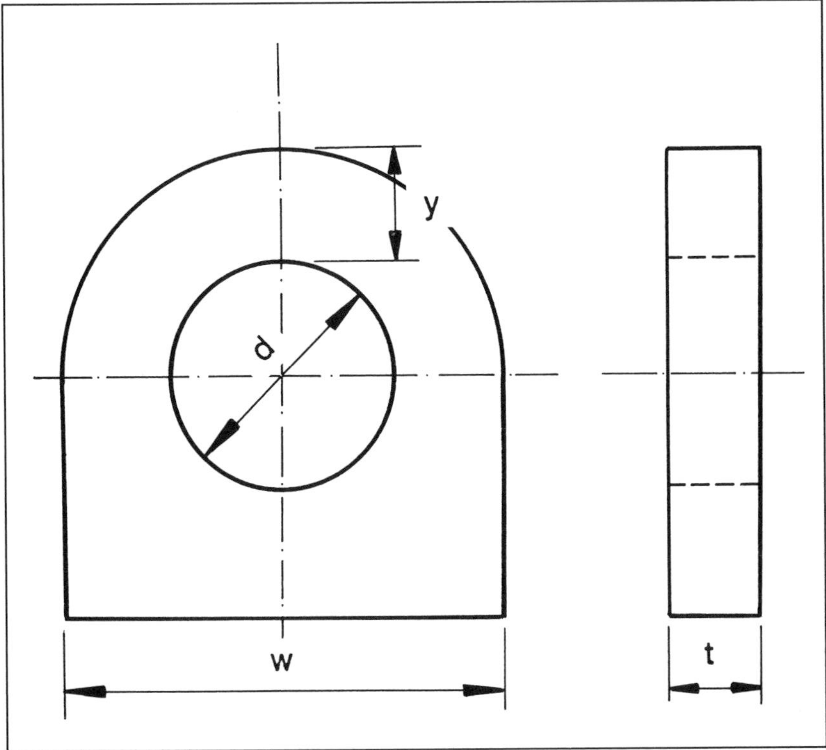

Typical chainplate dimensions

There are fairly standard procedures for working out the size of chain plates which are in mechanical engineering terms known as 'eye ends', and may be found in most engineering books. The following tables show typical sizes for chainplates for a given wire size and pin size and are based on the two most popular construction materials.

Maintenance: standing rigging
Standing rigging is generally good at resisting corrosion provided that the equipment is regularly maintained and can last many seasons use. Of course the only way to keep check on the state of the rigging is by careful observation and one of the most important tools to have at hand is a magnifying glass. The easiest way to check the rigging is when the mast has been unstepped and is lying on a set of trestles.

Checking the fittings
Starting from the top check each tang and eye fitting for cracks and signs of wear. Any welds that are present in a fitting should also be checked. Shroud tangs are particularily vulnerable when the mast is being raised, lowered or stored. The tang can sometimes be pushed into the mast wall both damaging the mast and the tang and sometimes even shearing the split pin in the process. This is particularly dangerous if the mast is re-stepped without the split pin being replaced as there will be nothing to hold the clevis pin in place.

Fittings that show signs of corrosion should be carefully studied as this will have removed some of the material making the fitting weaker and thus more prone to some form of damage such as a crack.

Hole elongation is an indication of either an old fitting or overloading and will require the fitting to be replaced. In addition to this it is very important to check that the particular stay is only being used for the purpose that it was intended. If the fitting has been deformed as a result of overloading then there is a good chance that the other fittings in that particular stay are overloaded as well and it may be necessary to increase the size of the fittings and stays all round. However, merely increasing the size of the rigging may just transfer the higher loads to a part of the mast that was not originally designed to take such loads. If this is the case then you should consult the spar manufacturer.

It is very important that the pin and hole sizes of any fitting match as a difference in sizes not only means that their strengths are not matched, but point loading may occur which will further weaken the fitting.

Clevis pins should be checked for any flats or bends along their length which again may be an indication of overloading and should be investigated. Shackles should be investigated in the same way especially where they are situated near the gunwales as they are prone to collision damage either with other boats or when docking.

The split pins (cotter pins in USA) that secure the clevis pins should be checked to make sure that they have not been under load due to any splaying of the fitting. These pins are not intended to carry any load and can shear quite easily, often with disastrous consequences.

Swaged fittings should be studied very carefully as they can sometimes split or crack, especially if they were not correctly fitted when the rigging was made. If there are any signs of this they should be replaced without question. The area where the wire meets the swage should be checked thoroughly both for the condition of the swage and the wire as this is often where failure occurs.

Rigging screws should be carefully watched for signs of cracking or wear on the end fittings and the body, in particular the threads should be checked for corrosion. Damaged or missing parts of the thread will reduce the load bearing surface and hence overload the remaining threads which may in turn lead to a chain reaction and eventual failure. The threads should be adequately lubricated to both ease their operation and afford some protection against corrosion.

Checking the wire

Each rigging span should be checked for splintering. Once one strand breaks there is a good chance that further strands in the same area will also break. In some cases a single broken strand may not mean that the stay has to be replaced immediately and a reasonable method to use in order to establish whether the wire can be continued to be used is the '5% test'.

1) Multiply the diameter of the wire by 8 and note as the 'Test Length'.
2) If along the wire's length more than 5% of the strands are broken for a given 'Test Length', then the complete wire should be replaced.
eg. For 6mm 1x19 stainless steel wire

Test Length = 8 x 6
= 48 mm

If more than 1 strand (5% of 19) is broken per 48 mm on any part of the wire's length, then discard wire.

Broken strands should be treated very seriously especially on stays that take sails particularily if their luffs are hanked to the stay. A broken and protruding strand can be caught by a hank which will tend to unravel the strand causing it to bunch around the stay. In some cases this could prevent the sail from being lowered altogether.

Spares and tools

The following list concerns the rigging only and is by no means exhaustive, but is a guide to some of the spares and tools that should be carried especially if the boat is to be sailed over long distances away from specialized rigging services.

a) Bulldog clips
b) Length of wire at least 2 x the longest stay length
c) Clevis pins and split pins
d) Drifts for split pins
e) Norseman/Staylok eyes and forks
f) Talurit/Nicropress ferules and fitting tool
g) Wire cutters or bolt croppers
h) Hacksaw
i) Pliers
j) Spanners
k) Screwdrivers

4: Running rigging

This chapter concerns only the running rigging that is directly associated with the *spars* on the boat as well as a limited range end fittings and terminations. Because the subject is so broad, this section of the book is intended as a guide to some of the equipment available along with some suggestions on sizes. In addition to this, the equipment available changes frequently as new materials and techniques become available. Therefore a yacht owner would be well advised to contact a specialist rigging company for specific information in order to develop a detailed specification.

Wire types

Because most of the running rigging turns over a number of sheaves, flexibility is an important factor when considering the type of material that should be used. It is for this reason that when wire is considered for items such as halyards 7x19 construction is favoured in most cases. Wire that is constructed by this method is available in two materials, stainless steel and galvanized steel. The stainless steel wire is very good in terms of corrosion resistance but is slightly less flexible than the galvanised equivalent. In addition to this it is also slightly more expensive.

As with standing rigging there is a wide range of methods of end termination, but the most common by far is the thimble eye which is fastened by means of a 'talurit' or 'Nicropress'.

Rope types

Unless a reel type winch is used, rope tails will be necessary in order to cleat off the control lines. In most cases, reef lines and other miscellaneous running rigging will be entirely rope with exception of those that carry very high loads such as outhaul lines and kicking strap controls.

There are many types of materials and construction methods available for such tails and a specialist rigging company should be consulted for the latest options. The most popular types however fall into the

Halyard reel winch

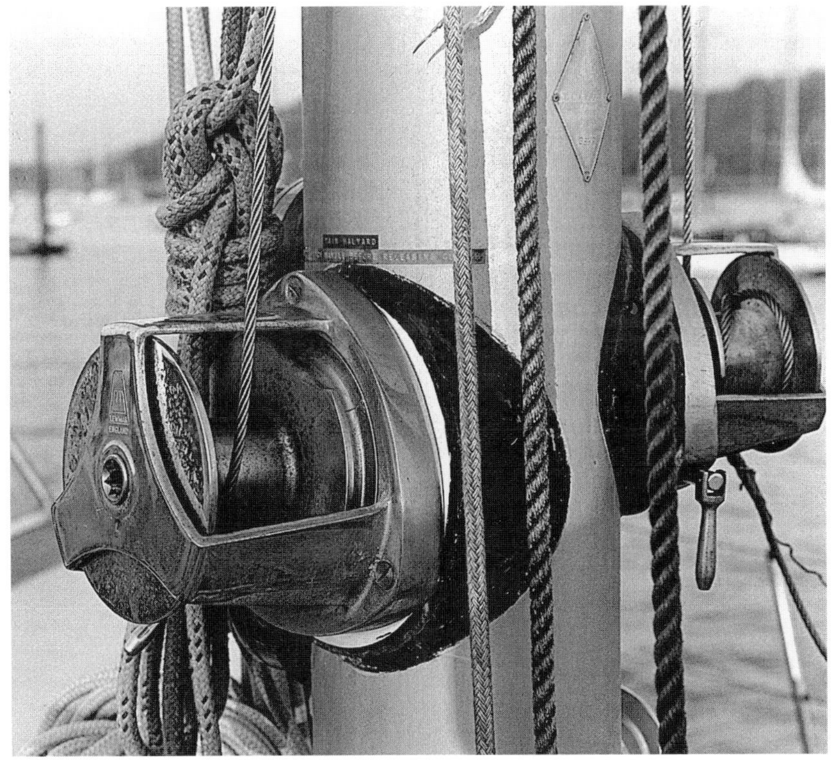

following categories:
a) Dacron. This is a polyester rope and is the most popular type used for running rigging. Its high strength, low stretch and relatively low price make it a very popular choice for most applications.
b) Kevlar. This is aramid fibre used as a core with a polyester braid line sheath. This type of rope has gained in popularity especially for lines that require very low stretch such as halyard tails on racing halyards. Although Kevlar rope possesses higher strength properties than the equivalent polyester braidline sizes the material does have its limitations in that it does not perform well when it is deflected through sharp angles. Large diameter sheaves are required in order to minimize the fatigue and in areas where there are sharp deflections wire should be used. This has led to a great many of racing yacht halyards being constructed primarily from Kevlar line, but with short wire tails at the top end of the halyard where it passes through deflectors such as spinnaker halyard bullseyes on fractional rig masts. The length of the tail would normally be sufficient to travel from the bullseye up the mast and over the sheave where it is then spliced into the Kevlar, which then travels all the way down the mast and back to the winch or cleating arrangements. This has the advantage that as the wire chafes in the area of the bullseyes, the damaged length may be cut off and the remaining wire may be re-formed as a thimble eye.

Another advantage of Kevlar for racing yachts is that due to its higher breaking strength, a smaller diameter may be used than for the polyester braidline type halyard, and therefore the weight aloft may also be reduced.
c) 'Spectra'. This is a relatively new type of rope which possesses a higher breaking strength and lower stretch factor than even Kevlar. However, its high price generally prohibits its use on all but the top racing yachts. The core material is the fibre itself and it is sheathed in polyester braidline. Its principal applications are the same as Kevlar i.e. halyards and items that need low stretch control lines, but it can in a lot of cases offer lower stretch and/or lower weight.
d) Gleinstein. This type of rope, (often referred to as "Cup Sheet" in the USA), combines low stretch characteristics with high abrasion resistance. These properties are achieved by producing a parallel core of polyester, (thus reducing the constructional stretch) and is covered in two layers of braid on braid sheath. It is this double sheath that gives the rope its high chafe resistance. Gleinstein's most popular applications are for control lines that are subject to high loads with a high risk of chafe whilst requiring low stretch properties. These would include items such as:
i) Spinnaker guys
ii) Reefing lines
iii) Genoa sheets
This type of rope can quite easily be identified as it is a relatively stiff rope to bend and almost feels as if it has a wire core. This stiffness can be attributed to the double sheath.

A distinct advantage of this type of rope over, say, Kevlar is that it retains a higher proportion of its strength when knotted or passed through an abrupt angle. In addition to this it is also cheaper than Kevlar and Spectra.

Configuration

The type and number of halyards, reef lines and other miscellaneous items that are required is directly dependent on the type of rig. For example, a masthead sloop rig will normally only require halyards for main, genoa and spinnakers. Whereas a cutter rig will require all of these plus at least one staysail halyard. The specific number of halyards will of course depend on the specific requirements for a particular boat and the table is therefore by no means definitive.

Having established how many halyards and additional control lines are required, it is now necessary to develop a rigging schedule so that this equipment can be manufactured. It is at this stage when it is necessary to establish the specific purpose of the yacht i.e. in terms of the materials used, the specification for a 35ft (10.7m) cruising yacht may differ dramatically from that of a 35ft (10.7m) racing yacht. The following specifications illustrate the difference between the cruising and racing spec for the same size yacht.

One of the most noticeable differences between the two specifications is that of the materials used for the rope tails.

Rope type summary for a given diameter and in ascending order of cost.

	Stretch	**Abrasion resistance**	**Deflection resistance**
Braidline	**	***	****
Gleistein	***	*****	***
Kevlar	****	***	*
Spectra	*****	***	****

* poor ** fair *** good **** v. good ***** excellent

Halyard option table

Item	Sloop	Cutter	Ketch	Yawl	Material
	Rig type				
Main halyard	1	1	1	1	Wire/rope
Main t.lift	1	1	1	1	Rope
Genoa halyard	1,2	1,2	1,2	1,2	Wire/rope
Spinnaker halyard	1,2	1,2	1,2	1,2	Rope
Spinnaker pole t.lift	1,2	1,2	1,2	1,2	Rope
Staysail halyard		1	0,1	0,1	Wire/rope
Mizzen main halyard			1	1	Wire/rope
Mizzen boom t.lift			1	1	Rope
Mizzen staysail hal.			1	1	Rope

When considering a racing yacht accurate control over the luff tension of both the mainsail and genoa is critical in order to obtain an optimum sail shape. As a result it is necessary to limit the amount of stretch in these halyards to an absolute minimum. However, it can be seen from the specification that the spinnaker halyards in this case are also Kevlar, the reason being that on modern day racing yachts the spinnaker halyards are in fact used as temporary genoa halyards when headsail changing is necessary. This is also the reason for there being two spinnaker halyards and one genoa halyard on the racing specification as opposed to two genoa halyards and one spinnaker halyard on a cruising specification. Very few cruising yachts do spinnaker peel changes and therefore only require one spinnaker halyard but often may wish to change headsails in which case two genoa halyards may be required. The racing yacht may need to peel change both spinnakers and headsails but in order to reduce the weight aloft only one genoa halyard is present. The spinnaker halyards can then be used as temporary genoa halyards as they are above the hounds height. (The genoa halyard should not be used for flying a spinnaker for two reasons a) the sheave box exit does not normally possess adequate anti-chafe fittings and therefore may seriously damage the halyard sheave box b) if the spinnaker is gybed the halyard will then be wrapped around the forestay making it very difficult to lower the sail and in some case damaging both the halyard and the forestay).

Developing the specification

Once the running rigging requirements have been established the sizes then need to be calculated. One of the fundamental differences between standing rigging and running rigging is that the latter tends to be far more susceptible to chafe and this is very often a more significant factor when considering sizes and materials than that of the direct load on the rigging. If a set of spars have been well designed chafe would have been an important consideration throughout the design of the spars. Sheaves and swivel leads

Rigging comparison for cruiser and racer options

Item	Cruiser No.	Cruiser Material Wire	Cruiser Material Rope	Cruiser Diam. (mm) Wire	Cruiser Diam. (mm) Rope	Racer No.	Racer Material Wire	Racer Material Rope	Racer Diam. (mm) Wire	Racer Diam. (mm) Rope
Main hal.	1	7x19	Tbr	6.0	12.0	1	7x19	Kev	6.0	8.0
Main t/lift	1	–	Tbr	–	10.0	0	–	–	–	–
Genoa hal.	2	7x19	Tbr	6.0	12.0	1	7x19 strp	Kev	4.0	8.0
Spin hal.	1	–	Tbr	–	12.0	2	7x19 strp	Kev	4.0	8.0
Spin t/lift	1	–	Tbr	–	10.0	1	–	Tbr	–	8.0

Tbr – Terylene braidline   Kev – Kevlar   Strp – Strop

(Courtesy Rouse Rigging)

Typical halyard size guide

Dimensions in mm

Boat size in feet	-18	18-24	24-30	30-36	36-44	44-54	54-66	66-80
Main hal.								
7x19 st	4.0	4.0	5.0	6.0	6.0	7.0	8.0	12.0
Braid	6.0	8.0	10.0	10.0	12.0	14.0	16.0	24.0
Genoa hal.								
7x19 st	4.0	4.0	5.0	6.0	6.0	7.0	8.0	12.0
Braid	6.0	8.0	10.0	12.0	12.0	14.0	16.0	24.0
Spin hal.								
7x19 st	4.0	4.0	5.0	6.0	6.0	7.0	8.0	12.0
Braid	6.0	8.0	10.0	12.0	12.0	14.0	16.0	24.0
Spin t.l.								
7x19 st	–	–	–	–	–	–	–	–
Braid	5.0	6.0	8.0	10.0	10.0	14.0	14.0	16.0
Main t.1.								
7x19 st	–	–	–	–	–	–	–	–
Braid	5.0	6.0	6.0	10.0	10.0	14.0	14.0	16.0
Mizzen main and staysail								
7x19 st	4.0	5.0	5.0	5.0	5.0	7.0	7.0	8.0
Braid	6.0	8.0	8.0	10.0	10.0	14.0	14.0	16.0
Staysail								
7x19 st	–	–	–	6.0	6.0	7.0	7.0	8.0
Braid	–	–	–	12.0	12.0	14.0	14.0	16.0

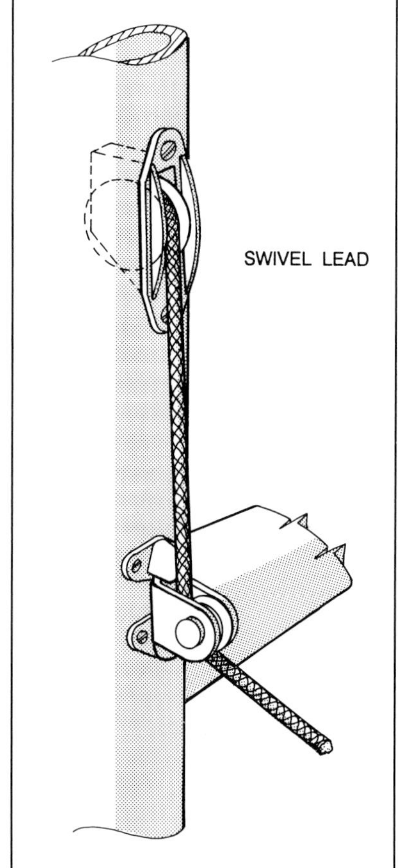

Left: Halyard or topping lift swivel lead prevents chafe on sheave cage

should have been positioned at all areas where the halyards are required to turn through an angle in order to reduce the effect of compression on the inside face of the rigging thus reducing the chance of damage to the rope. However, many factors such as the space available on a spar, inevitably make this

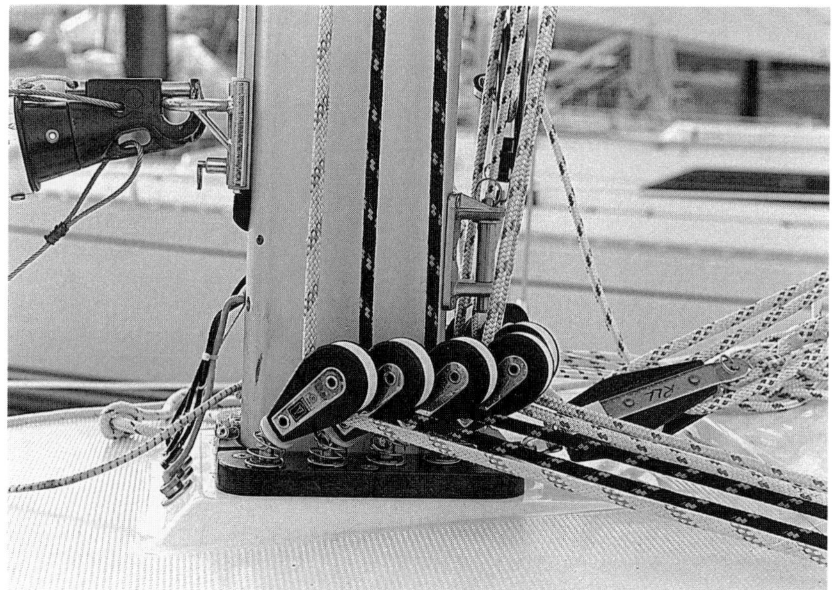

Deck mounted halyard lead blocks

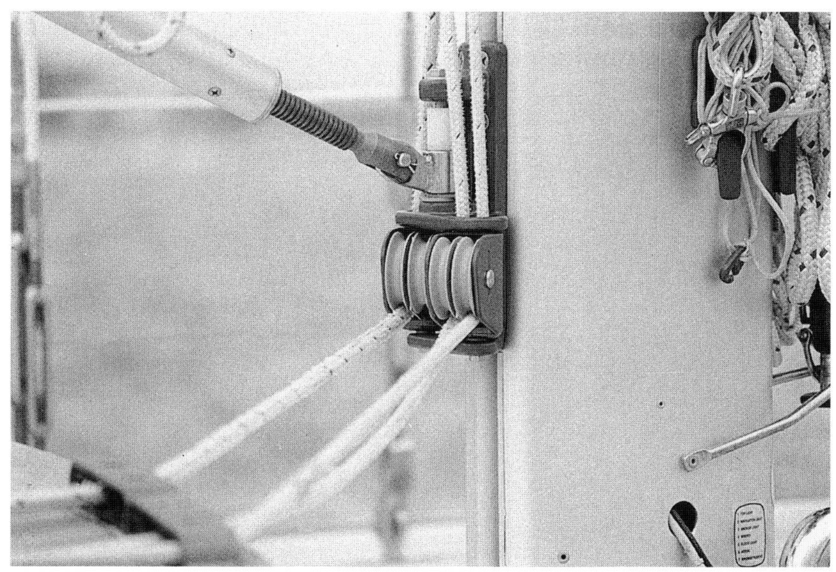

Halyard swivel leads at base of mast

design process a difficult compromise. This is very apparent on racing spars where windage and weight, especially aloft, is critical. In the design chapter we discussed the importance of establishing the yacht's purpose as a guide to the specification that should be drawn up. This again is the case for running rigging and also makes it very difficult to lay down hard and fast rules as to the sizes and materials that should be employed. For example, a "round the cans" maxi yacht may consider that weight and windage are such important factors that the owner must resign himself to having to replace halyards and running rigging on a fairly regular basis. On the other hand, for a Whitbread round the world maxi the halyard chafe would be one of the biggest concerns. Spars and their associated fittings where the halyard are concerned would be designed primarily to reduce the chances of chafe to an absolute minimum.

The dynamic loadings (or shock loadings) also make it difficult to define specific sizes without going into detailed calculations. The tables show typical rigging sizes which have been based on a wide range of historical data and have been split into the two categories – racing and cruising. The important point to bear in mind when developing the specification is that the breaking loads of each component in the item of rigging should as far as is possible be matched. (See table overleaf for rope breaking loads)

End fittings
The most popular type of end fitting for halyards fall into two categories, 'D' shackles and snap-shackles. There are many different makes of such fittings and in most cases the rigging company will specify a particular type that will suit the breaking load of the complete rigging system. Of the many types of shackles that are available the main variations can be listed as follows:

a) Strip Shackles. These shackles are generally only available in small sizes and are stamped from 316 grade stainless steel.
b) D-Shackles. These are generally available in two sizes, the standard D-shackle and the large D-shackle. The difference being the distance between the inside surface of the pin and the bearing surface of the D. These shackles are forged from 316 grade stainless steel and are available in a wide range of sizes.
c) Bow Shackle. This is similar to the D-shackle but is wider than the D part of the shackle. This type is also forged from 316 grade stainless steel.
d) Twist Shackle. Again forged from 316 stainless steel and similar to the bow shackle but the

Halyard size guide – racing

Dimensions in mm

Item	class					
	¼ ton	½ ton	¾ ton	1 ton	2 ton	50 ft IOR
Main hal.	6 Kev	5 7x19 8 Kev	5 7x19 10 Kev	6 7x19 10 Kev	7 7x19 12 Kev	8 7x19 14 Kev
Genoa hal.	6 Kev	4 7x19 8 Kev	4 7x19 8 Kev	5 7x19 10 Kev	6 7x19 10 Kev	7 7x19 12 Kev
Spin. hal.	6 Kev	4 7x19 8 Kev	4 7x19 8 Kev	5 7x19 8 Kev	6 7x19 10 Kev	7 7x19 12 Kev
Spin. t/lift	4 Kev 6 Tbr	4 Kev 8 Tbr	6 Kev 8 Tbr	8 Kev	8 Kev	8 Kev 10 Tbr

Kev = Kevlar
Tbr = Terylene braidline
7x19 = 7x19 wire

(Courtesy Rouse Rigging)

Min break load table – ropes

Diam	7x19	Synthetic fibre				Braided rope	
(mm)	St.St	Nylon	Terylene	Polyprop	Kevlar	Gleistein	Terylene
2.5	274						
3.0	510						
4.0	907	320	295			475	
5.0	1420	500	400		600		
6.0	2040	750	565	550	950	575	650
7.0	2780	1020	770				
8.0	3630	1350	1020	960	1750	1060	1175
9.0	4511	1700	1270				
10.0	5670	2080	1590	1425	2600	2080	1800
11.0	7950	2500	1910				
12.0	8160	3000	2270	2030	3500	2770	2575
13.0		3500	2720				
14.0	11100	4100	3180	2790	5700	4000	3650
16.0		5300	4100	3500		5900	4525
18.0		6700	5100	4450		7030	5675
20.0		8300	6300	5370		8300	7925
22.0		10000	7600	6500			
24.0		12000	9100	7600		11900	10200
26.0		13400	10100	8600			
28.0		15300	12200	10100			
32.0		20000	15700	12800			
36.0		24800	19300	16100			
40.0		30000	23900	19400			
44.0				23400			
48.0		42000	33500	27200			
52.0				31500			

(Courtesy of Spencer Rigging)

D is twisted through 90 degrees.
e) Snap-Shackles. These are used most commonly for halyards that require frequent un-clipping from the sails such as genoa and spinnaker halyards.

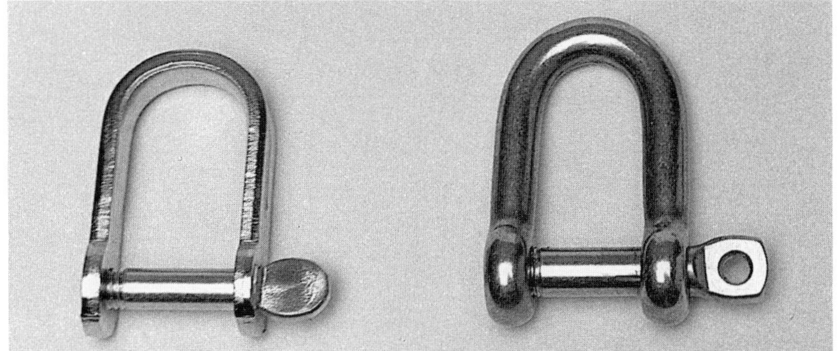

Strip Shackle

D Shackle

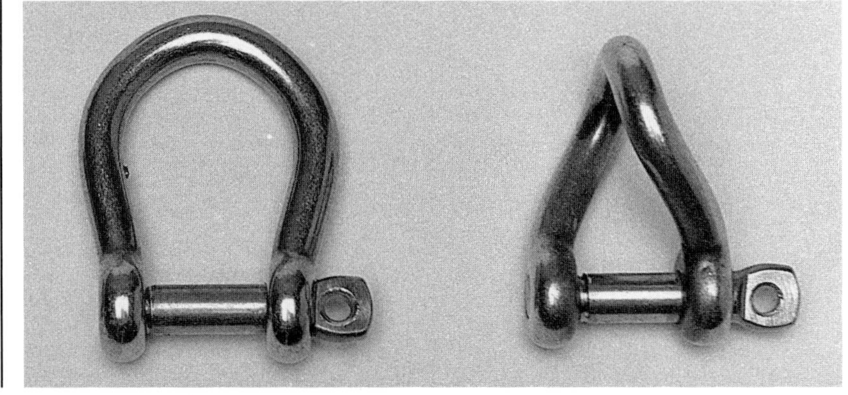

Bow Shackle

Twist Shackle

(Courtesy Norseman Gibb Ltd.)

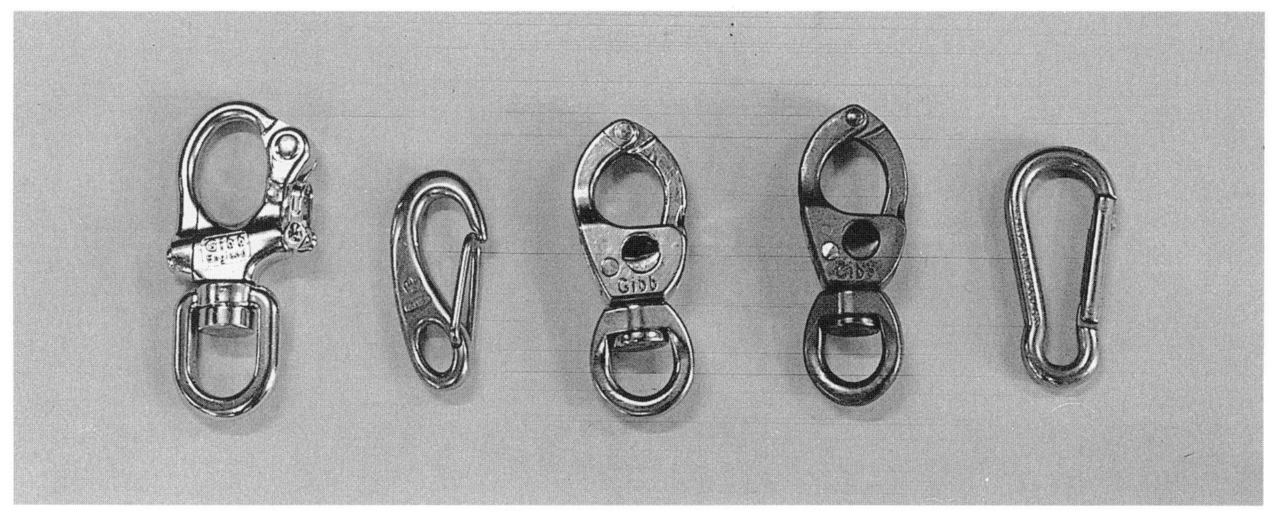

Halyard (above) and sheet (below) attachments

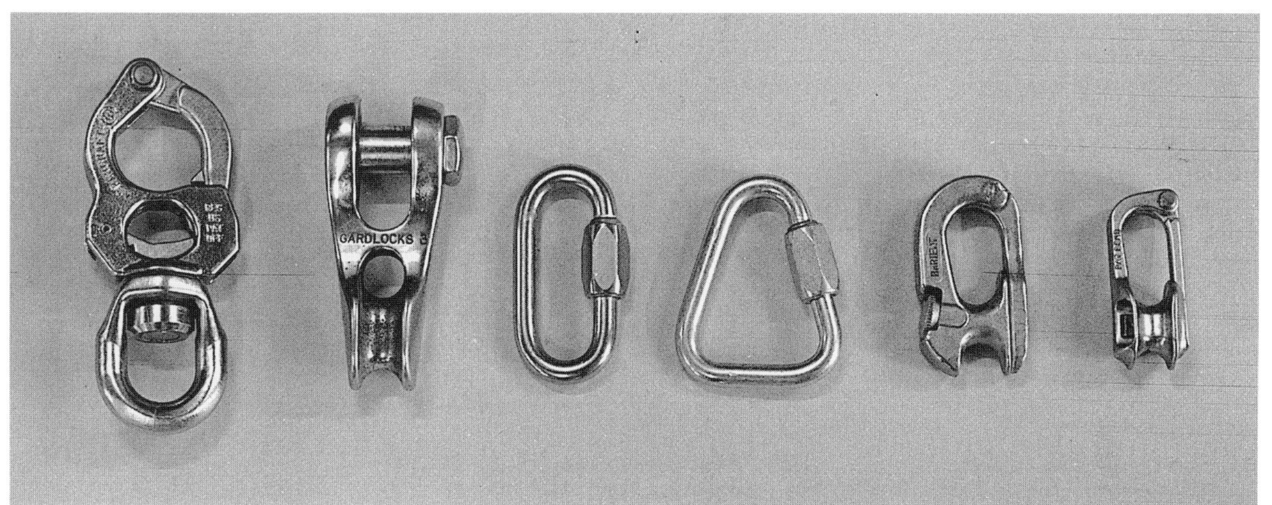

Typical working loads – shackles

Pin diam.		Breaking load (kg)		
(mm)	**(ins)**	**Std. 'D'**	**Large 'D'**	**Bow**
3	$\frac{1}{8}$	140	–	130
4	$\frac{5}{32}$	320	–	–
5	$\frac{3}{16}$	380	–	190
6	$\frac{1}{4}$	510	–	200
8	$\frac{5}{16}$	–	790	410
10	$\frac{3}{8}$	1400	–	510
11	$\frac{7}{16}$	–	1660	–
13	$\frac{1}{2}$	2350	–	760

5: Stepping a new or old mast

Information required

Unless your boat is a strict one-design you will need to supply the mast manufacturer with some initial data in order that he can establish the section or sections that are most suitable for your boat. Ideally a sail plan should be presented to the manufacturer, but this is not always possible, especially if the boat is second hand or the original design office no longer in existence. In such a case the information that will be required may vary slightly depending on the manufacturer but essentially it is as follows:

a) I * + Height of the forestay attachment above datum. In the case of a keel stepped mast this will usually be at the sheer line in way of the mast. For deck stepped masts measure to the stepping point at deck.
b) J * + Horizontal distance between the forward face of the mast and the forestay fitting at the bow.
c) P * + Luff length of the mainsail.
d) E * + Foot length of the mainsail.
e) FL + Forestay length (Channel Handicap only).
f) BAS * Height of boom gooseneck attachment above datum.
g) CPW Horizontal width between chain plates at deck level. For aft swept spreaders the distance aft from the forward face of the mast will be required.
h) RMC * Righting moment of the boat at 1' heel. or if this is unavailable, waterline length of the boat and displacement.

or

i) DISPLACEMENT + If RM not available or Channel Handicap
j) SPREADERS Number of pairs of spreaders (not including jumper struts or diamonds).
k) RIG TYPE Masthead or fractional
l) STEPPING Is the mast deck stepped or keel stepped ?
m)PURPOSE An outline of the intended use e.g. Racer, Cruiser, Cruiser/Racer.
n) MISC. Additional items or features that are required ie: Cutter rig, babystay, masthead electrics etc.

If your boat has an International Offshore Rule or International Measurement System rating, the data denoted with '*' can be read directly off the certificate. Be sure to check whether the units of measurement are metric or imperial. Data denoted with + that can be read off a Channel Handicap System rating certificate.

From this information the mast manufacturer can calculate the stiffness of mast required which will be expressed as a 'required set of inertias' whose units will be either in cm4 or in4. These will then be compared with the inertias of the sections available and hence a suitable section can be specified.

Assuming that the quotation and specification are suitable and the order is placed, the manufacturer will then require some further information in order to produce a set of spar drawings. This will include measurements such as: mainsheet and kicking strap attachments, bury dimensions, halyard exit positions etc.

Having established the correct specifications a set of spar drawings will be produced. Most manufacturers have a similar format for their drawings such as the example shown. The drawing is generally in compressed form and not to scale. It will show a diagram matic representation of the mast complete with all its fittings which are numbered and itemized on the right hand side of the drawing. On the left of the drawing are the heights of the various fittings relative to datum. Additional stiffening that may be

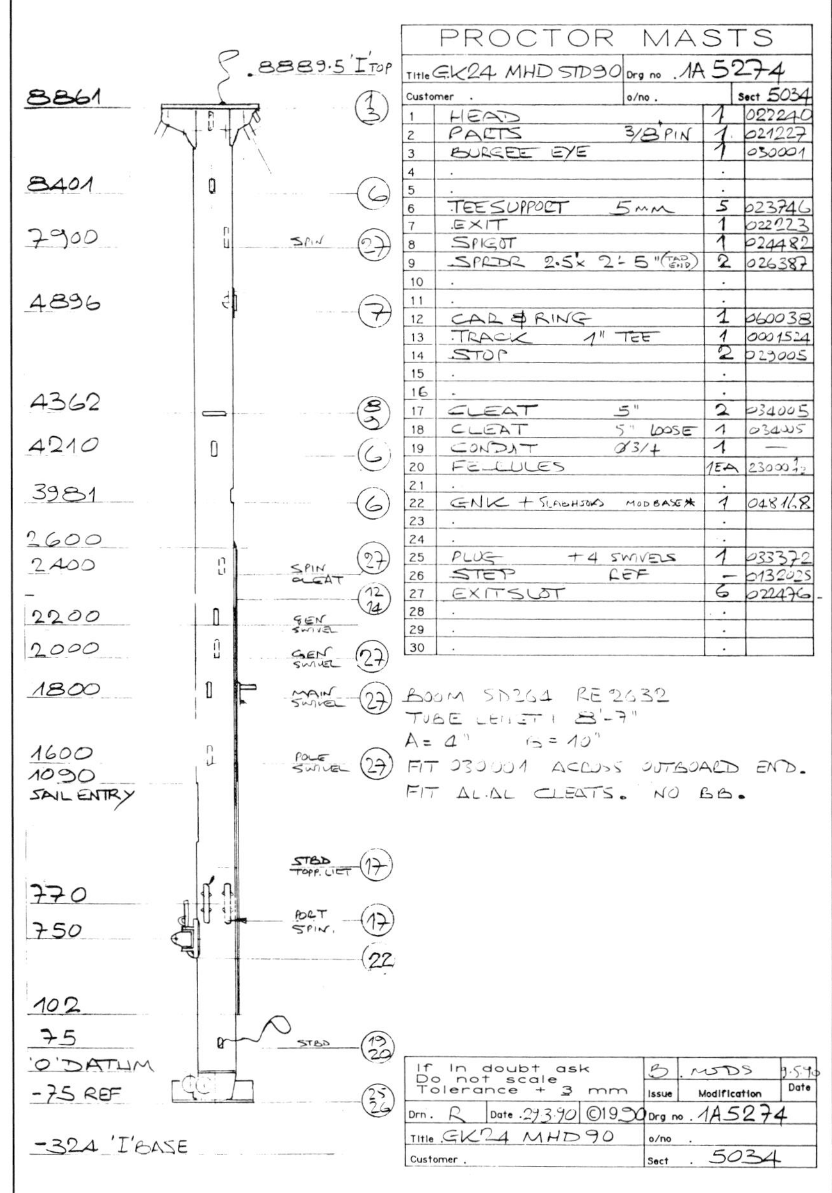

Typical drawing by mast manufacturer

required will also be detailed and usually expressed as a set of heights between which the stiffening will be fitted.

Approving various spar drawings

Before manufacture of a mast commences the drawings will need to be approved. Understandably this is often a problem for many owners as they are not used to reading spar drawings and as a result, problems tend to surface only when the mast is being stepped, by which time it is often difficult to alter the spar. However the following points are a guide as to how to approve the spar drawings and satisfy yourself that the mast will be to the correct specification.

The mast

1) Find the datum position of the boat. For a deck stepped mast this will be simple as the datum will generally be the bottom of the mast tube. (An allowance will have to be made for the height of the heel plug which may differ from the original.)

For a keel stepped mast the datum will usually be the sheerline of the boat at the longitudinal position of the mast. In order to find this take a piece of line and attach it with plasticine (or similar) to the inside face of the gunwale on each side of the boat, at right angles to the centreline of the boat, and tension until it is taut. It will now be possible to measure precisely both the height of datum above the mast step and the height of the deck above datum.

If the mast you are ordering is a direct replacement for an existing mast you will be able to compare the positions shown on the mast drawing to the actual positions on the current mast. The following notes are a guide to help you check these measurements.

2) Mark the datum position on the existing mast.

3) Attach the end of a long tape measure to the datum position and stretch it along the mast securing at intervals with adhesive tape.

4) Starting at datum, working up the mast, check the heights of fittings, exits, lights etc. with the new mast drawing. (If the positions of some fittings such as shroud tangs are critical, check with the manufacturer whether their dimensions are to pin centres or bearing surfaces). Whilst checking the heights of halyard exits check that the mast drawing shows the necessary exits on the correct side of the mast. An exit on the opposite side to the drawn side will usually be dotted. As each position is confirmed tick the measurement on the mast drawing or, if it is incorrect, mark on the correct dimension.

5) Re-attach the tape measure at datum but this time extend it down the mast to measure the positions of fittings and exits on the 'bury'. Again check off against the mast drawing

Above and below: Finding the sheerline of the boat

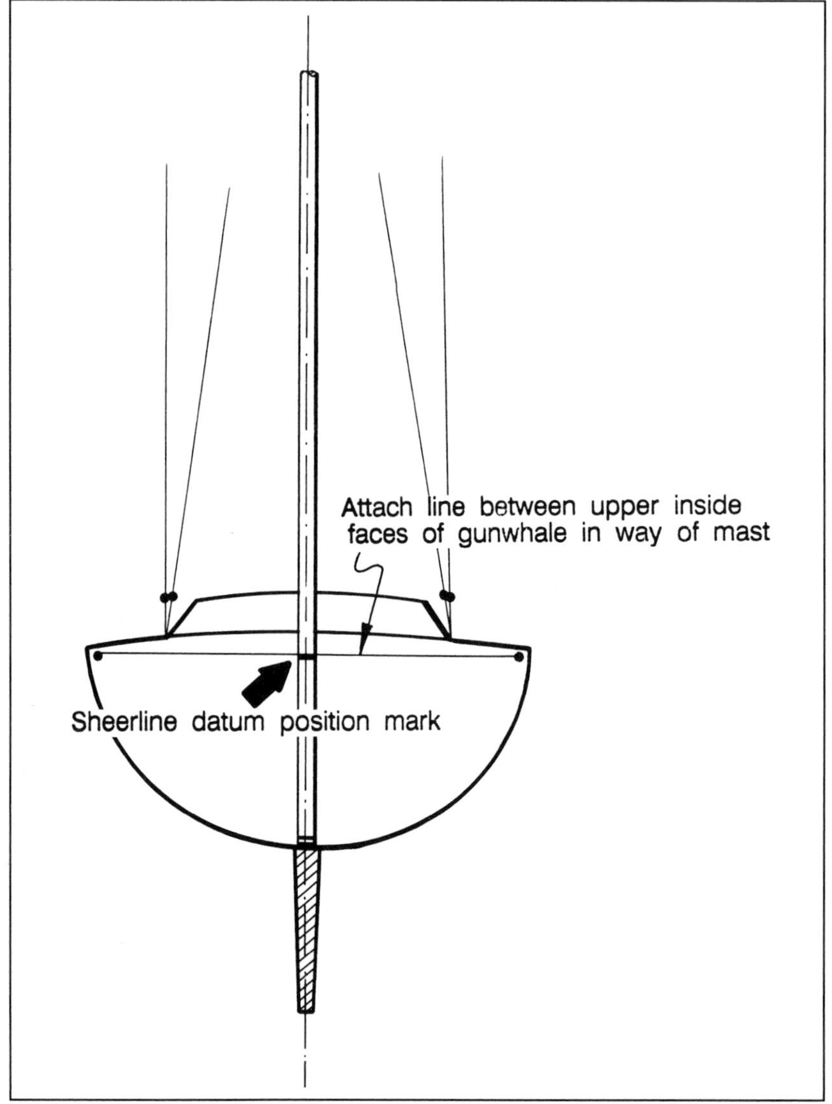

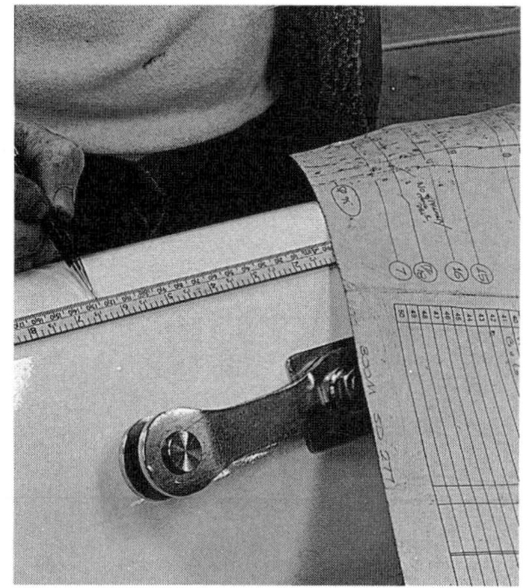

Checking the positions of fittings

confirming or amending as necessary.

6) Measure the pin diameters of all rigging attachments and check against the drawing. If your mast is fitted with 'T-terminals' the size shown on the drawing should be the same as the respective rigging diameter. Therefore it will be necessary to measure the rigging in order to check. Some 'T-terminals' cover a range of wire sizes.

7) If the new mast is to be of a larger section to the original make sure that the deck ring can accommodate this larger size. There are few problems more frustrating than a mast that is too large to fit in the boat!

8) If an existing boom is to be used in conjunction with a new mast make a note on the mast drawing of the boom gooseneck arrangement. Similarly make a note of the kicking strap attachments (if required) both on the under-side of the boom and on the aft face of the mast.

The boom

1) Rig up the existing boom in its correct position and attach a tape measure to the aft face of the mast and extend it along the boom to the outboard end.

2) Measure the distance between the aft face of the mast and the black band on the outboard end of the boom. This

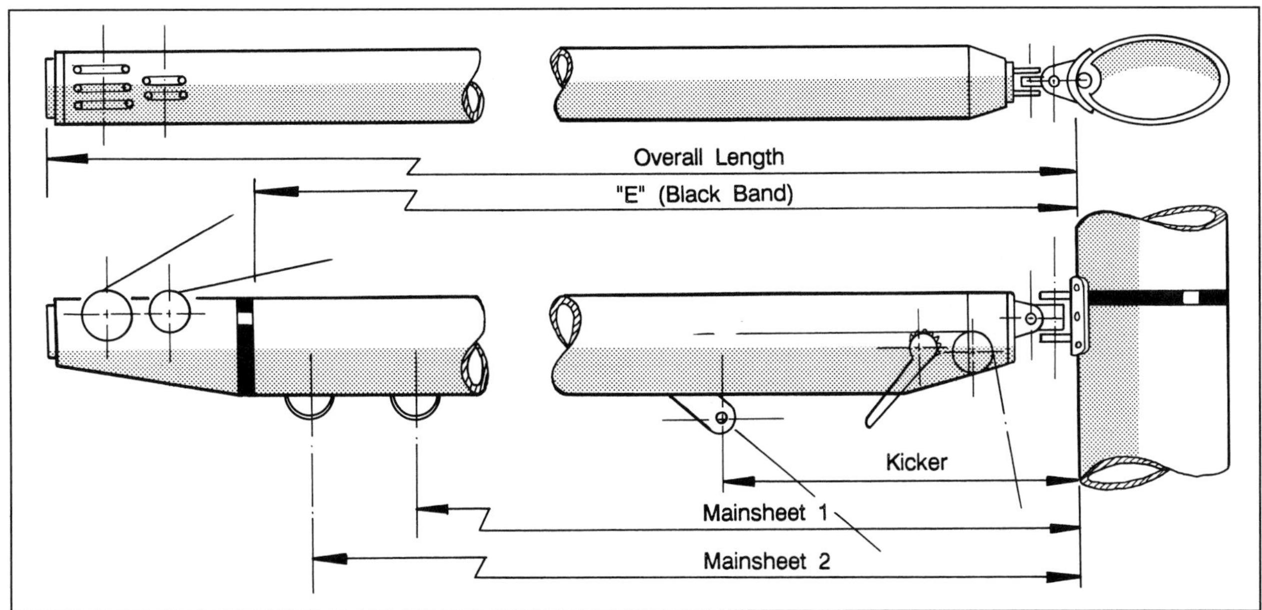

Required boom details

is the 'E' measurement. If the boat is new and does not possess any spars, this dimension can be checked with the designer.
3) Measure the number and positions of the mainsheet attachments from the aft face of the mast.
4) Measure the position of the kicking strap attachment.
5) Check the number of reef lines required against the boom drawing and amend if necessary. At the inboard end check the positions of the reef line exits.

The spinnaker pole
1) With the spinnaker pole set at right angles to the centreline of the boat, measure the distance between the forward centreline of the mast and the outboard end of the pole. This will give the 'SPL' measurement. In most cases this will be the same dimension as the 'J' measurement which is the horizontal distance between the forward face of the mast and the genoa tack fitting.
2) Check that the end fittings are as required e.g. plunger fittings at each end, cup and slider inboard end etc. Also check whether the pole end tripping arrangements are internal or external.

Having thoroughly checked the spar drawings they must then be signed and returned to the manufacturer. It is very important that any outstanding queries are taken up with the manufacturer as alterations are always much more difficult and expensive once the mast is under construction.

Spanning the mast for rigging: measuring the boat.
If standing rigging is required the mast will need to be measured accurately in order to assess the individual rigging lengths. This is often carried out by yacht riggers. In some cases however this will not always be possible and the owner of the boat will need to supply the lengths of the individual rigging spans.

Measuring individual spans on the mast that are relative to positions of fittings on the mast is a simple task. The problems in measuring the spans begin when the distance between a shroud tang and the deck is required for spans such as the cap shrouds or lowers. This need not be a problem however if the following sequence is followed.
1) Most spar and rigging manufacturers use the sheer line of the boat in the way of the mast as the datum mark for keel stepped masts. Therefore the first step is to establish the datum position inside the boat as described above.
2) Measure the vertical distance between the datum and the bearing point of the mast step.
3) Measure the vertical distance between the datum and the outside surface of the deck at the mast gate. Be sure to measure the position of the deck and not the mast collar as this will be the position that is referred to on the spar drawings.
4) Take a straight edge that is long enough to span the width of the boat to its gunwales in the way of the mast. Position this batten at right angles to the centreline of the boat, and on the line between the chain plates. The batten should rest on top of the mast gate and preferably bear directly on the deck.

In many cases this will not be possible as the deck collar will be the bearing point in which case the height of the deck ring above the deck will need to be measured. This height will need to be deducted from any subsequent measurements.

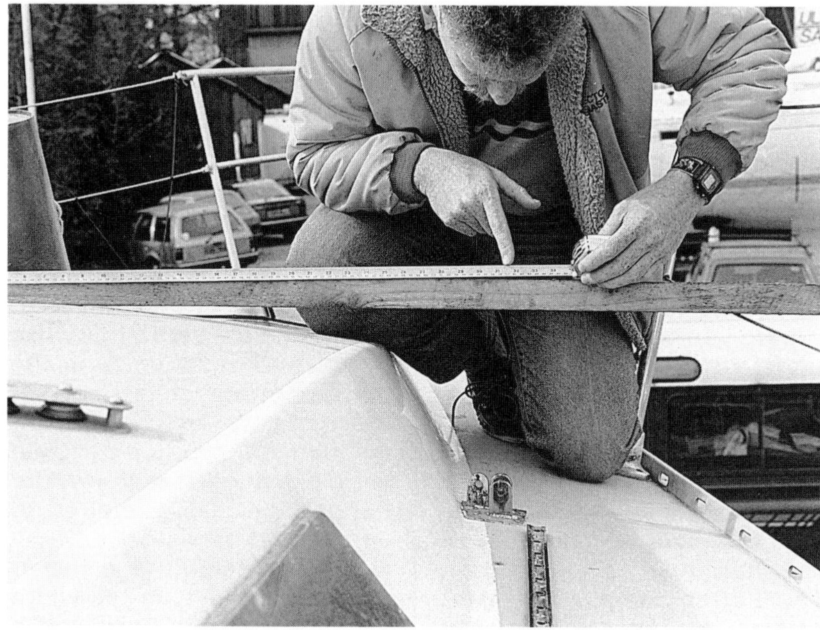

Measuring the chainplate position

5) For rigs with aft swept spreaders the straight edge should still be positioned as above and the horizontal distance of the chain plates aft of this line should be measured.

6) With the straight edge set up across the boat, measure the vertical distance between the bearing surfaces of the chain plate holes and the under-side of the straight edge. A large set square will help establish when you are vertically above the chain plate. Do this for each rigging attachment point on the chain plates. Make separate measurements for the port and starboard sides of the boat. It is often easier to mark the batten on each side and then measure the horizontal distances directly off the batten.

7) For each rigging point measure the horizontal distance from the centreline of the boat to the chain plate attachment. Again a large set square will help with this measurement.

8) The same process can be used to establish the position of the forestay and backstay attachments relative to the sheer. This is however more difficult to establish due to the length of the boat as straight edges over 20ft are hard to come by!

9) By fastening one vertical upright at the bow and stern, fasten a line between the two uprights and balance with a spirit level. Make sure that the line is taut and free from deflections along its length. This does of course rely on the boat being level to start with. If the boat is not level then the amount and direction of inclination will need to be measured and allowed for when levelling the line.

10) Having set up the line fore and aft make sure that it just touches the same position as the previous straight edge was resting on at the deck ring area.

11) Measure and note the vertical distance between the bearing surface of the forestay attachment and the under-side of the line. Repeat this process for the backstay attachment.

12) Note the horizontal fore and aft positions of the rigging attachments by measuring between each upright and the centre of the transverse straight edge.

13) If running backstays are required, measure the vertical distance between the fore and aft line and the top of the upper guard wire or pushpit. The horizontal distance aft of the transverse straight edge should also be measured.

14) If an inner forestay and/or a babystay is required, again measure the vertical distance between the bearing surface of the rigging attachment and the fore and aft line. Then measure the horizontal distance between the attachment position and the transverse straight edge. The measurement of the boat should now be complete and this information needs to be transferred to the mast in order that

accurate spanning can take place.

Spanning the mast for rigging: measuring the mast
Measuring the mast needs to be carried out in two stages. First the athwartships rigging lengths should be spanned off and then the fore and aft rigging lengths should be measured.

1) With all spreaders in position, lay the mast on two or more trestles with its spreaders lying horizontal. Support may be required underneath each spreader to prevent the mast from rolling over onto its side.

2) Take the batten that was used to measure the chain plates and position it at right angles to the mast, at the height of the deck in the way of the mast. This position can be measured and marked on the mast as the height of the deck above datum was measured.

3) With the batten set at the correct height on the mast, fasten securely with line and/or adhesive tape.

4) Make sure that the chain plate width is clearly marked on the batten on each side and for each span of rigging.

5) Take a long tape measure and attach the top to the cap shroud tang on the port side. A note should be made as to whether you are measuring to the pin centre or the bearing surface of the tang. Whichever way you decide to measure it all measurement positions must be consistent.

6) Extend the tape over the path that the cap shroud will take, ie. over each spreader tip and down to the batten.

7) Note the measurement at the corresponding position on the chain plate batten.

8) Now repeat the process for the starboard cap shroud.

9) Move down to the next rigging span which will be an intermediate or a lower shroud and repeat the process from 5 to 8.

Having spanned off the

Spreader heights above datum can be measured by attaching a line between the spreader tips and measuring down the mast to the datum position

Spanning the mast

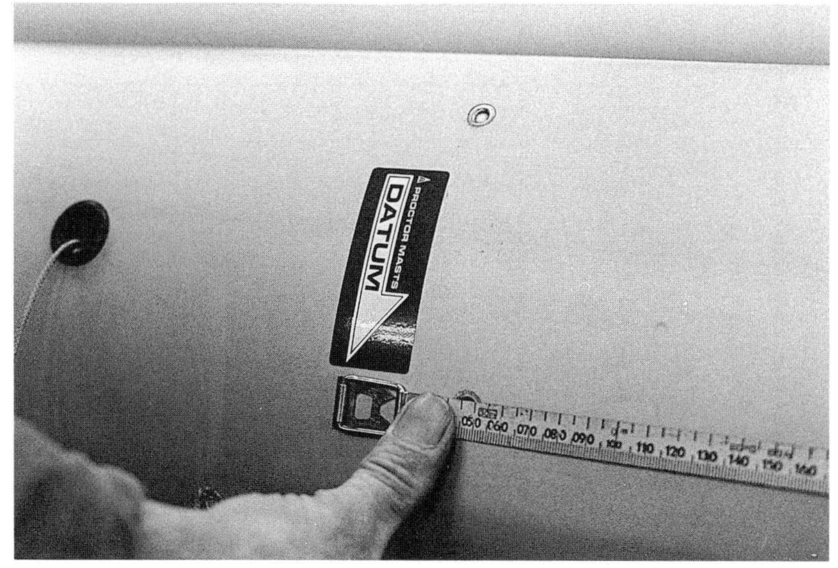

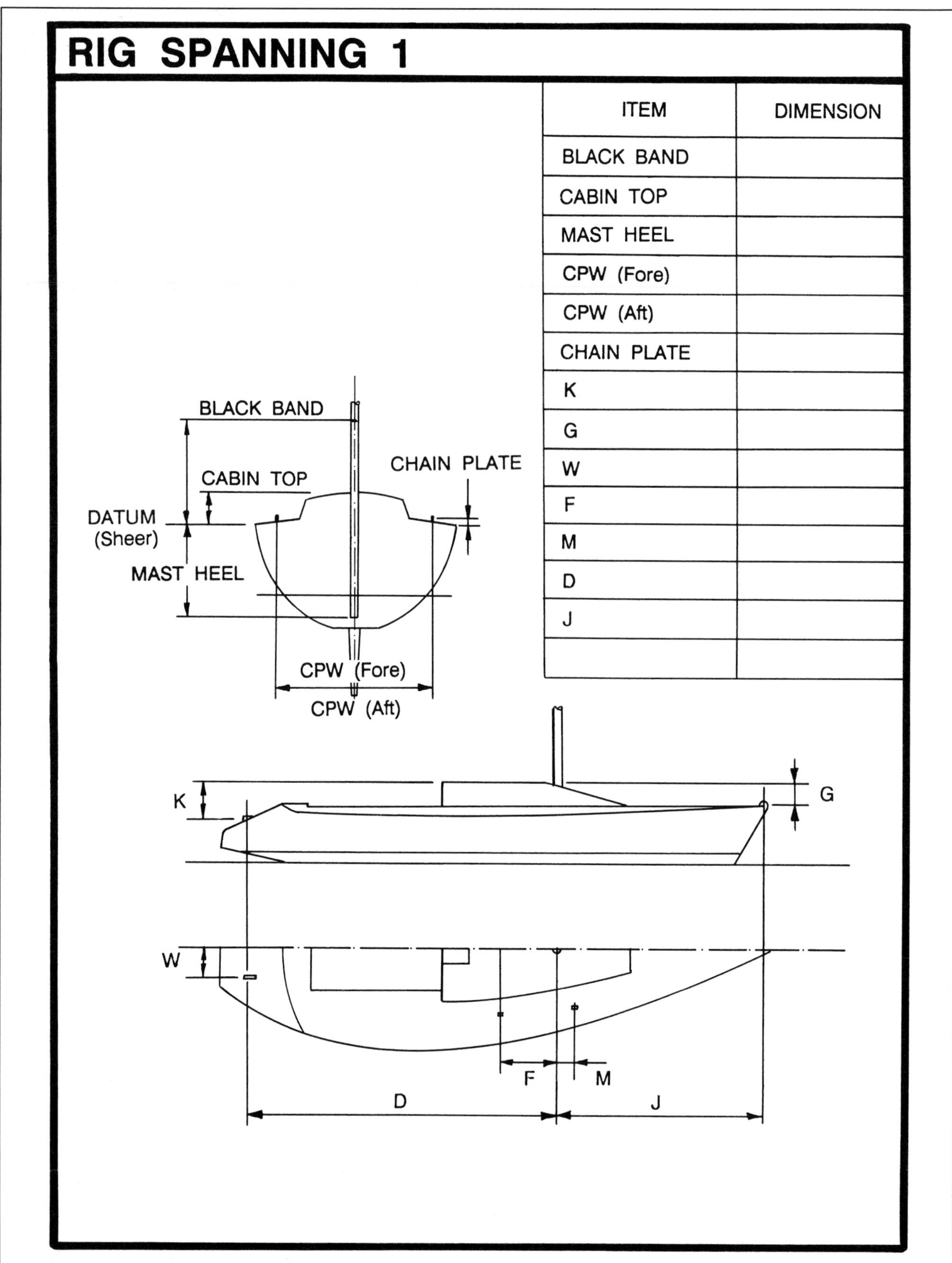

RIG SPANNING 1

ITEM	DIMENSION
BLACK BAND	
CABIN TOP	
MAST HEEL	
CPW (Fore)	
CPW (Aft)	
CHAIN PLATE	
K	
G	
W	
F	
M	
D	
J	

Drawings on this and the following three pages: Spanning off tables

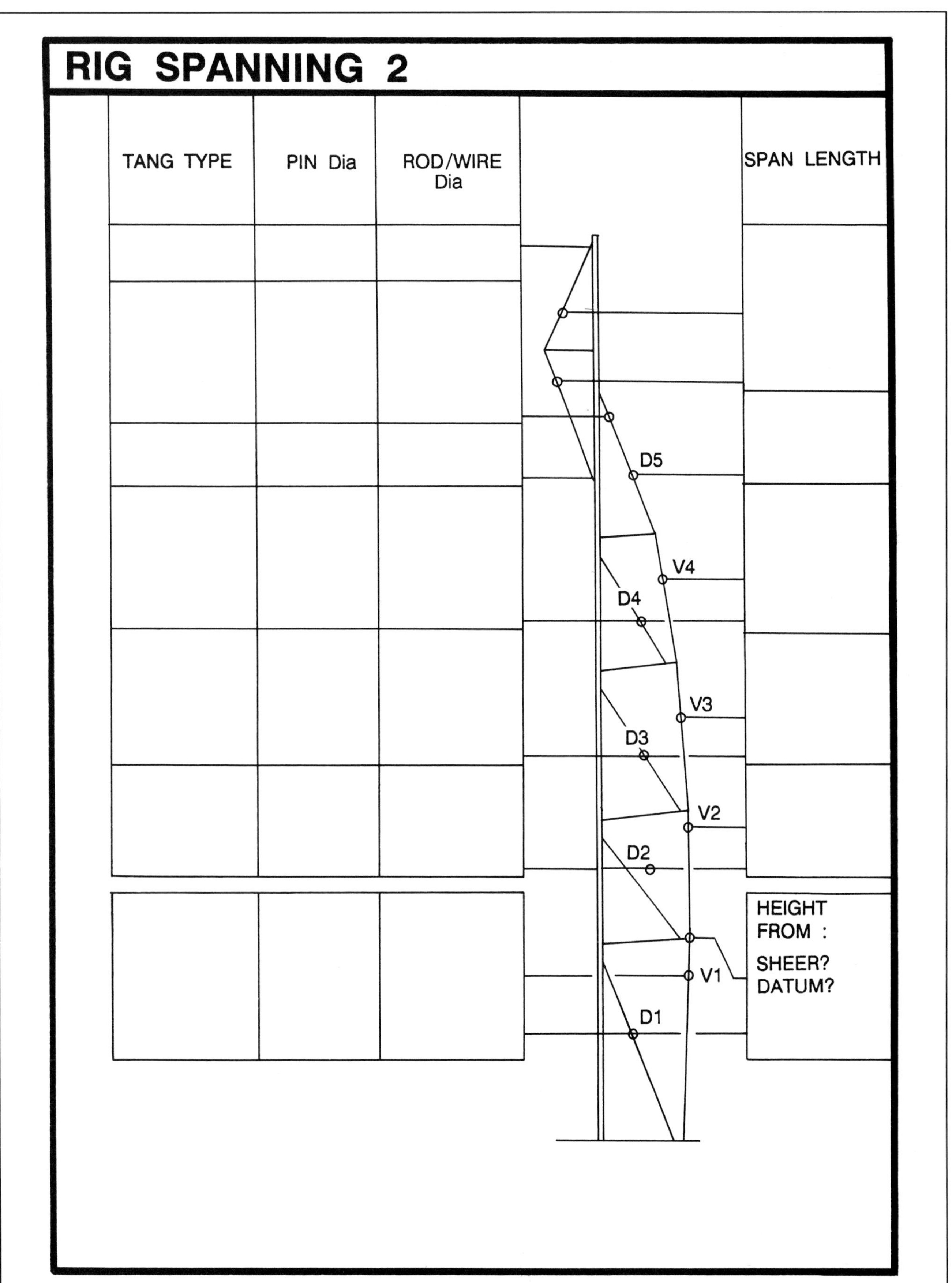
RIG SPANNING 2
TANG TYPE
PIN Dia
ROD/WIRE Dia
SPAN LENGTH
D5
V4
D4
V3
D3
V2
D2
V1
D1
HEIGHT FROM :
SHEER?
DATUM?

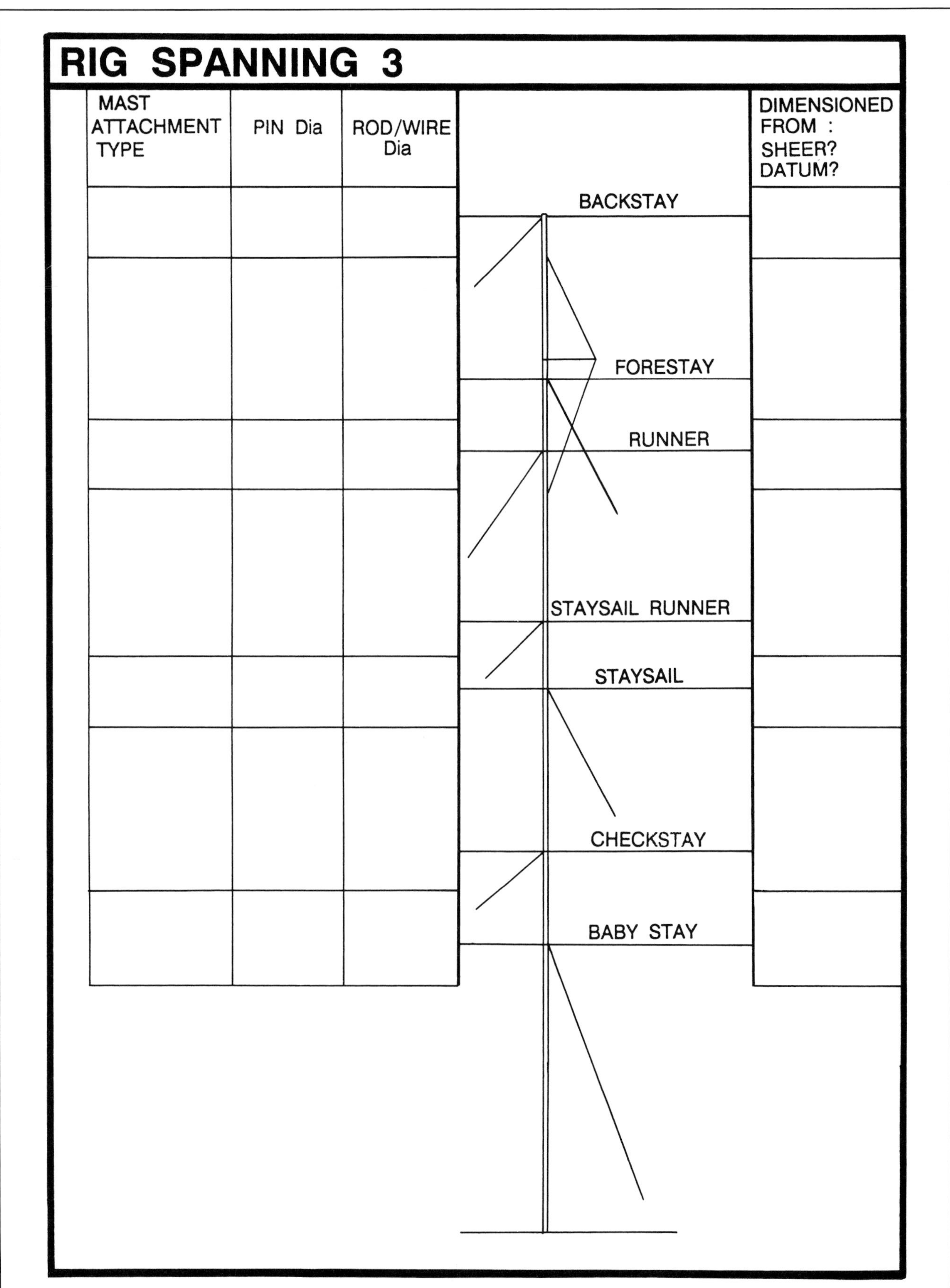
RIG SPANNING 3
MAST ATTACHMENT TYPE
PIN Dia
ROD/WIRE Dia
DIMENSIONED FROM : SHEER? DATUM?
BACKSTAY
FORESTAY
RUNNER
STAYSAIL RUNNER
STAYSAIL
CHECKSTAY
BABY STAY

RIG SPANNING 4

ANGLE	TIP TYPE &/or SIZE

CONTINUOUS Or
DISCONTINUOUS RIGGING ?

NOTES :

athwartships rigging, turn the mast through 90' and support. (The spreaders may need to be removed to do this.)
1) Using the horizontal plumb line that was used to measure the boat, set up the position of forestay and backstay attachments relative to the mast and deck.
2) The positions of these can be represented with the use of items such as: ground stakes, pegs, oil drums etc.
3) Using the same system as described above, measure the rigging spans, again making a note of whether the measurement is between pin centres or bearing surfaces.

Having spanned the mast, the measurements can be given to a rigging company who will make allowances for the dimensions of terminations and other fittings.

Checking a new mast on arrival or re-stepping an existing mast

Having received your mast from the manufacturers the stepping and installation can now begin. Be warned! This can become a very expensive operation if the mast and boat are not checked before attempting to step. This operation can of course usually be left to the boatyard, assuming that they have a mast stepping facility. It is however recommended that you at least check over the mast once it has arrived if only to make sure that you have received what you ordered and that it is in good condition. The following is a suggested checklist from delivery to just prior to stepping.
1) Lay the mast on two or more trestles making sure that it does not sag excessively along its length.
2) Carefully remove the polythene wrapping without using a knife, if possible, especially if the spars have a painted finish.
3) Find the datum position which should be marked on the mast and compare it to the datum position shown on the mast drawing.
4) Check the principal dimensions of the mast against those shown on the mast drawing such as:
a) Overall height
b) Height of forestay pin (if fractional rigged)
c) Height of spreaders
d) Height of lower black band or boom gooseneck.
e) Bury length. (see cutting bury)
5) Check that the pin sizes of the standing rigging attachments match both the sizes shown on the mast drawing and the actual pin sizes of the standing rigging itself.
6) Check the number of halyards and their exit positions and compare to the turning block and cleating arrangements on deck.
7) Check that the required electrical equipment such as: navigation lights, wind instruments, aerials etc. have been fitted to the mast. Taking care to make sure of the voltage requirements, check to make sure that this equipment works. Note: If there is any doubt as to the safety of the masthead equipment whilst stepping the mast,

ITEM	No. Off	WIRE				ROPE			END FITTINGS		Shackles	Rigging Screw	Toggle	Overall Length mtr.	REMARKS	
		Dia. mm.	Const.	Mat'.	Cutting Length	Dia. mm.	Type	Cutting Length	Top	Bottom						
FORESTAY	1	7	1x19	s/s	-	-	-	-	S.E.	N.S.L	-	-	7/16 F.E.	13.000		
BACKSTAY	1	3	1x19	s/s	-	-	-	-	S.E.	N.E.	-	-	FIT AT -	14.000		
CAP SHROUDS	2	7	1x19	s/s	-	-	-	-	T.T.	N.S.L.	-	-	-	12.000		
INTERMEDIATE	2	6	1x19	s/s	-	-	-	-	T.T.	N.S.L.	-	-	-	9.000		
LOWERS	2	8	1x19	s/s	-	-	-	-	T.T.	N.S.L.	-	-	-	5.500		
RUNNERS	2	6	1x19	s/s	-	-	-	-	S.E.	N.E.	-	-	-	12.800		
CHECKSTAYS	2	3	1x19	s/s	-	-	-	-	S.E.	N.E.	-	-	-	7.000		
BABYSTAY	1	3	1x19	s/s	-	-	-	-	T.T.	N.E.	-	-	-	6.200		
JUMPERS	2	5	1x19	s/s	-	-	-	-	S.F.	N.S.L.	-	-	-	TO SUIT		
MAIN HALY	1	5	7x19	s/s	17.000	10	WHITE BRAID	18.000	* T.T.E.	PLAIN	5/16 KEY PIN		-	-	*SUPPLY LOOSE ENDS	
GENOA HALY	2	5	7x19	s/s	15.500	10	BLUE BRAID	17.00	* T.T.E	PLAIN	3.5/8 SNAP	-	-		*SUPPLY LOOSE ENDS	
SPIN HALY	2	-	-	-	-	10	RED BRAID	29.000	S.R.E.	PLAIN	3.5/8 SNAP	-	-			
SPIN LIFT	1	-	-	-	-	8	RED BRAID	19.000	S.R.E.	PLAIN	3.5/8 SNAP	-				

NOTE: "OVERALL LENGTH" Includes all fittings, other than hydraulic cylinders, e.g. rigging screws, toggles, shackles etc. It is measured from centre to centre of the fixing pin or hole in the end fitting, or to the bearing point on T terminals, hooks, shackles or swaged balls. The length of rigging screws is measured at the mid point of adjustment. Measurements quoted are for new wire or rope prior to any stretch which may occur during service.

ABBREVIATIONS:

S.T.E.	Soft Talurit Eye	N.E.	Norseman Type Eye
T.T.E.	Thimble Talurit Eye	N.F.	Norseman Type Fork
S.E.	Swaged Eye	R.T.W.S.	Rope to Wire Splice
S.F.	Swaged Fork	S.R.E.	Soft Rope eye splice
T.T.	'T' Terminal	T.R.E.	Thimble Rope eye Splice
S.R.S.	Swaged Rigging Screw	S.T.E./S.R.E.	Soft Eye Rope to Wire connection.
S. Ball	Swaged Ball		

Typical rigging schedule sheet

remove it and refit later from a bosun's chair.
8) Make sure that the cables for the electrical equipment exits in the correct place(s). Sometimes the wires may emerge from the bottom of the mast tube in the case of 'overlength' masts, in which case they will need to be fed to their correct exit positions before stepping commences. If this is not done it will not be possible to fit the heel plug.
9) Smear grease or vaseline over any exposed electrical terminals to prevent corrosion.
10) With the spreader roots in the horizontal plane fit the spreaders. Tape over any sharp edges on split pins etc.
11) Dress the mast with its standing rigging.
12) Secure all shrouds to the spreaders either with the clamp that may be provided or with seizing wire making sure to cover any sharp edges.
13) If you have the spanning details of the mast (as described in 'Spanning the mast for rigging') the position of the deck can be measured and marked onto the mast. By setting up a batten at right angles to the mast the height and width of the chain plates can be simulated on the mast. The lengths of the rigging spans can then be checked against the batten.
14) Make sure that all rigging screws are the correct way up. For this to be the case they will all turn in the same direction to tighten.
15) Dress the mast with its running rigging by drawing each halyard through, one at a time, with its respective draw line. Be sure to tie a 'figure of eight' in the tail of each halyard once they are reeved.
16) The halyards should be marked at a reference point such as the exit position at their lower end to show their maximum hoist.
17) The main halyard should be positioned so that the upper edge of the mainsail is in line with the under-side of the black band. The splice should not be laying over the sheave at the masthead.
18) The genoa and spinnaker halyards should be positioned so that the upper end of the top halyard splice is just below the sheave. This will ensure that the splice does not lay on the sheave. The lower end of the halyard should be marked where it emerges from the exit, as above.
19) If a one piece neoprene mast coat is to be used, make sure that it is fitted and that it is the correct way up!
20) Check that there are no eyes or external fittings on the bury of the mast that will prevent it from passing through the deck at the mast gate.

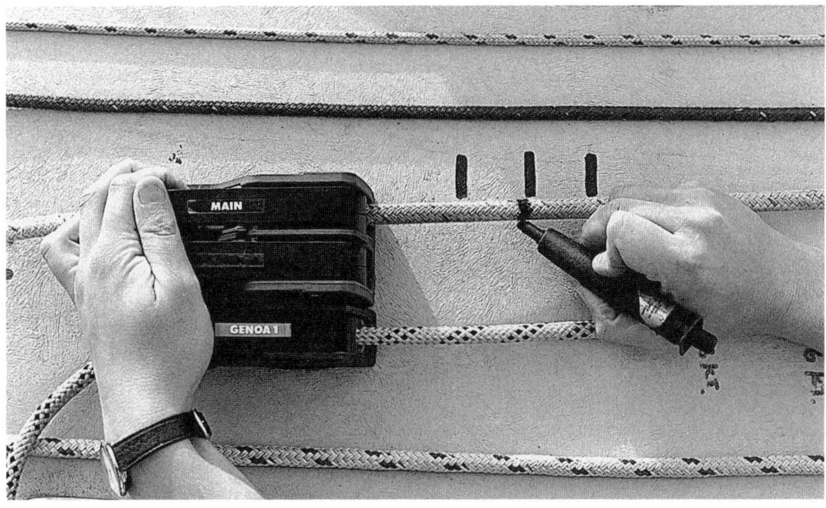

Marking full hoist on halyards

Additional checklist for re-stepping an existing mast.
1) Check over the mast thoroughly for cracks, dents and bulges both inside and out.
2) Check shroud tangs for cracks or signs of elongation of the holes. Also check the clevis pins which should be the correct diameter and length for the tang. The clevis pins should be straight, those that are bent should be replaced immediately. The split pins should be replaced if there is any doubt about their condition. 3) Any shroud tangs that are found to have larger hole diameters than those of the pin should be checked to see whether this pin size is adequate

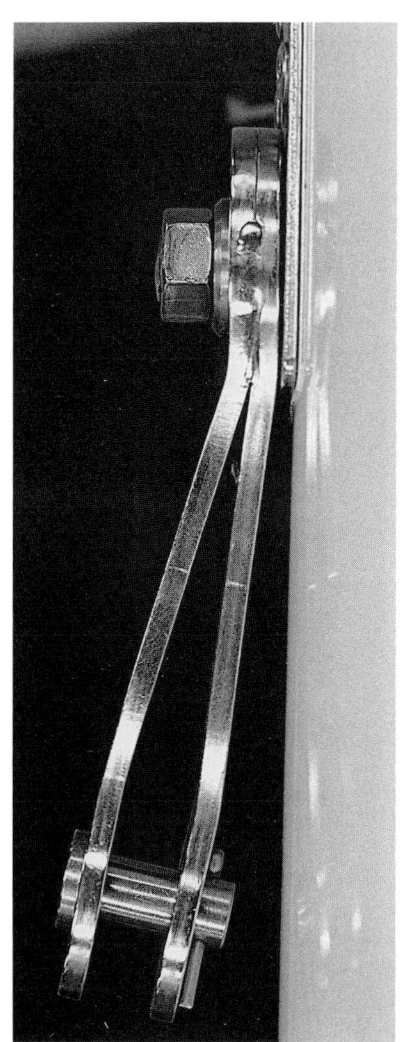
Clevis pins should always be the correct length

(see rigging table). If the pin size is adequate then the shroud tang should be bushed to prevent a point loading between the pin and tang.
4) With the aid of a magnifying glass carefully check each rigging termination for signs of cracking and/or corrosion. In addition check the wires for broken strands close to the end fitting (especially if swaged fittings have been used).
5) Make sure that each rigging span has sufficient articulation at each end by means of rigging toggles.
6) Check the mast for corrosion both inside and out especially in the following areas:
a) Joints between dissimilar metals.
b) Areas near electrical cables.
c) Heel area of the mast.
7) Check the spreader cups or spigots (if fitted) for cracks or bends. In particular check that the mast wall does not have a concave dent in the area of the spreader attachments.
8) All sheaves should be smooth without scores that could damage halyards and should turn freely without tight-spots.
9) Sheave cages should be free from sharp or scored edges as these could damage halyards. A sheave cage that has been badly scored or grooved suggests that the halyard is poorly aligned or that it requires some form of guide or deflector. It is very important that halyards do run correctly as the resultant chafing to the mast can form stress raisers which can in turn result in mast failure.
10) Check the luff track fastenings if applicable.
11) Wearing gloves, run your fingers along the full length of each rigging span and check for snags or broken strands.
12) Dress the mast with its standing rigging and check for signs of the rigging being misaligned.
13) Check inboard and outboard ends of the spreaders for signs of stressing or cracking.

Spreader end protection covers

14) Fit spreader end covers to protect the leech of the genoa. Wheels can be fitted which not only protect the sail from damage but also help the sail to pass over the end of the spreader when tacking. Whichever method you choose to protect the sail it is important that there are no sharp edges on the spreader tips.

Checking the boat before stepping.

1) Measure the size of the deck opening and check this against the mast for the whole length between the heel fitting and the kicking strap gooseneck.
As a guide, mainly for cruising yachts, the deck ring needs to be:
a) 25% larger fore and aft
b) 30% larger athwartships than the mast section dimensions in order that the mast chocks can be fitted.
2) Make sure that the mast step is securely fastened.
3) In the case of deck stepped masts, make sure that the step is positioned directly over the

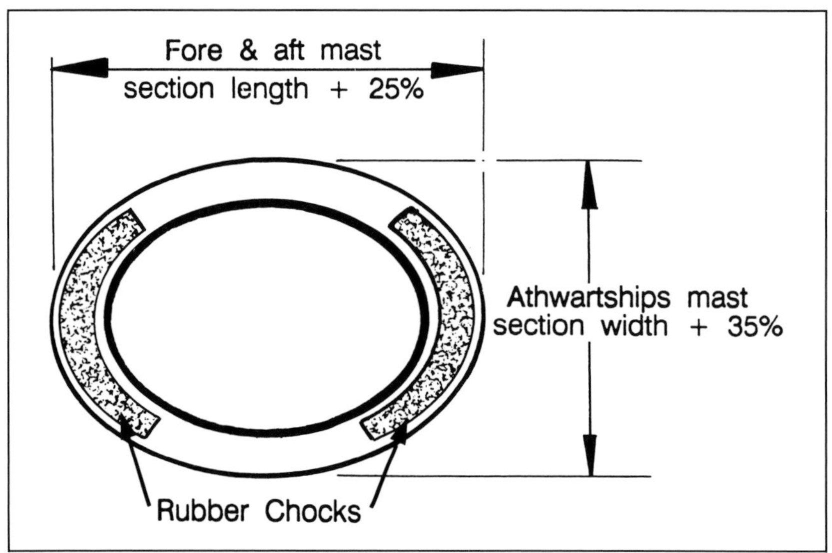

Typical mast gate dimensions

support under the coachroof.
4) Check that there are sufficient fastening holes for the required number of stays!
5) Check that the holes on the chainplates are not elongated and are the correct size for the corresponding rigging sizes.
6) Check that all the rigging screws and bottom terminations can fit comfortably onto the chainplates without distorting the path of the rigging spans.
7) Electrical cable connections should be on the correct side of the mast step and at the correct height to match up with the exits on the mast. (For fitting additional cables see later section)
8) The mast step should be directly under the deck opening but this is sometimes not the case. If the two are not in line, make a note of the difference as this will help with the tuning of the mast later on.
9) If the halyards pass through turning blocks on deck a set of deck tie-downs will be required below deck. These will prevent the deck from lifting when the halyards are tensioned.

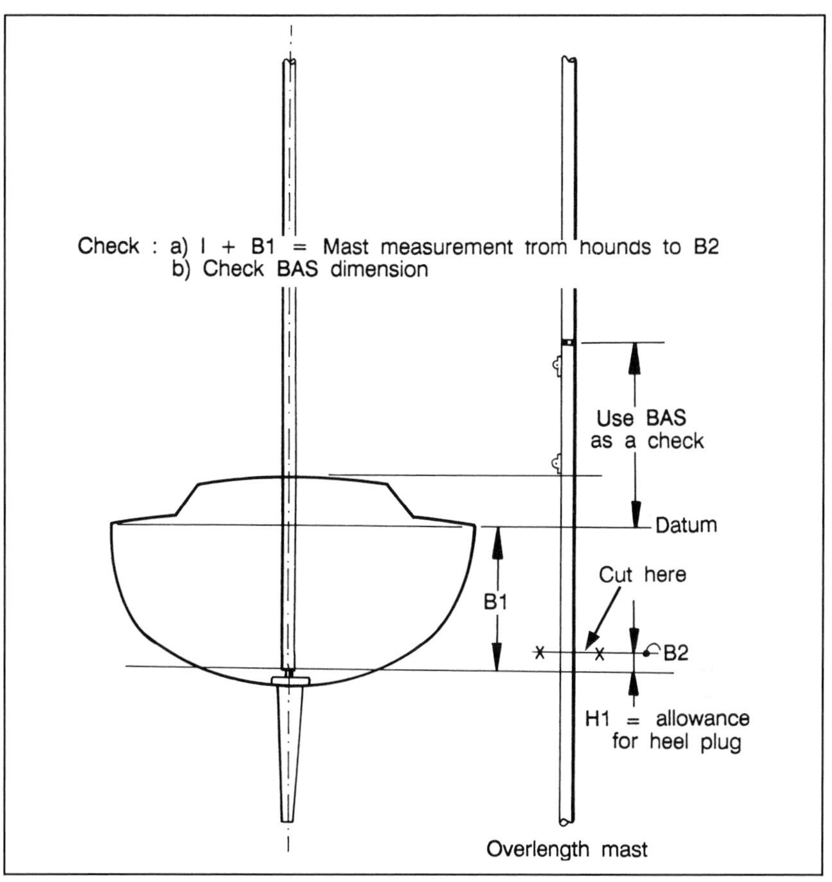

Cutting the bury

Cutting the bury
If bury dimensions of the boat have not been issued to the mast manufacturer the mast is often supplied 'overlength'. That is to say that all the measurements above the deck are correct, but the length of the mast below the deck is longer than required. This can often give a nasty shock to all concerned at the moment of reckoning when the mast is stepped in the boat, if the bury has not been cut!

Cutting the bury is critical. As a result it should be the last operation before the mast is stepped. The checks that follow will help to confirm the measurement.
1) With a datum measurement set up on the boat (as described in Chapter 5) measure the vertical distance between the bearing surface of the mast step and the datum (B1).
2) Find the datum mark on the mast and transfer the dimension B1 extending downwards, marking its position on the mast.
3) With the heel plug loose, measure the vertical distance between the bearing surface of the mast step and the bearing surface of the mast tube (H1).
4) Subtract this dimension (H1) from the bury dimension (B1) on the mast and mark as the bury cutting line (B2).
5) As a final check take the 'I' measurement for the boat and add the bury dimension (B1) as measured. Now measure the actual dimension between the same points on the mast itself and the measurements should be exactly equal.
6) The next stage is to cut the excess mast tube. In the case of cruising boats this cut should be exactly at right angles to the centre of the luff groove. (Racing boats sometimes have their bury's cut at a slight angle to help induce pre-bend.)
7) Fit the heel plug so that the mast wall is bearing on the lip of the heel casting. The heel plug can then be fastened with screws or rivets. It is not necessary to pepper the heel area with fastenings as the mast is in compression anyway and these fastenings serve only to hold the heel plug in place and prevent any splaying of the tube. The mast should now be ready to be stepped.

Stepping the mast
In most cases a boatyard will be involved in stepping the mast(s) and it will rarely be a consideration for the owner. However there are instances where you may wish or have to step the mast yourself. The following notes relate to the three types of mast stepping (also see Chapter 6).
a) Keel stepped masts. These

type of masts are perhaps the easiest masts to step as once the mast is in place the deck offers a degree of support whilst the rigging is connected.
1) The mast should be laid on trestles near to the boat and fully dressed with its rigging. Make sure that the rigging spans are lying correctly and do not pass over or around spreaders and also that they are not twisted.
2) Check that all the rigging screws are the correct way up. They should all turn the same way to tighten.
3) Mark the mast step for the position that you wish to step the heel.
4) Attach the mast lifting strop at or as near as is possible to the centre of gravity. The centre of gravity can be assessed by lifting the mast just off the trestles with the strop and adjusting so that the mast just balances.

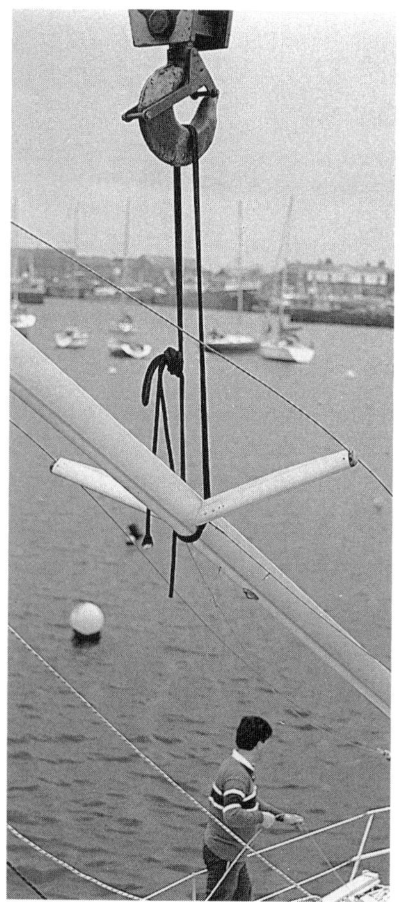

Slinging the mast

5) Attach a strong line from the strop down to the gooseneck fitting to prevent the strop from sliding up the mast. Be sure to anchor this line to a strong point on the mast as this line will need to support almost the full weight of the spar. If in doubt contact the spar manufacturer.
6) Hold the heel of the mast and carefully raise the mast into the near vertical position.
7) Move the heel over the mast gate and carefully lower the mast into the boat.
8) With the mast sitting on its step and whilst it is still supported by the crane, attach the rigging to the chain plates and tighten hand tight. Halyards can also be used as temporary support.
9) Remove the mast strop.
10) Fit the deck chocks in the desired position to give the correct amount of pre-bend if it is required. (See Setting Up.) On racing boats the J measurement will dictate where the chocks should be positioned in order to keep the rating the same. Therefore make sure you know this measurement and arrange the chocks accordingly.
11) In order to fit the chocks securely it may be necessary to attach lines to the mast at deck level to pull the mast forward or aft.
12) A later diagram shows some of the types of mast collar and chocking arrangements.

b) Deck stepped masts. Whilst these types of masts require less in the way of fitting, they do need careful handling as the deck does not support the mast.
1) The mast should be laid on trestles near to the boat and fully dressed with its rigging. Make sure that the rigging spans are lying correctly and do not pass over or around spreaders and also that they are not twisted.
2) Check that all the rigging screws are the correct way up. They should all turn the same way to tighten.
3) Mark the mast step for the position that you wish to step the heel.
4) Attach the mast lifting strop at or as near as is possible to the centre of gravity. The centre of gravity can be assessed by lifting the mast just off the trestles with the strop and adjusting so that the mast just balances.
5) Attach a strong line from the strop down to the gooseneck fitting to prevent the strop from sliding up the mast. Be sure to anchor this line to a strong point

A popular method of chocking the mast at the deck is to use 'T' shaped wooden shims

on the mast as this line will need to support almost the full weight of the spar. If in doubt contact the spar manufacturer.
6) Hold the heel of the mast and carefully raise the mast into the near vertical position.
7) Lower the mast onto the mast step.
8) With the mast sitting on its step and whilst it is still supported by the crane, attach the rigging to the chain plates and tighten hand tight. Halyards can also be used as temporary support.
9) Remove the mast strop.
10) On racing boats the 'J' measurement will dictate where the mast heel should be positioned in order to keep the rating the same. Therefore make sure you know this measurement and position the heel accordingly.
c) Tabernacle stepped masts. These types of masts are generally found on boats up to about 25ft (7.6m). Above this size the rigs tend to become too difficult to handle. There are two types of tabernacle stepping (right). The first is the conventional fabricated type which although it is fairly unsightly does offer good support to the mast when it is in the process of being raised or lowered.

The compression of the mast is transferred to the deck by means of either: wedges driven in under the bottom of the mast tube or, the pivot holes on the mast are elongated allowing the mast to sit directly on the step when vertical.

The second type is that of the extended heel. This system is much cheaper than the tabernacle and is identical to the deck stepped mast in that the compression is taken directly by the heel plug. The following are notes on the operation of such systems.
1) When hoisting a mast it is usually raised from the stern forward. This allows more deck space to be used and hence a better lever can be achieved on the mast for the initial lift.
2) A lifting strut should be fitted

Tabernacles (above) and hinging heel plug (below)

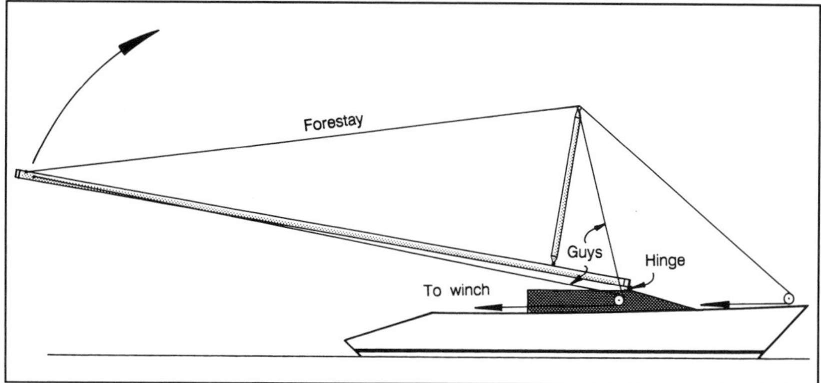

Raising a tabernacle mounted mast

to the forward face of the mast.
3) Transverse support will also be required and this can be achieved by attaching a line to each side of the mast. This support is very important particularly in the case of the hinging heel plug which can be seriously damaged if the mast is allowed to slew whilst it is being hoisted.
4) Connect the side shrouds and backstay making sure that the rigging screws are the correct way up (They should all turn the same way to tighten).
5) Make sure that the rigging screws are free to rotate on the chain plates as the mast is hoisted and that they do not snag. If the chain plate is a 'U' bolt type, PVC tape can be used to prevent the rigging screw toggle from toppling over and jamming.
6) Carefully hoist the mast to its vertical position and connect the forestay.
7) For the fabricated tabernacle type fit either wedges between the under-side of the mast tube and the deck or fit the additional securing pin.
8) Tension the rigging.

IMPORTANT – BEWARE OF OVERHEAD POWER CABLES WHEN HOISTING OR LOWERING MASTS BY ANY METHOD.

Fitting electrical cables

When the mast is lying down you may wish to fit electrical equipment in addition to that supplied by the manufacturer which will entail leading cables down the mast.

The very first item that must be checked is that the respective cables are of the correct diameter and type for their given task. Incorrect sizes can cause large resistances and high voltage drops resulting in poor efficiency of the equipment.

All cables must have some form of protection from chafe be it a conduit or tension device. If this is not present halyards may chafe or even get tangled with electrical cables. Cables that are free inside the mast are also a noisy irritation when the boat is at anchor. There are three ways in which electrical cables are usually installed in a mast.

a) Internal conduit. The conduit will be fitted up to the height of the appliance(s), typically right up to the mast head to carry the cables for the masthead electronics. The presence of an internal conduit can usually be seen by pairs of rivets equally spaced up the outside of the mast. These are the fastenings for the conduit. However in some cases manufacturers incorporate internal tracks into the mast extrusion which can carry a clip on type of conduit which is usually plastic. In this case the only way of identifying the conduit's existence is to remove the heel plug and look inside the mast.

If the mast does not have any conduit, (as is sometimes the case), it is usually possible to fit one of the two types. For the clip on type it is merely a case of purchasing the necessary lengths of extrusion and sliding it up the track. The aluminium type will take longer to fit but is essentially fairly simple as follows.

1) With the correct length lay the conduit along the outside of the mast along a path which is as straight as possible but avoids areas such as: halyard exits, spreader roots, winch pads etc.
2) Fasten the conduit to the outside of the mast with pvc tape.
3) At intervals of approximately 1m drill pairs of holes through the conduit and mast wall to suit 3/16in (4.8 mm) rivets.
4) Having removed the heel plug from the bottom of the mast,

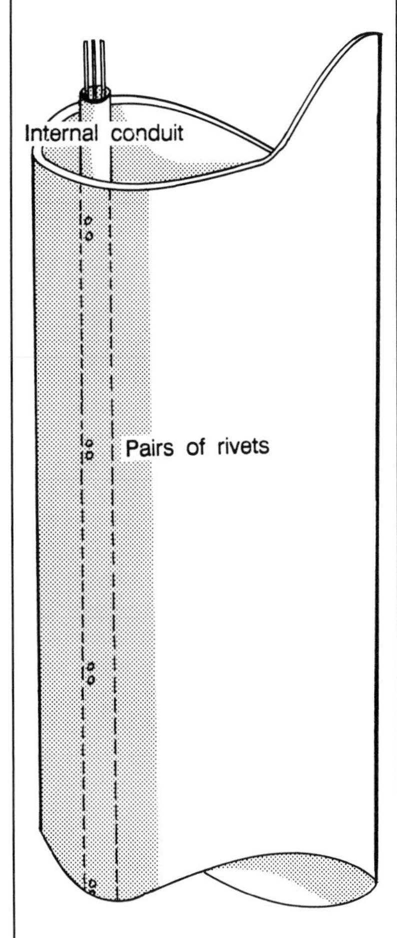

Cable conduits

Electrical cables – recommended sizes

Item	No.core	Area (mm²)	Volts	Watts
Tricolour nav. light	2	2.50	12/24	25
Tri-white nav. light	3	2.50	12/24	25 +10
Anchor light	1	0.75	12/24	10/25
Windex light	2	0.75	12	3
VHF aerial	co-axial			
Steaming light	2	1.50	12	10
	2	2.50	12	25
Deck light	2	1.50	12/24	35
Deck/steaming light	3	1.50	12	10 +20

The conduit is temporarily attached to the outside of the mast to drill the holes before it is fitted inside the mast

turn the mast over so that the holes are now on the lower side. Slide the drilled conduit up the inside of the mast in the same orientation as when the holes were drilled.

5) By carefully aligning the conduit the respective holes can be picked up.

6) Starting from the top of the mast and working down fasten the conduit with pairs of 3/16″ (4.8 mm) rivets.

7) If the relevant wire exits are not in place they can now be drilled through the mast wall and conduit. Make sure that the holes are positioned exactly where the conduit is lying.

8) It is very important that every cable exit, top and bottom, has a rubber grommet to prevent the chafing of electrical cables against the mast wall. Such grommets also provide a form of sealing for the mast preventing water from running down the inside of the mast.

If the mast is new it will have been fitted with a draw line to which you can attach your cables and pull them through the mast. If however you are fitting an additional cable you will need to attach a drawline to one or all of the cables and withdraw the cable(s) from the mast. Then attach the additional cable and pull all back through with the drawline taking care not to break the drawline. In either case you will find the task considerably easier with two people, one to feed the cables in and the other at the opposite end of the mast to draw them through.

Usually the cables will be installed by feeding them in from the bottom of the mast and drawing them out at their respective exits up the mast. However in some cases such as masthead units this is not possible as the top of the cable has a sealed unit which cannot be broken. It is therefore important to check which way the cables should be aligned before you start to feed them in.

It is worth remembering that PVC cable can create a considerable drag and therefore the mouse line should be of sufficient strength and fastened securely. This is particularly important when removing the cables at the end of the season, especially when the mast is to be left outside, as some line will rot and break easily. In order to reduce the friction when pulling cables through the mast heel plug should be removed which will allow a more direct pull on the drawline.

b) Tension type conduit. This system is often found on racing boats where weight must be kept to a minimum. It involves using a wire or low stretch Kevlar line which is tensioned inside the mast and has the electrical cables taped to it.

When the mast is new and this system is required the tension wire or line will be fitted at the factory without the electrical cables (unless otherwise specified). In order to fit cables you will need to attach a drawline to the wire or Kevlar and withdraw the tension system. Then lay out the wire or Kevlar alongside the mast and tape the electrical cables to it. Make sure that there is some slack in the electrical cables in order to allow the wire or Kevlar to stretch a

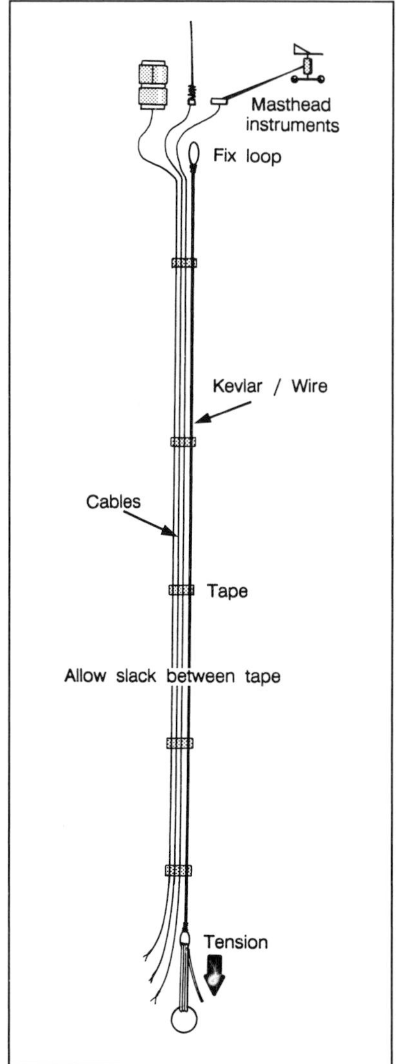

Tension type conduit

External conduit often used for large diameter co-axial cables for radar systems

little without the cables becoming tensioned once the system is tightened within the mast.

The tension wire and cables should then be attached to the draw line and fed into the mast in the same way as for the internal conduit.

Once the system is in the mast the top end of the tension wire or conduit should be fastened securely. Just below the bottom exit position a fixed eye should be fitted. The lower end of the tension wire can then be tensioned by means of a lashing purchase between the wire and the fixed eye.

b) If you are fitting an additional cable to an existing system you will need to attach a drawline and withdraw all the cables. Then tape your additional cable to the tension line, as above, and re-fit.

c) External conduit. This type of conduit is most often used when a radar cable needs to be fitted. Such cables are generally too large in diameter to fit inside a single conduit along with the masthead electrical cables and thus either an additional conduit or an external type needs to be fitted.

To fit the conduit:

1) Stretch a length of drawline along the proposed path of the cable(s) and fasten at each end.

2) Cut the correct length of conduit and temporarily fasten it to the outside of the mast with PVC tape.

3) Drill 3/16in (4.8 mm) pairs of fastening holes at approximately 1m intervals along the length of the conduit.

4) Fasten the conduit with 3/16in (4.8 mm) rivets.

5) Attach the drawline to the cable and pull through the conduit in the same way as for the internal conduit described above.

6: Setting up and tuning

The mast, spars and rigging may be installed safely in a yacht by, say, an ordinary boat yard. Yet much needs to be done to make such a rig effective. The process of adjusting all components of the rig to give the desired results, when sailing on any point, is known as 'tuning'. The static parts of tuning is known as 'setting up'; subsequently final tuning has to be done after sailing trials.

Then there are yet further and continuously optional adjustments on some mobile components. These might include backstays and inner stays with tackles, lever adjusters, or releases.

For some readers, this Chapter 6 is almost certainly central to the book. No one else but the owner, or the person to whom he has delegated, will get the rig into shape after the yard installs it and before the crew maintain it. Here I have given precise directions for all common modern rigs to enable each to be set up and tuned as it should be.

For a racing yacht, the rig must be tuned to offer the most efficient and well balanced characteristics in order to obtain the very best performance at all times. For a cruising yacht, the performance aspect is not necessarily the most important feature, but such features as balance on the helm are necessary, especially if the yacht is sailed short-handed. A yacht of any type that is difficult to steer on a straight course and has a tendency to broach is an unnerving experience and, to say the least, undesirable.

Often the most noticeable difference between a badly tuned yacht and a good one is the feel of the helm. Some boats have extreme weather helm making it very difficult to steer the boat and others have the opposite, lee helm, which is both difficult to control and dangerous. (Dangerous as the boat will bear away and eventually gybe if the helm is released.) Normally there should be no excuse for either case as these problems can usually be ironed out by correctly tuning the rig. Such examples of poor handling characteristics are only two of many tuning factors which this section of the book will cover.

As we have seen in Chapter two there are many different types of sail plans which have differing types of rig. The way in which these rigs are tuned vary on the type concerned and therefore before you can begin to tune the rig you will need to establish (if you do not already know) which type of rig you have. In this chapter we will study the most popular versions. These can be split into the following categories:

a) 1 Spreader

'In line'	Masthead	Continuous rigging
	Fractional	Continuous rigging
'Aft swept'	Fractional	Continuous rigging

b) 2 Spreader

'In line'	Masthead	Continuous rigging
	Fractional	Continuous rigging
'Aft swept'	Fractional	Continuous rigging

c) 3 Spreader

'In line'	Masthead	Discontinuous rigging
	Fractional	Discontinuous rigging

d) 4 or more spreader

'In line'	Masthead	Discontinuous rigging
	Fractional	Discontinuous rigging

There are of course many other configurations, but to discuss each one would be a very laborious process. Instead, the above represent the most popular rig types for racing and cruising alike.

Here is a reminder of some of the terminology:

a) 'In line'. This refers to the orientation of the spreaders, which are in this case set at right angles to the centreline of the boat.

b) 'Aft swept'. In this case the spreaders are set aft to the centreline of the boat, usually 20-30 degrees.

c) 'Masthead'. Indicates the position of the forestay top attachment, in this case at the top of the mast.

d) 'Fractional'. Again refers to the forestay position which is at a position below the masthead.

e) 'Continuous'. This describes the rigging system that is employed. Each span in this case extends from the mast shroud fitting down to deck level to a turnbuckle.

f) 'Discontinuous'. Some or all of the rigging spans are terminated at the spreader tips which have link ends. As a result there are fewer turnbuckles at the chainplates.

Helm balance

As mentioned earlier, the most noticeable effect of poor mast tuning is that of the balance of the helm. Before commencing the tuning of the rig let us first study the reasons for this effect.

If the underwater lateral profile of the yacht is considered there is a point on the profile about which the section can be balanced. One way to find this would be to cut out the profile from a piece of cardboard and balance this section on a single point. This point is known as the Centre of Lateral Resistance (CLR) and can be considered as the position through which all the lateral forces act whilst the underwater profile remains this shape. As the boat heels so the profile changes, altering the distribution of area, hence changing the position of the CLR. To begin with we shall consider only the profile with the boat in its upright position.

For the sail plan there is also a position through which all the forces can be considered to act and this is known as the Centre Of Effort (CE). Unfortunately this cannot usually be imagined in the same way as the CLR as the genoa either overlaps or falls short of the mainsail. To find the sail plan's CE each sail must be considered individually and then combined to find the resultant position.

Having ascertained both the CLR and the CE we are now concerned with the horizontal separation of the two positions, called the 'lead', as it is this that governs the balance of the helm. The lead of a particular boat is usually expressed as a percentage of the waterline length of the boat which, for sloop rigged yachts, is usually about 18%.

With the value for 'lead' at less than 18% the boat will tend to have weather helm as it will try to slew round to a head to wind position. Conversely if it is much greater than 18% the boat will tend to develop 'Lee helm' and try to bear away downwind.

The degree by which the yacht tries to deviate from a straight

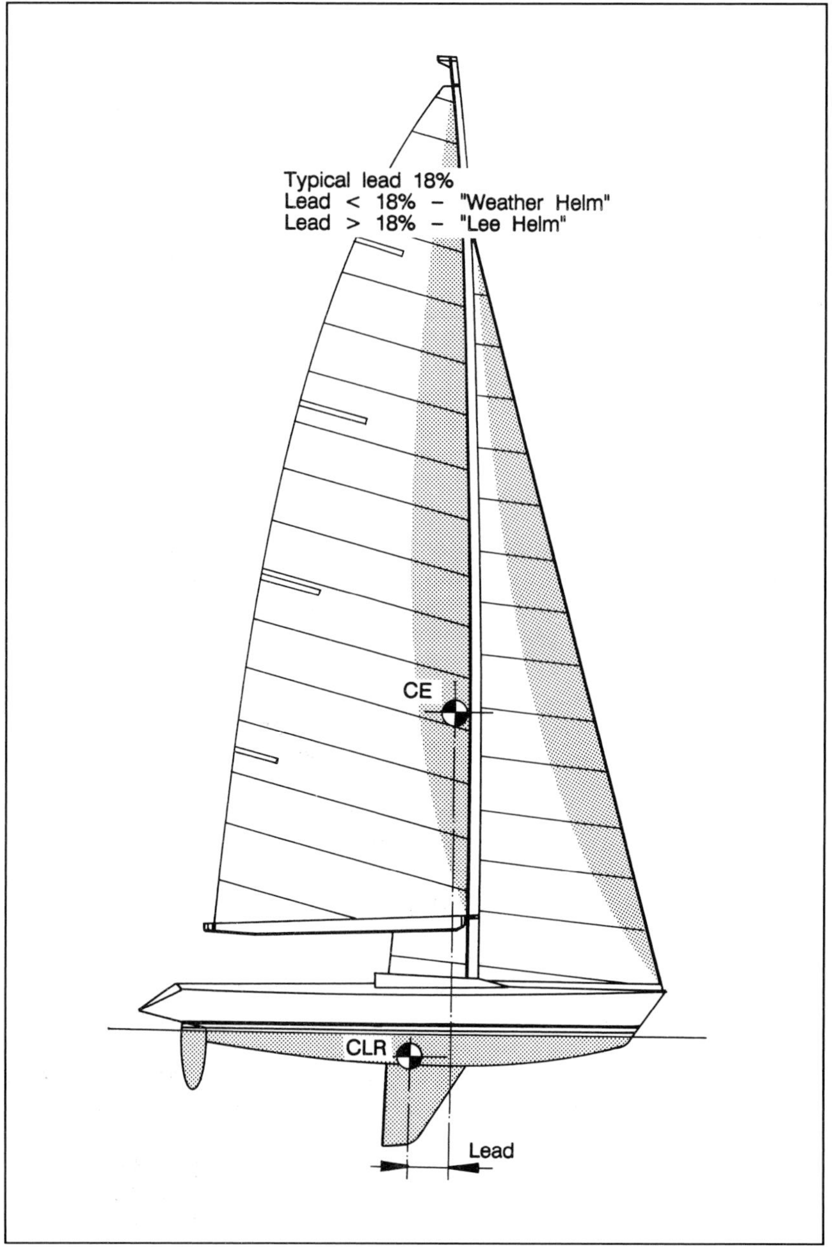

CLR vs CE and lead

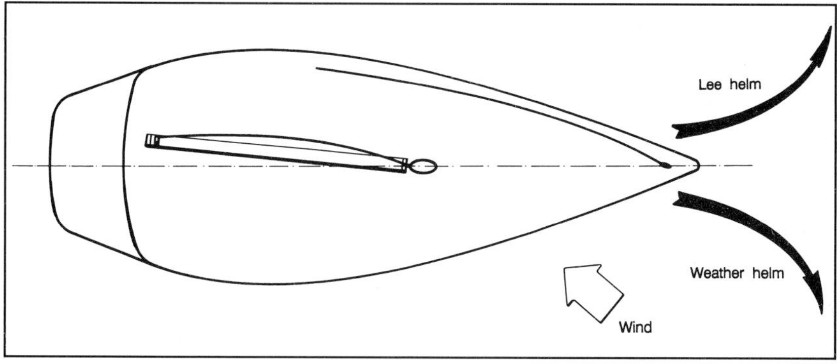

Weather and lee helm

course is dependent on the percentage of lead. That is to say that the greater the horizontal distance between the two then the greater the force steering the yacht off course.

It is generally considered that boats should be set up so as to have slight weather helm for both reasons of safety and performance. The safety of weather helm is that if the helm is released then the boat will gradually head up into wind and virtually stop. If the wind or waves push the bow of the boat away and the sails fill, the boat will again round up into the wind until the sails cease to drive the boat. However it is important that there is not too much weather helm that the boat heads up so violently that it tacks through the wind. From a performance point of view, most helmsmen prefer a slight amount of weather helm to give the boat some 'feel' when on the wind. Again it is important that there is not too much weather helm which causes high drag, slows the boat, tires the helmsman or even makes the boat uncontrollable.

One way to measure the amount of weather helm is to sail on the wind with full mainsail and the number one genoa and measure the angle at which the helm is set to maintain a straight course. This can be done by marking the stock and deck area in degrees. An acceptable value should be between 2 and 5°. The boat's balance will be discussed in more detail later.

There are two ways that the lead and hence the balance of a boat can be changed. The first is to move the CLR. This is generally not a practical solution as either the keel will have to be moved or the underwater profile of the boat changed. A much easier way is to alter the position of the CE which can be achieved by either altering the fore and aft position of the sail plan with the heel of the mast or altering the rake.

Preliminary tuning

If your mast has just been stepped and is sitting in the boat with its rigging set at 'hand tension' you can continue

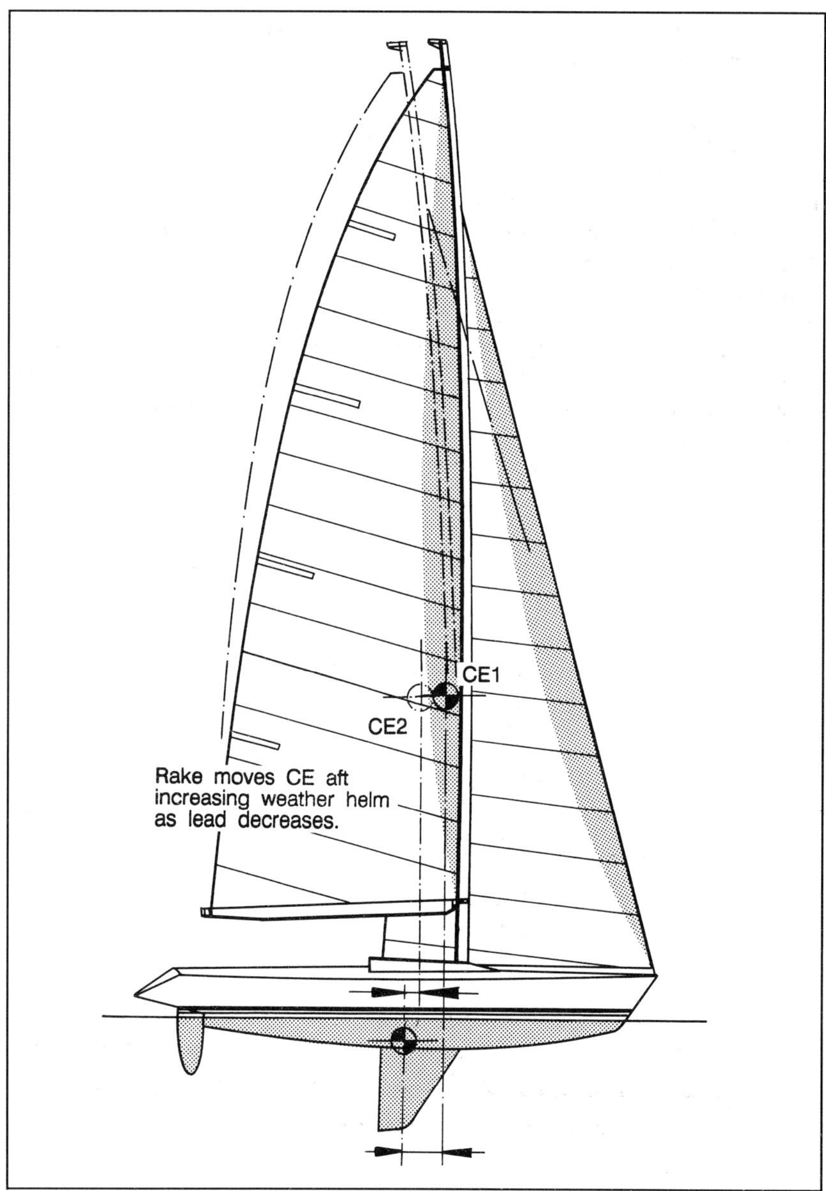

Altering rake affects lead

through this section to tune the mast. If however you are about to re-tune your rig from scratch you will need to slacken off the rigging to about 'hand tight'.

Next make sure the boat is floating to her marks and upright. If the boat is listing to one side or trimmed by the bow or stern this must be corrected before any tuning can begin.

The first stage is to move the heel of the mast to its correct position. Ideally this position would have been decided before the mast was stepped so that it could be lowered onto exactly the correct spot. Unfortunately this is rarely the case and the heel must be moved afterwards. It is for this reason that the rigging will need to be fairly slack otherwise it will be very difficult to move the heel. If you are in any doubt as to the initial position of the heel you should consult either the designer or yacht manufacturer who will often be able to advise you on the initial setting. Alternatively, if you are class racing, study the top boats and the position of their heels.

The position of the heel has, to a certain degree, the same effect for most of the common types of rig, ie: masthead or fractional, deck stepped or keel stepped. Pre-bend and mast rake are the two main factors that are affected by the position of the heel. To start with we shall consider the keel stepped rig.

Mast rake

The amount of mast rake is varied by either the longitudinal position of the mast heel and/or the length of the forestay.

The advantages of aft mast rake are:

a) Better upwind performance
b) Centre of effort of the sail-plan is lowered making the rig more controllable in strong wind.

Too much aft rake can have the following effects:

a) Increased weather helm
b) Boom hits water when reaching and can cause broaching
c) Main sets badly downwind with a tendency for the boom to swing onto the centreline of the boat
d) Difficulty in obtaining correct bend characteristics
e) The centre of effort of the sail plan is lower and hence light airs performance is sacrificed
f) Excessive aft rake can position low clew genoas below an effective sheeting point
g) The leech of the genoa becomes more open thus de-powering the sail. (This can sometimes be used to advantage in strong wind.) Ideally the rake requirements are such that the boat goes faster to windward with its mast raked aft, and faster downwind with its mast upright or raked forward. In light winds the mast is set in its most forward raked position and progressively raked farther aft as the wind strength increases.

The best way to achieve these requirements is to set the mast up with the maximum rake required and then use a spare genoa halyard as a temporary forestay carefully to pull the mast upright when sailing

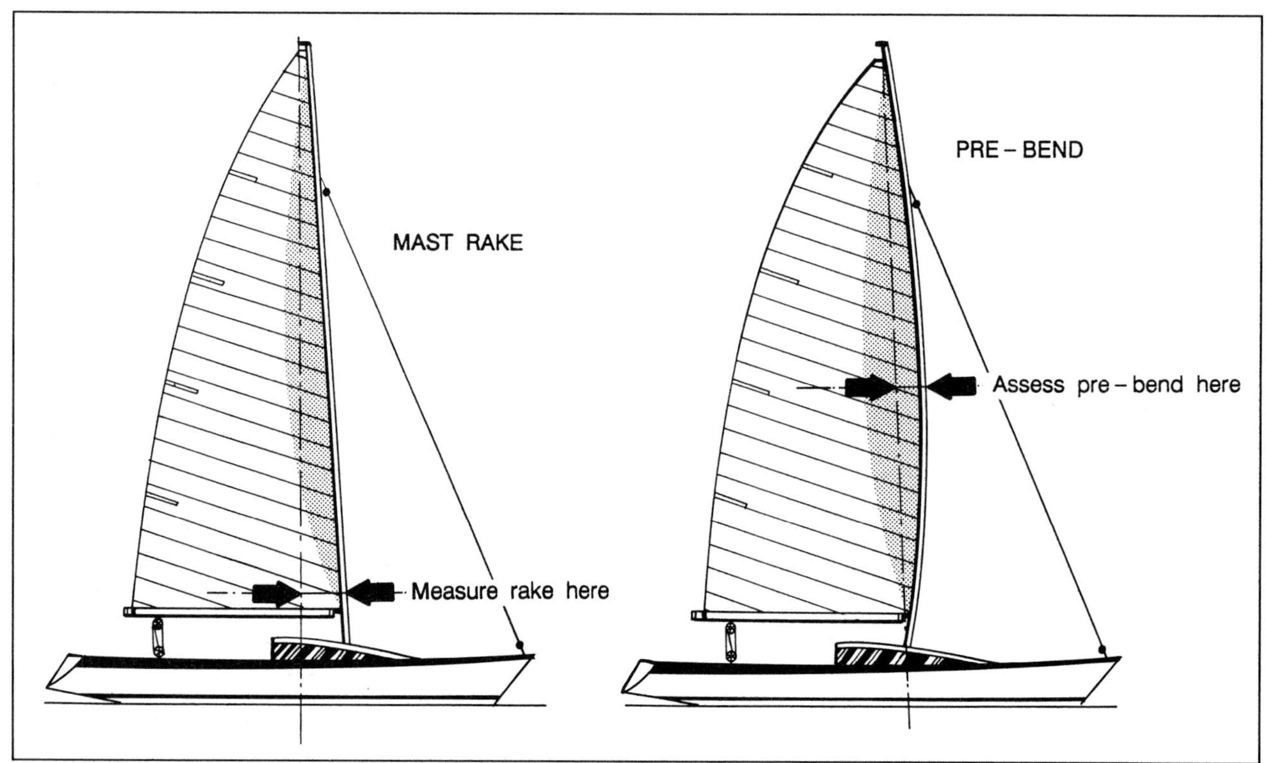

Pre-bend and Rake

downwind or in light airs. This is often best achieved with in-line spreaders. Aft swept spreaders will resist the forward pull of the genoa halyard.

The amount of mast rake required will of course depend on the balance of the boat and the sailmaker's requirements. To set the rake:

1) Remove the mast chocks from the deck ring and sight up the mast from below deck to make sure that there are no sharp deflections about the deck.

2) Set up a plumb line from the masthead to just below the gooseneck and measure the distance from the aft face of the mast to the line at gooseneck height. Typical values for rake would be:

a) Masthead rig:	1% – 2% 'I'
b) Fractional rig:	2% – 3% 'I'

(where 'I' is the height of the foretriangle)

Therefore for a 10 m (32.8 ft) fractional mast the distance between the aft face of the mast and the line at gooseneck height would be between 200 – 300 mm (7.9 – 11.8 in).

3) Moving the heel forward will increase the amount of rake. Conversely moving it aft will reduce the rake. (Assuming that the forestay length is not altered)

Pre-bend

Most racing boats and some cruising boats have their masts set up bowing slightly forward; this is known as 'pre-bend.' This is defined as the amount of bend held in the rig when the boat is at rest. ie Before the main is hoisted and the backstay is tensioned. This bend may be necessary for two reasons:

a) In light airs, when the backstay (or running backstays if fitted) are slack, a fine entry is achieved on the mainsail.

b) To ensure that when the backstay (or running backstay), is tensioned the mast bends in the correct direction, ie. middle forwards.

There are a number of ways in which pre-bend can be achieved which include:

a) Angling the spreaders aft.

b) Fitting chocks behind the mast at the deck, in the case of a keel stepped rig.

c) Positioning the masthead such that the hounds attachment is forward of the chain plates and deck ring.

d) If twin lower shrouds are fitted then the forward lowers should be fitted forward of the mast gate and tightening these stays will tend to pull the lower panel of the mast forwards.

The degree of pre-bend required depends almost entirely on the cut of the mainsail and therefore you should consult your sailmaker to establish the amount of pre-bend that they have allowed for.

In order to measure the amount of pre-bend in a mast, set up a line from the masthead to the gooseneck and tension sufficiently to take up the slack. Be careful not to over-tension this line as you may induce bend, particularly on fractional rigs. The amount of bend should

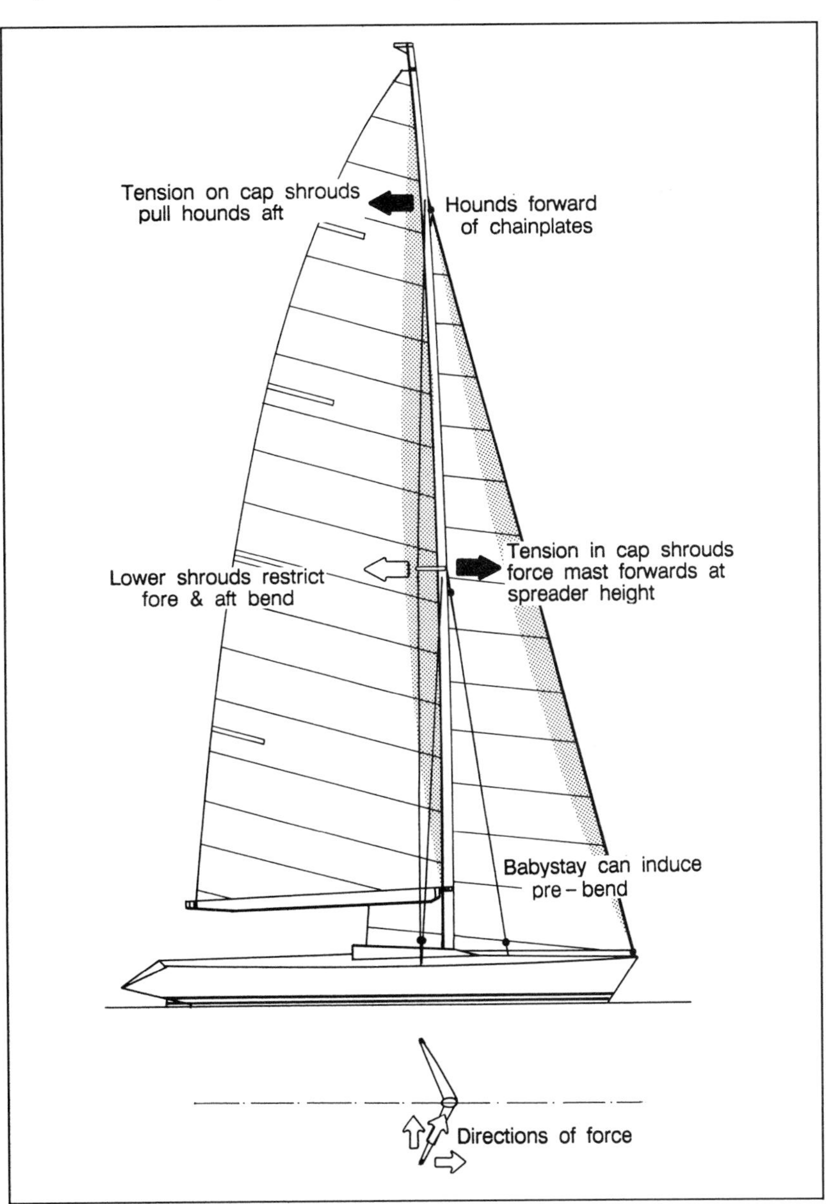
Tension on cap shrouds pull hounds aft
Hounds forward of chainplates
Lower shrouds restrict fore & aft bend
Tension in cap shrouds force mast forwards at spreader height
Babystay can induce pre – bend
Directions of force

Altering pre-bend on aft swept rigs

Typical pre-bend dimensions

Boat size	approx 'I' dimen. (m)	(ft)	pre-bend (mm)	(in)
¼ Ton	8.6	(28.22)	51	(2.0)
½ Ton	10.5	(34.54)	64	(2.5)
¾ Ton	11.4	(37.40)	69	(2.7)
1 Ton	14.6	(47.90)	76	(3.0)
2 Ton	16.1	(52.90)	86	(3.4)
50ft IOR	18.4	(60.37)	104	(4.1)

Fore and aft bend alters shape of sail

then be assessed at about mid span where the deflection will be greatest

Initial tuning
So far we have discussed the basic position of the mast without any tension in the rigging which is essentially the same for most rigs. The amount by which a set of rigging is tensioned is virtually impossible to define precisely not least because it is so difficult to measure the pre-tension in rigging accurately. However the following notes attempt to set out some of the guidelines that can be used in order to achieve a well balanced rig.

This section has been divided into the six most popular types of modern rig. To make the notes specific to each case and therefore easier to follow, each section can be read independently depending on which type of rig you are setting up. Therefore there is inevitably some degree of repetition between the various sections.

Whilst each type of rig has its specific tuning requirements there are some important points which are common to most rigs which include the following:

a) If new rigging has been fitted the rig will need to be re-adjusted after the yacht has been sailing for a few hours. This is necessary as the rigging will stretch a greater amount initially which will need to be allowed for.

b) Excessive shroud tension – beware! This is probably the most common cause of rig set up problems and its effect is often severely underestimated. Not only can it hinder the performance of the rig but it can bend the boat! For tuning purposes it is often better to err on the side of under-tensioning.

c) Rigging stretch. For the same size, wire rigging stretches more than rod rigging and therefore rigs using the former tend to need more pre-tension in order to take out some of the stretch.

d) Rigging loads. Defining and then measuring rigging loads is usually difficult without sophisticated and expensive equipment which is usually only found on out and out racing yachts (see *Equipment*).

However for wire rigged yachts approximate pre-tension loads can be established quite simply. eg.

For 1 x 19 Stainless Steel Rigging:

Cap shroud pre-tension approx. = 15% Breaking load of wire (assuming cap shroud angle 10 – 11°).

This can be simply measured in two ways:
1) Use a simple tension gauge (as described in Chapter 8.)
2) Measuring the elongation (stretch) in the wire from its slack condition. Then using a simple formula the tension can be calculated.

Load (Kg) = Elongation (cm) x Breaking load (Kg)/Stretched wire total length (m)

The measuring process would be as follows:
1) Measure and note the total length of each cap shroud from pin to pin in their slack condition.
2) Measure and note the cap shroud diameter and check corresponding breaking load (See Chapter 3).
3) Mark the lower pin position on both sides. (This should be the position at which the lower end of the rigging was measured to in 1) above.
4) Calculate 15% breaking load of the relevant wire size.
5) Tension the cap shrouds EVENLY on each side. The mast should not be allowed to bend athwartships otherwise a false reading will be obtained.
6) Measure the elongation.
7) Add the elongation to the original wire length to give the stretched wire length.
8) Calculate the load in the wire.

Example: 30 ft (9.1 m) LOA Yacht

Cap shrouds = 6.0 mm (0.025 in)

Wire length = 8.53 m (28.0 ft)

From table, Break Load = 2880 Kg

Therefore 15% Cap load = 432 Kg

Rigging is tensioned:

Elongation = 13 mm

Therefore Wire length = 8.543 m

$$\text{Load (Kg)} = \frac{1.3 \times 2880}{8.543}$$

$$= 438 \text{ kg}$$

This corresponds to approximately 15% cap shroud breaking load.

Individual rig tuning: Spreader rigs. In line spreaders: masthead/fractional

1) Having established the heel position, take the slack out of the rigging, enough to enable the mast to stand up safely. 2) From below look up the aft face of the mast, through the deck, if keel stepped, and towards the top of the mast. Check that the mast is straight through the area of the deck and that there is no deflection as a result of the mast bearing on the deck. Do not be surprised if you find that in order to keep the mast straight over its whole length you cannot pass it through the exact centre of the hole in the deck. This sometimes occurs where the deck hole is not in the exact centre of the boat.
3) Mark a position at the toe rail in the way of the mast on either side of the boat. Using a halyard cleated off at the appropriate length check that the mast is standing vertically in relation to the boat by positioning the lower end of the cleated halyard over the mark on each toe rail. Note: Make sure that the halyard you are using is below the forestay attachment point and on (or as close as possible) to the centreline of the mast.
4) Do not overtighten the rigging at this stage. All you are trying to do is to get the mast to stand perpendicular to the boat. As a result you will only need slight tension to hold the mast up and in many cases you will be able to adjust the rigging by hand.
5) By adjusting the forestay length (by means of the turnbuckle or link plate) and/or the heel position set the required amount of mast rake.

Centring the rig in the boat

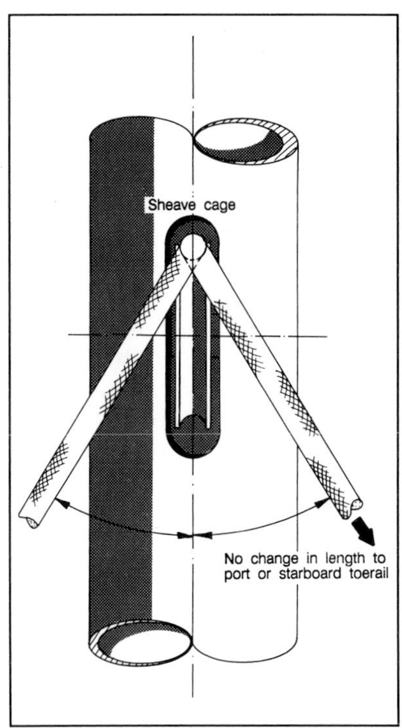

Halyard must be on forward centreline of mast

6) Before adjusting the athwartships rigging tension the desired pre-bend must be set. Once initially set the pre-bend can then be altered following sailing trials to optimise the sail and weather conditions that you require. As with all aspects of tuning it is important to make a record of the pre-bend setting which will help you to both make further adjustments more precisely and repeat performance when the mast is re-stepped. (see tuning sheet)
7) Set up a guide line between the top of the mast and the gooseneck by using the main halyard or similar. Do not over-tension this as you may induce bend in the spar.
8) Tension the permanent backstay until you have achieved the required amount of pre-bend. Cleat off the backstay and move to the side shrouds which now can be tensioned.
9) Tighten the lower shrouds a few turns at a time on each side. Make sure that you remember the number of turns you are putting on each side in order that you tension up the rigging evenly. Each time you tighten the shrouds as a pair (ie port and starboard) check that the mast is straight athwartships by looking up the mainsail track on the aft face of the mast.
10) Continue to tighten the lower shrouds until they are reasonably tight. ie Using the correct size and length spanner the rigging screws should become fairly difficult to tighten further. (Avoid using adjustable spanners as their use can damage the rigging screw bodies.)
11) Check the mast again for athwartships straightness. Do not begin to further tighten the rigging until you have done this.
12) In the same manner as the lowers tighten the cap shrouds a few turns at a time, again checking the mast for straightness both athwartships and fore and aft.
13) At this stage the cap shrouds do not need to be as tight as the lowers.
14) Release the tension on the backstay and sight up the mast in both the fore and aft and athwartships direction. Check that you are happy with the bend or lack of and replace the locking pins in the rigging screws.
15) Fit the mast chocks securely. Then fit the mast coat (if keel stepped mast.)
16) Make sure that the mast heel is fastened to the step to prevent it moving either fore and aft or jumping off the step.
17) The rig should now be ready for fine tuning.

Fine tuning under sail

Whilst a mast can be set up

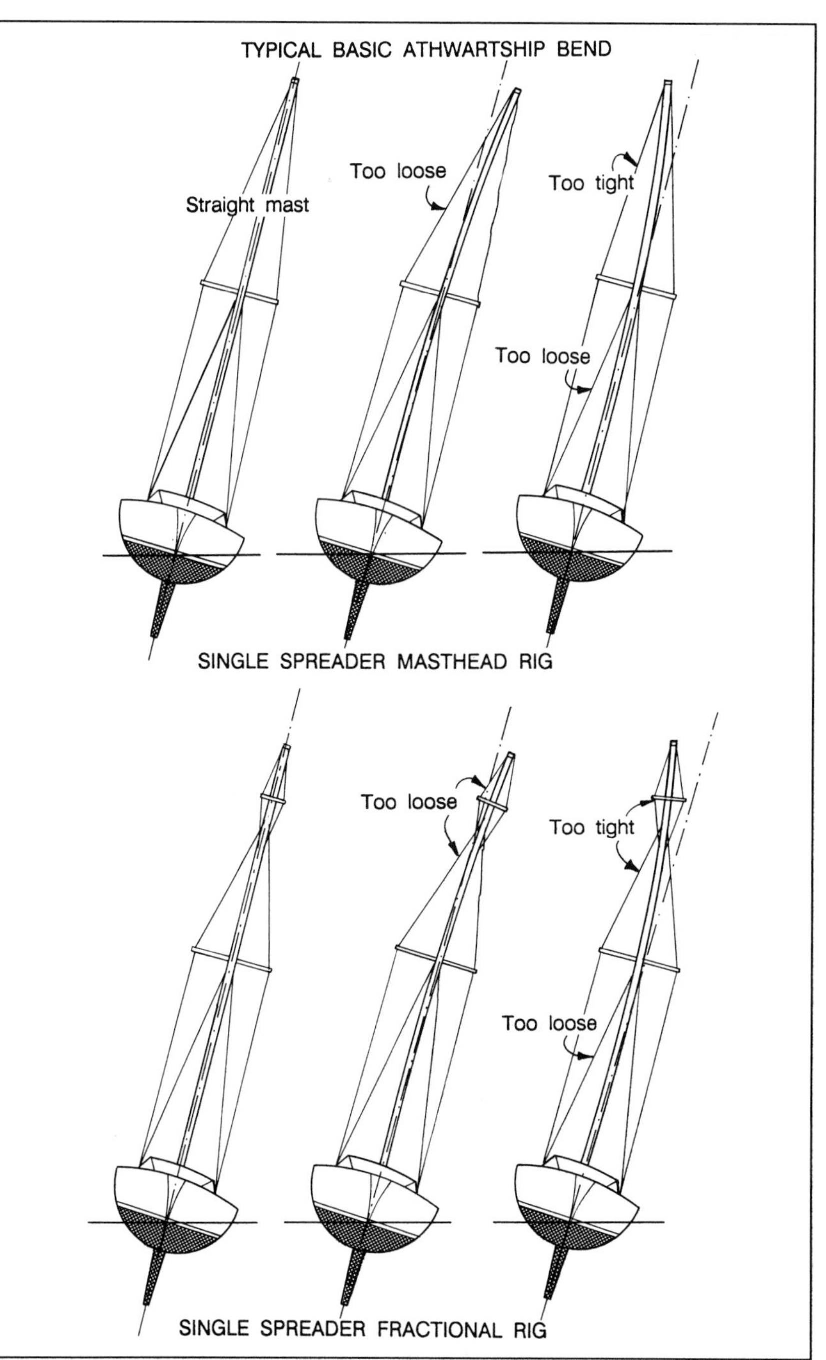

Typical mast bends

fairly accurately whilst on its mooring, sailing trials are an essential part of setting up and tuning. One of the main factors on mast tuning is the stretch in the rigging and the effect of this can only be seen when the rig is loaded. It is for this reason that cap shrouds are often tighter than lower shrouds and the additional stretch must be taken out by pre-tensioning the rigging.

Conditions for fine tuning under sail should be such that the boat can be comfortably sailed on the wind. Do not attempt to tune the mast in rough sea conditions.

As a rule of thumb:
a) Full sail ie. full main sail and No. 1 genoa
b) Sail close hauled with crew in position
c) Flat water
d) 10 – 15 degrees heel

The leeward cap shrouds should just be going slack. The lower shrouds should remain relatively tight.

Before adjusting anything:
1) Check the mast on both tacks.
2) Make a note of the current settings.
3) Sight up the aft face of the mast and assess the straightness.

There are two ways of adjusting the rigging now either; Heave-to, lower the sails and adjust the rigging or carefully adjust whilst under sail. The latter requires extreme care but is a more efficient method.

If you do decide to adjust the rigging whilst under sail be sure to only adjust the leeward rigging. If you attempt to move the windward turnbuckles whilst under sail you will most probably damage them.

If you are tuning under sail make sure you only adjust the leeward shrouds two turns at a time. This is very important as high compression loads can be induced into the mast whilst tuning under sail and excessive loads could damage the mast and even the boat.

If you find that you have been tightening the shrouds continuously without any apparent effect – STOP!

Heave to, in order to lower the sails and check the tension in the rigging. If the shrouds seem excessively tight then there is a good chance that the boat is bending or the chainplates are moving. If this is the case, slacken off the rigging and investigate the boat's structure and the chain plates.

If you find instead that the mast falls off to leeward excessively and cannot be controlled with additional capshroud tension – STOP!

This is an indication that the mast is severely overloaded as a result of too much tension and is buckling under compression. The rigging must be fully slackened and the tuning process must begin again. This time you will have to watch carefully to prevent over-tensioning. Do not attempt to re-tune the mast by progressively slackening the rigging, you must start again from scratch. (See fall off section.)

Having set up the rig athwartships, the balance of the helm can now be adjusted if necessary. As described earlier, this balance is mainly a function of mast rake. Mark the head of the rudder stock or the wheel. Set up the boat with the following conditions;
a) Full sail ie. Full main and no. 1 genoa
b) Sail close hauled with crew in position
c) Flat water
d) 10 – 15 degrees heel

Thus: Weather helm angle = 2 to 5 degrees

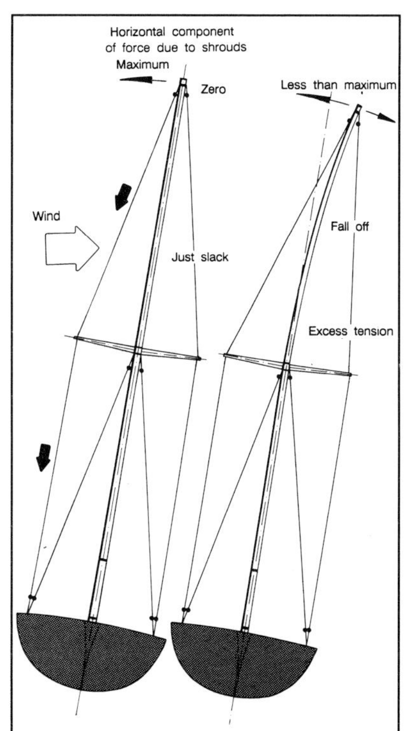

Left: Effect of excess leeward shroud tension

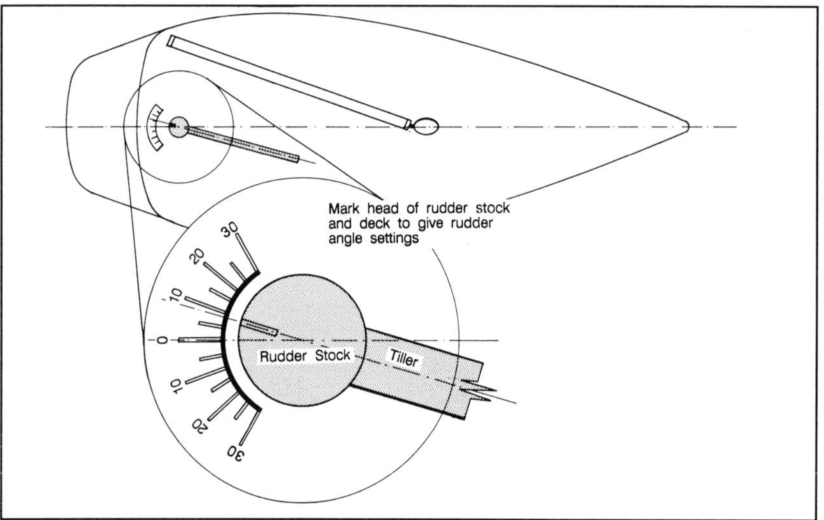

Below: Marking up the rudder stock helps check the amount of 'helm'

Weather helm angle

The 'weather helm angle' should = 2° – 5°
If your helm angle does not correspond to this then:

Helm Angle	Rake adjustment	Result
<2 degrees	Increase aft rake	+ Weather helm angle + Upwind performance
>5 degrees	Reduce aft rake	– Weather helm angle + Helm control – Broaching tendency

Where: + = increased
– = decreased

1 Spreader rigs – aft swept spreaders – fractional
Whilst this type of rig may look very similar to the in line version, it is in fact a very different rig to set up. These types of rigs have evolved to simplify the fractional rig by dispensing with the need for running backstays. It is therefore ironic that they are in fact more difficult to set up than the conventional in-line type. The reason for this is that the aft swept rig is a compromise in terms of the fact that the forestay tension comes primarily from the cap shroud and backstay tensions. As a result the athwartships rigging cannot be tensioned without affecting the fore and aft support. It is therefore very difficult, if not impossible, to achieve the perfect settings for all wind strengths.

In addition to this the sweep back of the spreaders means that when the cap shrouds are tensioned, fore and aft bend is induced into the mast. This bend is checked by the lower shrouds. If a degree of pre-bend is required, it is important to make sure that the lower shrouds are not over tensioned as they will tend to reduce this bend.

The setting up of a racing rig is usually more critical than that of a cruising boat. However the initial settings should be the same.

1) Having established the heel position, take the slack out of the rigging, enough to enable the mast to stand up safely.
2) From below look up the aft face of the mast, through the deck and towards the top of the mast. Check that the mast is straight through the area of the deck and that there is no deflection as a result of the mast bearing on the deck. Do not be surprised if you find that in order to keep the mast straight over its whole length you cannot pass it through the exact centre of the hole in the deck. This sometimes occurs where the deck hole is not in the exact centre of the boat.
3) Mark a position at the toe rail

Below: Effect of rake and bend on cap shrouds

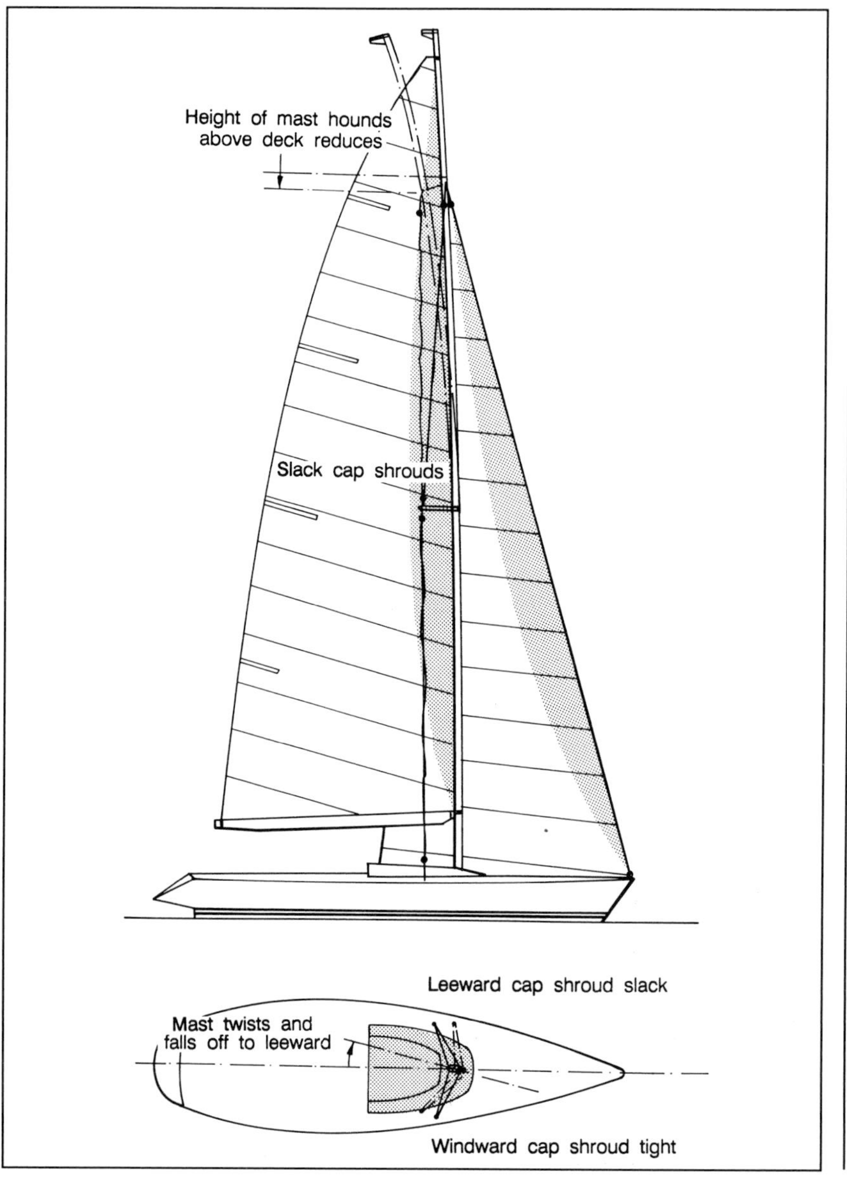

in the way of the mast on either side of the boat. Using a halyard cleated off at the appropriate length check that the mast is standing vertically in relation to the boat by positioning the lower end of the cleated halyard over the mark on each toe rail.

Note: Make sure that the halyard you are using is below the forestay attachment point and on (or as close as possible) to the centreline of the mast.

4) Do not overtighten the rigging at this stage. All you are trying to do is to get the mast to stand perpendicular to the boat. As a result you will only need slight tension to hold the mast up and in many cases you will be able to adjust the rigging by hand.

5) By adjusting the forestay length, (by means of the turnbuckle or link plate), and/or the heel position set the required amount of mast rake.

6) Before adjusting the athwartships rigging tension the desired pre-bend must be set. Once initially set the pre-bend can then be altered following sailing trials to optimise the sail and weather conditions that you require. As with all aspects of tuning it is important to make a record of the pre-bend setting which will help you to both make further adjustments more precisely and repeat performance when the mast is re-stepped.

7) Set up a guide line between the top of the mast and the gooseneck by using the main halyard or similar. Do not over-tension this as you may induce bend in the spar.

8) Slacken completely the lower shrouds.

9) With a combination of tension on the permanent backstay and the insertion of chocks behind the mast at deck level the required amount of pre-bend can be achieved. (On a deck stepped mast it will only be possible to induce pre-bend with the backstay.) Cleat off the backstay and move to the side shrouds which now can be tensioned.

10) Tighten the cap shrouds a few turns at a time on each side. Make sure that you remember the number of turns you are putting on each side in order that you tension up the rigging evenly. Each time you tighten the shrouds as a pair (ie port and starboard) check that the mast is straight athwartships. Also check the fore and aft bend against the guide line.

11) Continue to tighten the cap shrouds until the fore and aft bend starts to increase. As you tighten the cap shrouds periodically check the tension in the backstay which should start to decrease. At this point stop tensioning the caps and check that the mast is still straight athwartships.

12) In the same manner as the caps, begin to tighten the lower shrouds a few turns at a time checking the mast for straightness athwartships.

13) Continue to tighten the lowers until the fore and aft bend just begins to reduce.

14) At this stage the cap shrouds should be tighter than the lowers.

15) Release the tension on the backstay and sight up the mast in both the fore and aft and athwartships direction. Check that you are happy with the amount of bend.

16) Replace the locking pins in the rigging screws.

17) Replace the mast chocks if the mast is keel stepped and fit the mast coat.

18) Make sure that the mast heel is securely restrained from moving fore and aft. Ideally it should be bolted right through the heel and step to prevent the mast from lifting off the step altogether. (In a number of racing classes this is mandatory.) The rig should now be ready for fine tuning.

Fine tuning under sail

The conditions required for sailing trials should be the same as described in the previous section ie.

a) Full sail ie. Full main and no 1 genoa
b) Sail close hauled with crew in position
c) Flat water
d) 10 – 15° heel

The leeward cap shrouds and lowers should not be slack but neither should they be so tight as to impose high compression on the mast. If the leeward shrouds are allowed to go slack then the mast will tend to twist and move forwards. This will also allow the forestay to slacken and sag thus reducing the efficiency of the headsail. As the height of the hounds has reduced the cap shrouds will also slacken which will allow the mast to fall to leeward. A common mistake is to see this as fall off and to tighten the shrouds still further thus increasing the compression and hence worsening the situation.

Before adjusting anything:
i) Check the mast on both tacks
ii) Make a note of the current settings.

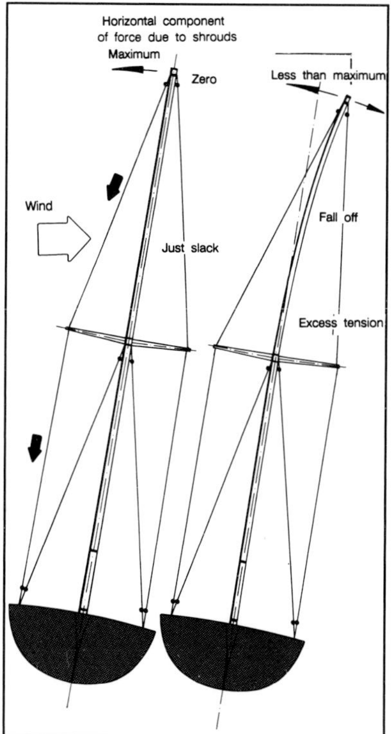

Effect of excess leeward shroud tension

iii) Sight up the aft face of the mast and assess the straightness.
iv) Watch the forestay and tension the backstay to the point where further tensioning ceases to have an effect on the forestay.

There are two ways of adjusting the rigging now either: Heave-to lower the sails and adjust the rigging or carefully adjust the leeward rigging whilst under sail. The latter requires extreme care but is a more efficient method.

If you do decide to adjust the rigging whilst under sail be sure to only adjust the leeward rigging. If you attempt to move the windward turnbuckles whilst under sail you will most probably damage them.

If you are tuning under sail make sure you only tighten the leeward shrouds a maximum two turns at a time on each side. This is very important as high compression loads can be induced into the mast whilst tuning under sail and excessive loads could damage the mast and even the boat.

If you find that you have been tightening the shrouds continuously without any apparent effect – STOP!

Heave-to in order to lower the sails and check the tension in the rigging. If the shrouds seem excessively bar tight then there is a good chance that the boat is bending or the chainplates are moving. If this is the case slacken off the rigging and investigate the boat's structure and the chain plates.

If you find instead that the mast falls off to leeward excessively and cannot be controlled with additional cap shroud tension – STOP!

This is an indication that the mast is severely overloaded as a result of too much tension and is buckling under compression. The rigging must be fully slackened and the tuning process must begin again. This time you will have to watch carefully to prevent over-tensioning. Do not attempt to re-tune the mast by progressively slackening the rigging, you must start again from scratch. (See Fall Off section.)

Having set up the rig athwartships, the balance of the helm can now be adjusted if necessary. As described earlier, this balance is mainly a function of mast rake.

Set up the boat with the following conditions:
a) Full sail ie. Full main and no. 1 genoa
b) Sail close hauled with crew in position

Related effects of aft swept rig

Item		
Backstay	+	–
Caps tension	–	+
Leeward lowers on athw.bend	+	–
Hounds height	below max.	max.

Where: + = tight
– = slack

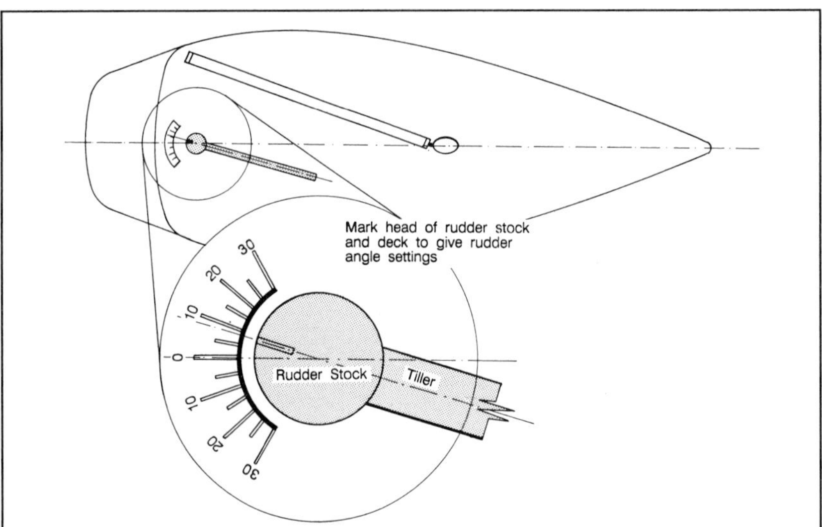

Marking up the rudder stock helps check the amount of 'helm'

Weather helm angle

The 'weather helm angle' should = 2° – 5°
If your helm angle does not correspond to this then:

Helm Angle	Rake adjustment	Result
<2°	Increase aft rake	+ Weather helm angle + Upwind performance
>5°	Reduce aft rake	– Weather helm angle + Helm control – Broaching tendency

Where: + = increased
– = decreased

c) Flat water
d) 10 – 15 degrees heel
Thus: Weather helm angle = 2 to 5 degrees

2 Spreader rigs – in line spreaders – masthead/fractional

As there is an extra set of spreaders and one additional span of rigging on each side, this type of rig is often considered to be considerably more difficult to set up than a single spreader version. This should not be the case so long as the rigging system is of the continuous type. It is unusual for a two spreader rig to employ a discontinuous rigging system (such a system is in the section on 3 spreader rigs) and therefore we shall only discuss tuning the continuous type in this section.

In addition to the intermediate shrouds there is often a set of additional fore and aft stays on this type of rig. There are two reasons for this:

a) If the mast is set up for a cutter rig an inner forestay will be required. This will necessitate a set of running backstays to provide the mast with fore and aft support against the inner forestay. (The running backstays on a masthead rig act more as preventers which restrain the centre panel from "panting" fore and aft.)

b) The bottom set of spreaders will be lower than on a single spreader rig of the same height. This means that there is little fore and aft support for the longer section of mast above the lower spreaders. An advantage of this system is that when setting the pre-bend into the spar the inner forestay can be used initially to set the amount of bend.

The tuning process is very similar to that described in the section entitled '1 Spreader rigs in-line masthead/fractional'.

For the initial setting details follow points 1-12 then continue with this section:

13) Take the slack out of the intermediate shrouds on each side but do not tension.

14) Sight up the aft face of the mast to check for athwartships straightness. Balance any deflection with just enough tension on one of the intermediates to straighten the mast.

15) Starting from the same side of the boat as with the other spans, begin to tension the intermediates a few turns at a time.

16) Continue to tighten until the slack has been taken out and slight pre-tension exists. These spans should be the slackest of the athwartships rigging. (The purpose of these spans is

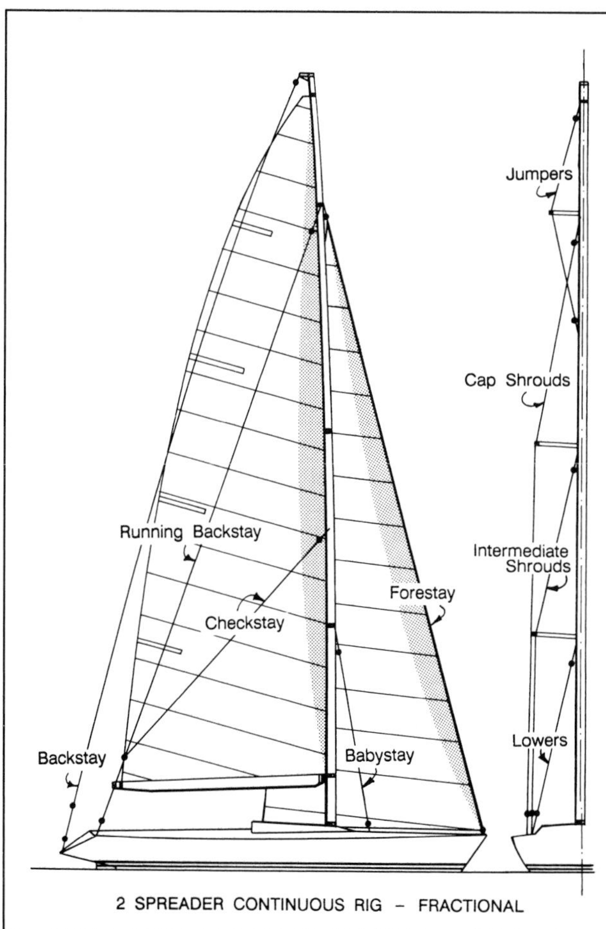

Two-spreader continuous rig – fractional

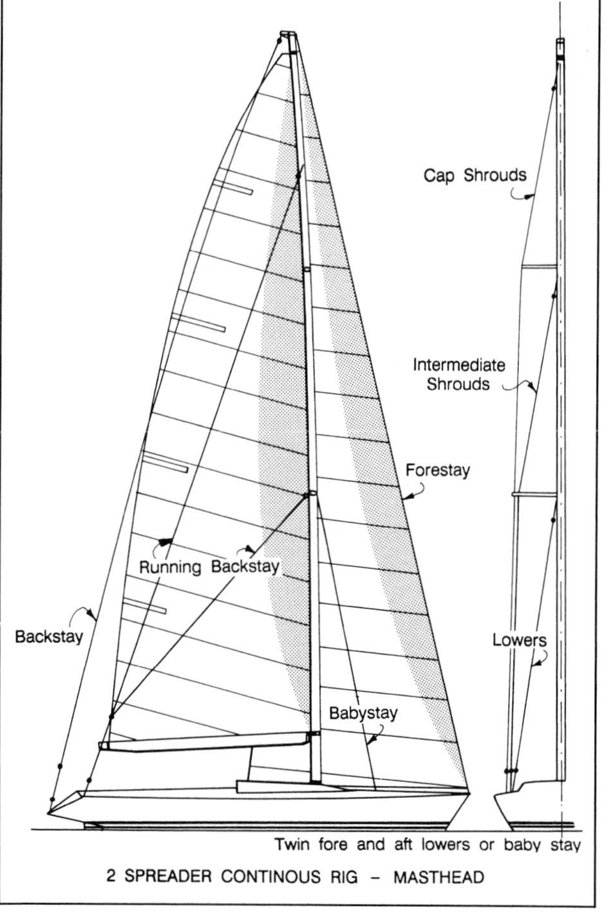

Two-spreader continuous rig – masthead

primarily to keep the middle of the mast in column and in most instances not to carry the main part of the supporting loads. When heavily reefed these spans do however carry a relatively high load.)

17) Release the tension on the backstay and sight up the mast in both the fore and aft and athwartships directions. Check that you are happy with the bend, or indeed lack of and replace the locking pins in the rigging screws.

18) Fit the mast chocks securely and fasten the mast coat.

19) Make sure that the mast heel is securely restrained from moving fore and aft. Ideally it should be bolted right through the heel and step to prevent the mast from lifting off the step altogether. (In a number of racing classes this is mandatory.)

Fine tuning under sail.

Whilst a mast can be set up fairly accurately whilst on its mooring, sailing trials are an essential part of setting up and tuning. One of the main factors on mast tuning is the stretch in the rigging and the effect of this can only be seen when the mast is loaded. For a given rigging diameter and material the stretch remains constant per metre. Therefore the longer the span the greater the stretch that has to be allowed for at one end. It is for this reason that cap shrouds are often tighter than lower shrouds as the additional stretch must be taken out by pre-tensioning the rigging.

Conditions for fine tuning under sail should be such that the boat can be comfortably sailed on the wind. Do not attempt to tune the mast in rough sea conditions. As a rule of thumb:

a) Full sail ie. Full main and no 1 genoa

b) Sail close hauled with crew in position

c) Flat water

d) 10 – 15 degrees heel

The relative leeward shroud

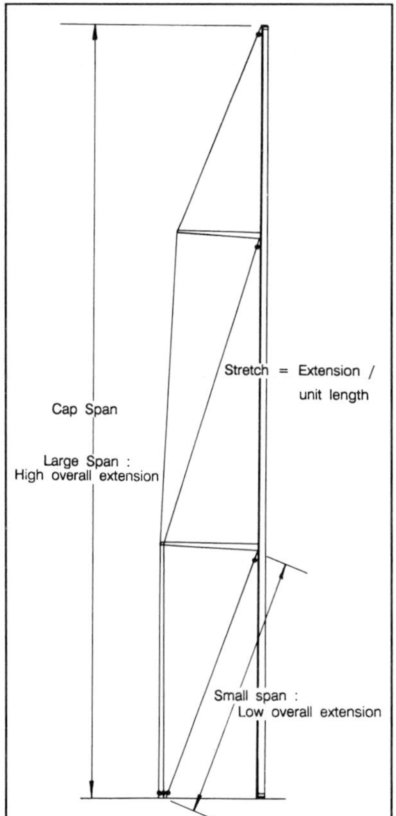

Stretch and span length

tensions should be as follows:

a) Cap shrouds should just be going slack.

b) Lower shrouds should remain relatively tight.

c) Intermediate shrouds should be slack.

The intermediate shrouds should have just enough tension in order to keep the mast in column. Therefore these are the last shrouds to be tensioned.

The very first item that must be checked is the athwartships straightness of the mast. Before adjusting anything:

a) Check the mast on both tacks

b) Make a note of the current settings.

c) Sight up the aft face of the mast and assess the straightness.

Be careful particularily when sighting up a fractionally rigged mast to establish whether the bend you are looking at is fall off at the top or windward lift in the middle. Be warned – the difference between the two can be very deceptive!

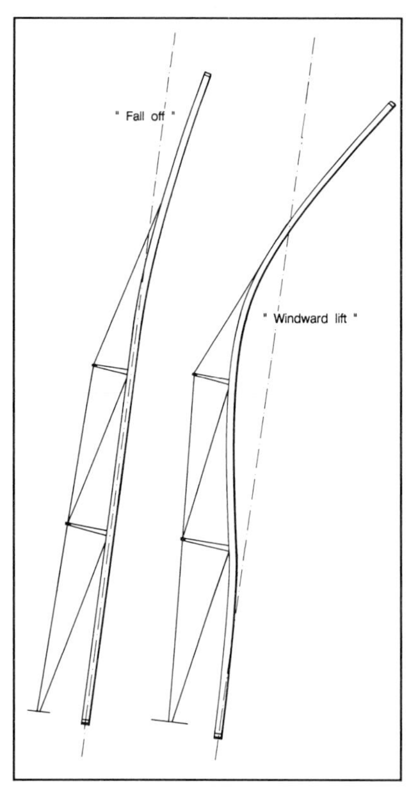

Fall off and windward lift

There are two ways of adjusting the rigging now either: Heave-to lower the sails and adjust the rigging or carefully adjust whilst under sail. The latter requires extreme care but is a more efficient method.

If you do decide to adjust the rigging whilst under sail be sure to only adjust the leeward rigging and no more than two turns at a time. If you attempt to move the windward turnbuckles whilst under sail you will most probably damage them.

If you are tuning under sail make sure you only tighten the leeward shrouds two turns at a time on each side. This is very important as high compression loads can be induced into the mast whilst tuning under sail and excessive loads could damage the mast and even the boat.

If you find that you have been tightening the shrouds continuously without any apparent effect – STOP! Heave-to, lower the sails and check the tension in the rigging. If the shrouds

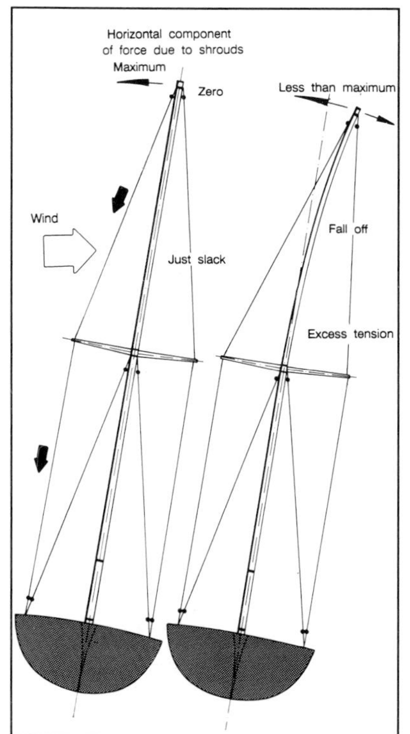

Effect of excess leeward shroud tension

seem excessively tight then there is a good chance that the boat is bending or the chainplates are moving. If this is the case slacken off the rigging and investigate the boat's structure and the chain plates.

If you find that the mast falls off to leeward excessively and cannot be controlled with additional cap shroud tension – STOP! This is an indication that the mast is severely overloaded as a result of too much tension and is buckling under compression. The rigging must be fully slackened and the tuning process must begin again. This time you will have to watch carefully to prevent over tensioning. Do not attempt to retune the mast by progressively slackening the rigging, you must start again from scratch. (See Fall Off section.)

Once you have set up the mast under full sail, now reef the mainsail so that the head of the sail is well below the hounds.

Set up the boat on the wind as described above and sight up

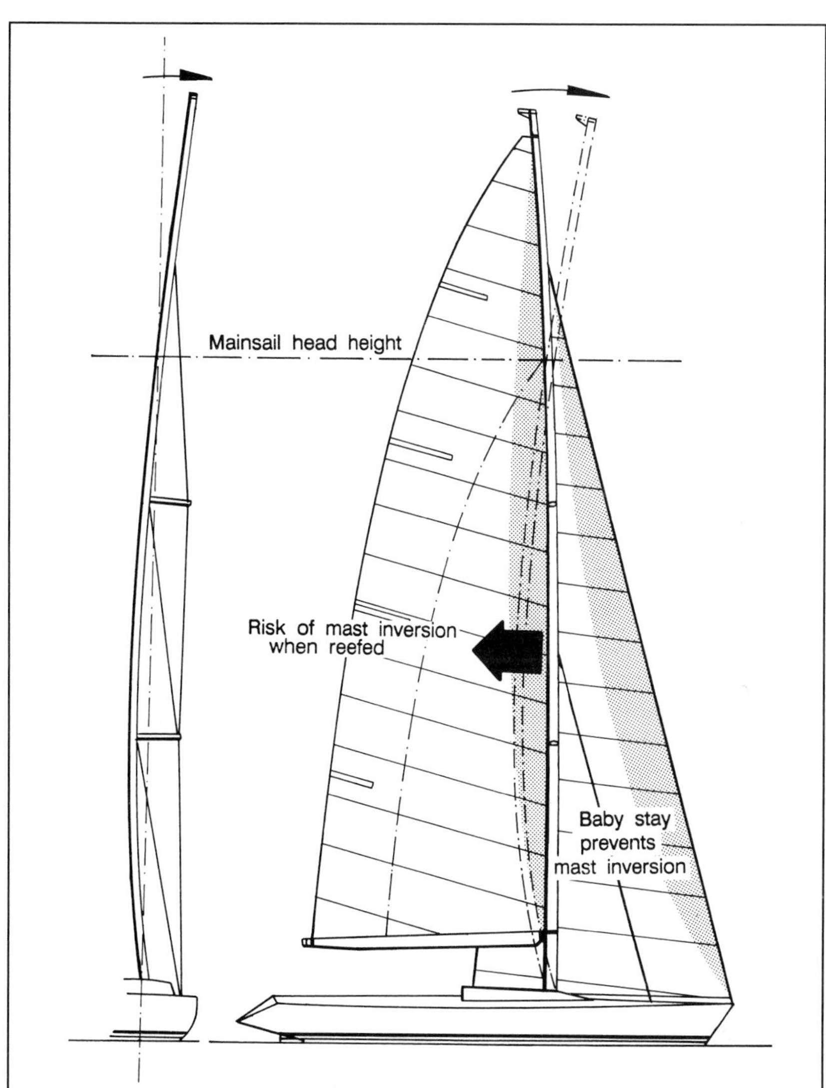

Checking the rig when reefed

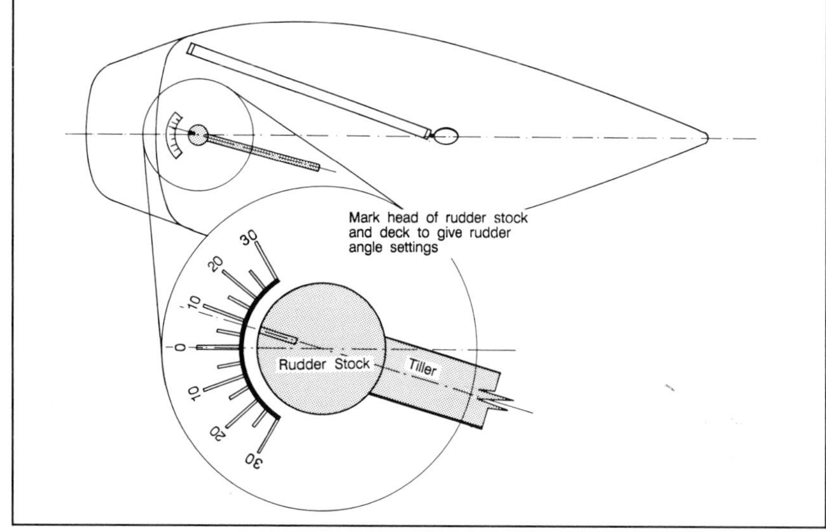

Marking up the rudder stock helps check the amount of 'helm'

the aft face of the mast looking for athwartships bend particularly in the intermediate attachment area.

Tighten the intermediate shrouds by just enough to straighten the mast on each tack. You will need to check the mast again in stronger airs where the intermediate shroud may have stretched and will therefore require tightening. DO NOT attempt to adjust this whilst sailing in strong winds.

Once the rigging tensions have been set return to a full mainsail sail-plan. Having set up the rig athwartships, the balance of the helm can now be adjusted if necessary. As described earlier, this balance is mainly a function of mast rake.

Set up the boat with the following conditions:

a) Full sail ie. Full main and no 1 genoa
b) Sail close hauled with crew in position
c) Flat water
d) 10 – 15 degrees heel

The 'weather helm angle' should = 2 to 5 degrees

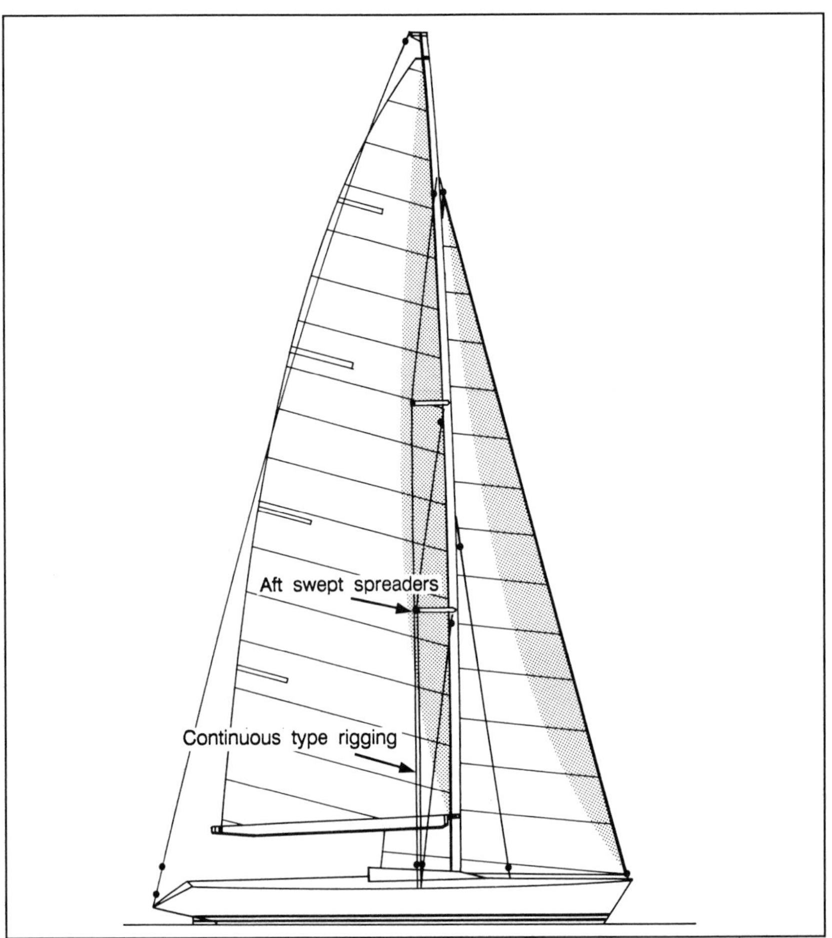

Two–Spreader continuous rig aft swept – fractional

Weather helm angle

The 'weather helm angle' should = 2° – 5°
If your helm angle does not correspond to this then:

Helm Angle	Rake adjustment	Result
<2 degrees	Increase aft rake	+ Weather helm angle + Upwind performance
>5 degrees	Reduce aft rake	– Weather helm angle + Helm control – Broaching tendency

Where: + = increased
– = decreased

2 Spreader rigs – aft swept – fractional

Rigs with aft swept spreaders are notoriously difficult to set up. The reason is that they are a compromise between fore and aft and longitudinal support. As a result when the rigging tensions are altered the effect is in two planes. Unfortunately the results are often conflicting and a compromise has to be made.

The fundamentals of setting up this type of rig are very similar to that of the single aft swept spreader system in the respect that the mast must be restrained both from fall off and twisting.

A two spreader rig is however often slightly easier than a single spreader rig. There is often an inner forestay fitted which is attached at approximately mid-height. As this stay supports the mast in the fore and aft direction it can also be used to control the degree of bend. (This stay can also assist in the initial setting of the pre-bend.)

This section considers continuous type rigging systems only as it is very unusual for a two spreader rig of this type to employ a discontinuous type system. (If you do have such a system the primary rigging tensions i.e. caps and lowers are the same as described in this section. Also see the section on 3 spreader rigs paying attention only to the notes relating to the diagonal spans.)

For the initial setting details follow points 1-12 in the previous section on 1 spreader aft swept fractional rigs and then continue with this section:
13) Take the slack out of the intermediate shrouds on each side but do not tension.
14) Sight up the aft face of the mast to check for athwartships straightness. Balance any deflection with just enough tension on one of the intermediates to straighten the mast.
15) Starting from the same side of the boat as with the other spans, begin to tension the intermediates a few turns at a time.
16) Continue to tighten until the slack has been taken out and slight pre-tension exists. These spans should be the slackest of the athwartships rigging. When tightening these stays pay particular attention to the fore and aft bend in the mast as over-tensioning will tend to reduce the pre-bend. (The purpose of these spans is primarily to keep the middle of the mast in column and in most instances not to carry the main part of the supporting loads. When heavily reefed these spans do however carry a relatively high load.)
17) Release the tension on the backstay and inner forestay, if fitted. Sight up the mast in both the fore and aft and athwartships directions. Check that you are happy with the bend, or indeed lack of and replace the locking pins in the rigging screws.
18) Fit the mast chocks securely and fasten the mast coat.
19) Make sure that the mast heel is securely restrained from moving fore and aft. Ideally it should be bolted right through the heel and step to prevent the mast from lifting off the step altogether. (In a number of racing classes this is mandatory.)

Fine tuning under sail
The conditions required for sailing trials should be the same as described in the previous section ie.
a) Full sail ie. Full main and no 1 genoa
b) Sail close hauled with crew in position
c) Flat water
d) 10 to 15 degrees heel

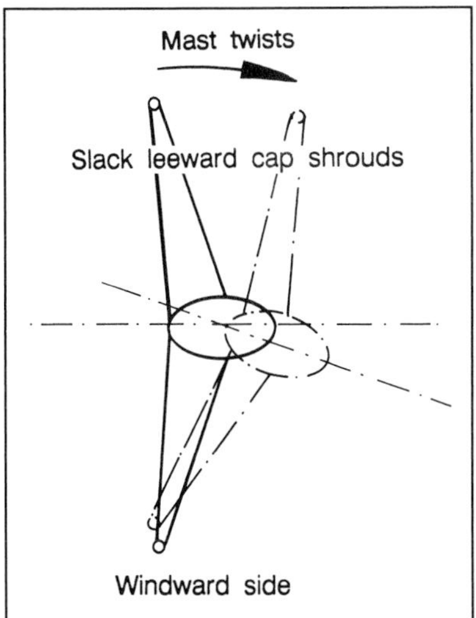

Effect of slack cap shrouds

The leeward cap shrouds and lowers should not be slack but neither should they be so tight as to impose high compression on the mast. If the leeward shrouds are allowed to go slack then the mast will tend to twist and move forwards. This will also allow the forestay to slacken and sag possibly reducing the efficiency of the headsail. It is possible to overtension the cap shrouds to such an extent that the mast becomes overcompressed and develops excess fore and aft bend. If this happens the effective height of the hounds will be reduced which will tend to slacken the cap shrouds. As the height of the hounds above the deck has reduced the cap shrouds will also slacken which will allow the mast to fall to leeward. A common mistake is to see this as fall off and to tighten the shrouds still further thus increasing the compression and hence worsening the situation.

Sight up the forward face of the mast and check that the spreaders are perpendicular to the centreline of the boat. If they are twisted so that the leeward spreaders are forward of perpendicular then the leeward cap shrouds are most likely too slack.

The intermediate shrouds have little effect on the twisting of the mast. Their primary effect is to keep the mast in column with the minimum of compression. Unlike an in-line spreader system the intermediates do affect the amount of fore and aft bend around the mid-height area. This has a large effect on the mainsail shape and fullness. If these shrouds are too tight they will prevent the middle of the mast from moving forwards and flattening the main. This will make the sail plan more difficult to handle in stronger winds where a flat sail is required. The lowers will also try to prevent the mast from bending in the fore and aft plane if they are overtightened and this will also make flattening the mainsail difficult. Therefore set the lowers so that they prevent the mast from travelling beyond the maximum position for flattening the main.

The net requirement is that when sailing on the wind as described above the intermediate shrouds should just be going slack. A summary of the relative leeward rigging tensions:
a) Cap shrouds – fairly tight
b) Lower shrouds – fairly tight
c) Intermediate shrouds – just going slack
Before adjusting anything:
1) Check the mast on both tacks.
2) Make a note of the current settings.
3) Sight up the aft face of the mast and assess the straightness.
4) Watch the forestay and tension the backstay to the point where further tensioning ceases to have an effect on the forestay. There are two ways of adjusting the rigging now either; Heave-to lower the sails and adjust the rigging or care

Effects of individual rigging spars

Item		
Backstay	+	–
Caps tension	–	+
Ints tension	–	+
Lowers	+	–
Hounds height	below max	max.

Where: + = increased tension
– = decreased tension

fully adjust the leeward rigging whilst under sail. The latter requires extreme care but is a more efficient method.

If you do decide to adjust the rigging whilst under sail be sure to only adjust the leeward rigging. If you attempt to move the windward turnbuckles whilst under sail you will most probably damage them.

If you are tuning under sail make sure you only tighten the leeward shrouds a maximum two turns at a time on each side. This is very important as high compression loads can be induced into the mast whilst tuning under sail and excessive loads could damage the mast and even the boat.

If you find that you have been tightening the shrouds continuously without any apparent effect – STOP! Heave-to in order to lower the sails and check the tension in the rigging. If the shrouds seem excessively tight then there is a good chance that the boat is bending or the chainplates are moving. If this is the case slacken off the rigging and investigate the boat's structure and the chain plates.

If you find instead that the mast falls off to leeward excessively and cannot be controlled with additional cap shroud tension – STOP! This is an indication that the mast is severely overloaded as a result of too much tension and is buckling under compression. The rigging must be fully slackened and the tuning process must begin again. This time you will have to watch carefully to prevent over-tensioning. Do not attempt to re-tune the mast by progressively slackening the rigging, you must start again from scratch.

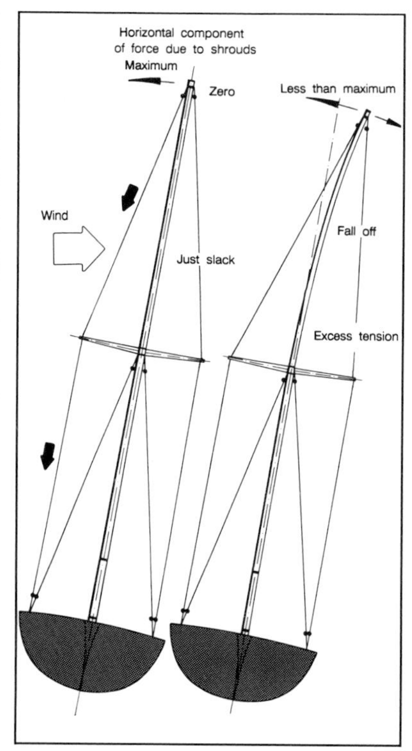

Effect of excess leeward shroud tension

Once you have set up the mast under full sail, now reef the mainsail so that the head of the sail is well below the hounds. Set up the boat on the wind as described above and sight up the aft face of the mast and look for leeward sag at about mid height.

Set the mainsail flat for heavy weather conditions and sight up the windward side of the mast and assess the fore and aft bend.

Tighten the leeward shrouds by just enough to straighten the mast athwartships on each tack and to prevent any twisting. Over-tensioning will reduce the fore and aft bend thus making the mainsail fuller. This will make the sail plan difficult to handle in strong winds.

Sight up the windward face of the mast to check that the fore and aft bend is still acceptable and that the mainsail has remained flat.

Even though you have tuned the mast for stronger winds you will need to check the mast again when you do sail in such conditions. The additional load may cause the rigging to stretch further and slight re-adjustment may be necessary. If this is the case DO NOT attempt to adjust the rigging whilst sailing.

Having set up the rig athwartships, return to a full mainsail sail plan and the balance of the

Weather helm angle should = 2° – 5°
To adjust to this:

Helm Angle	**Rake adjustment**	**Result**
<2 degrees	Increase aft rake	+ Weather helm angle + Upwind performance
>5 degrees	Reduce aft rake	– Weather helm angle + Helm control – Broaching tendency

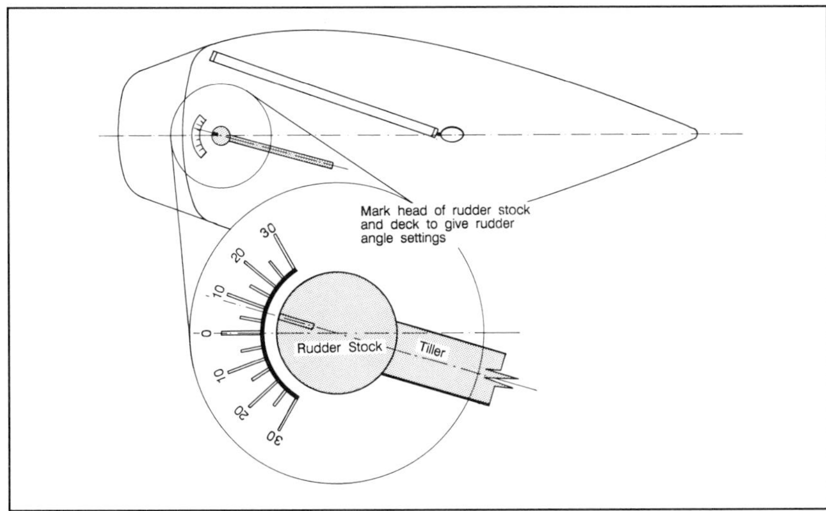

Marking up the rudder stock helps check the amount of 'helm'

helm can now be adjusted if necessary. As described earlier, this balance is mainly a function of mast rake.

Set up the boat with the following conditions:

a) Full sail ie. Full main and no 1 genoa
b) Sail close hauled with crew in position
c) Flat water
d) 10 – 15 degrees heel

The 'weather helm angle' should = 2 to 5 degrees

3 and 4 Spreader rigs – in line – masthead/fractional

These types of rig are most often found on a Grand Prix type racing yachts where the

Figures below and right: 3 and 4 Spreader rigs – discontinuous rigging

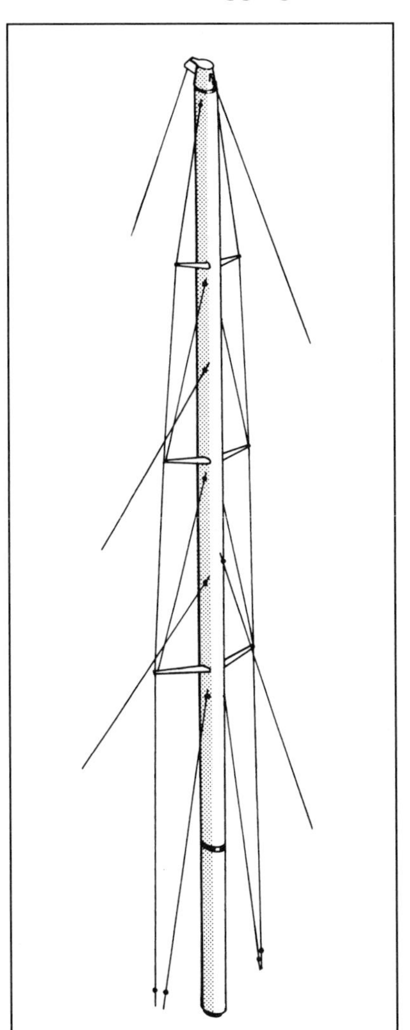

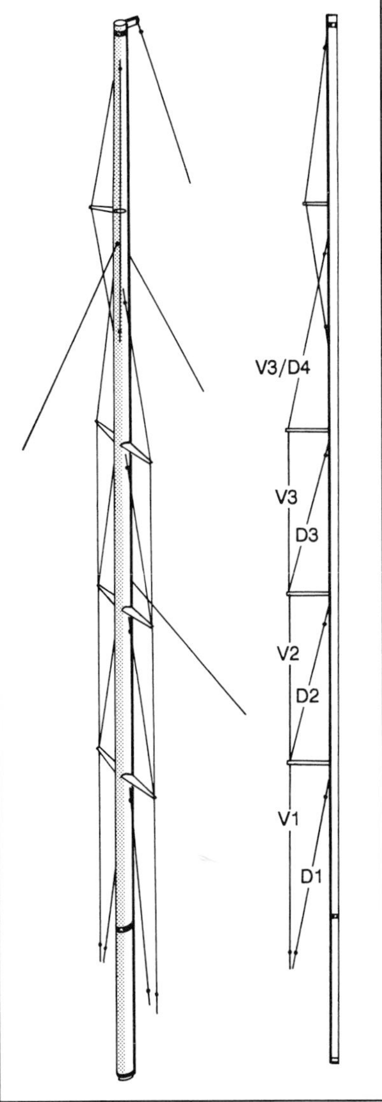

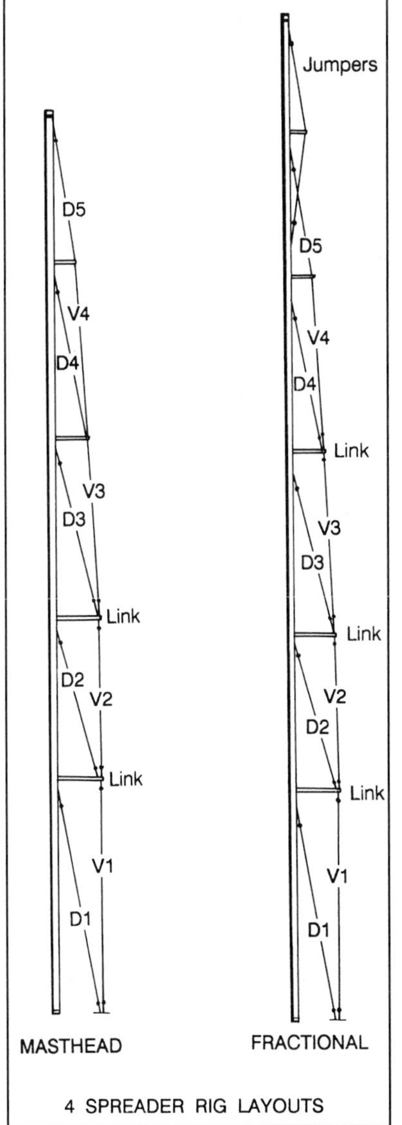

shroud base has to be kept to a minimum to enable close sheeting for good windward performance. There are however an increasing number of cruising yachts using this system for which the tuning procedure is the same. The only difference will be the extent that the rig needs to be tuned. The notes that follow are biased towards the racing yacht.

Some of the early 3 spreader rigs used continuous type rigging where the turnbuckles for each span were to be found at deck level or wherever the chainplates were mounted. This type of rig is very difficult to set up as a result of the stretch involved in each of the long spans to say nothing of the considerable congestion at the chainplates. A four spreader rig of this type would be nothing short of a nightmare with five sets of rigging screws on each side! Fortunately these continuous type systems for 3 and 4 spreader rigs are rare and a discontinuous type system is more common.

The discontinuous rigging system is often considered to be a recent development exclusively for racing craft. This in fact is not so. Link ends on spreader tips were commonplace on most multiple spreader yachts but were generally much larger and heavier than those of today. It was the racing fraternity that developed spreader bends for the continuous rigging system to cut down the weight at the spreader tips. Having said that it must be remembered that there were very few, if any, rigs with 3 and 4 spreaders at that time.

The main difference between continuous and discontinuous systems is that the intermediate rigging on the latter is terminated with a rigging screw at the spreader tip, often called a 'Tip Turnbuckle'. This can easily be seen as there are only two turnbuckles at the chain plate on each side. One is for the main vertical span (V1) and the other is for the lower span (D1). The remaining vertical spans are of a pre-set length and cannot be altered. The diagrams show the way in which the various spans are labelled. The discontinuous system has the following advantages:

a) The rigging sizes can be reduced to match the reduction in loading up the mast. A significant weight saving can be made by employing this system.

b) The stretch of the complete rigging system can be more carefully controlled as the individual rigging spans are much shorter (stretch is expressed as the increase in length from the original length therefore the longer the span, the greater the total stretch).

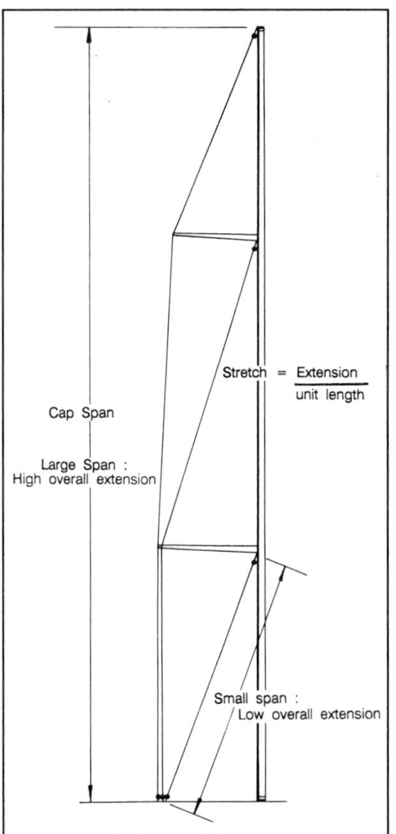

Stretch and span length

c) Repeatable performance and tuning are essential for the Grand Prix racing yacht even when the mast is being lifted in and out of the boat frequently. The discontinuous system means that only the two rigging screws at the chain plates need be slackened on each side to remove the mast. The diagonal spans can be left at their last setting.

d) With the shorter spans on this system each individual unit of rigging becomes more manageable when rigging, de-rigging or repairing. This is a significant advantage and sometimes a necessity on large yachts.

One of the most important points to remember when setting up a discontinuous rig is to make sure that before the mast is lowered into the boat the diagonal spans are as slack as possible. The purpose of these spans is to hold the mast in column with as little tension as is practically possible. Over-tensioning will result in an incorrect distribution of rigging load when under way, leading to excess compression and in some cases unnecessary 'fall off' towards the top of the spar. The advantages are clear to see but they can only be achieved with careful and often lengthy tuning process which is outlined as follows.

1) With the diagonals slack step mast in boat and by adjusting the D1 and V1 spans take the rigging up just enough to enable the mast to stand up safely.

2) Set up a guide line between the top of the mast and the gooseneck by using the main halyard or similar. Do not over-tension this as you may induce bend in the spar that will be difficult to maintain when you release the line.

3) Tension the permanent backstay until you have achieved the required amount of pre-bend. Cleat off the backstay and move to the side shrouds which now can be tensioned.

4) From below look up the aft face of the mast, through the deck and towards the top of the mast. Check that the mast is straight through the area of the

deck and that there is no deflection as a result of the mast bearing against the deck. Do not be surprised if you find that in order to keep the mast straight over its whole length you cannot pass it through the exact centre of the hole in the deck. This sometimes occurs where the deck hole is not in the exact centre of the boat.

5) Mark a position at the toe rail in the way of the mast on either side of the boat. Using a halyard cleated off at the appropriate length check that the mast is standing vertically in relation to the boat by positioning the lower end of the cleated halyard over the mark on each toe rail. Note: Make sure that the halyard you are using is below the forestay attachment point and on (or as close as possible) to the centreline of the mast.

6) Do not overtighten the rigging at this stage. All you are trying to do is to get the mast to stand perpendicular to the boat. As a result you will only need slight tension to hold the mast up and in many cases will be able to adjust the rigging by hand.

7) Once the mast is upright in the boat begin to tension the D1 spans a few turns at a time, in even amounts each side, making sure you note which side of the boat you started! Whilst doing this keep sighting up the mast athwartships and fore and aft to make sure the lower span remains straight.

A mast jack may assist in the tuning of the mast at this stage especially on large racing yachts where the pre-tension loads are high. (See Chapter 8.)

8) Continue to tighten the D1 shrouds until they are reasonably tight. ie using the correct size and length spanner, the rigging screws should become fairly difficult to tighten further.

9) Check the mast again for straightness. Once this has been done make sure that the mast is still vertical in the boat in the manner described in 3).

10) In the same way as the D1 spans, tighten the V1 shrouds a few turns at a time checking the mast for straightness. By attaching the main halyard to the top of the gooseneck fitting and tensioning slightly, deflection of the mast can often be seen more clearly. However do make sure that the topmast is straight and does not have an athwartships set in it before using this method as a guide.

11) As the V1s are tightened the spreader tips will progressively move downwards which in turn will tighten both the vertical and diagonal spans. Because of this it is important to ensure that the diagonals are slack when the mast is initially stepped as these relatively small diameter rods could become over-tensioned and begin to take the main loading off the vertical spans. This in turn could lead to loads beyond the capacity of the diagonals resulting in failure of the rod, its end fittings, or the mast wall.

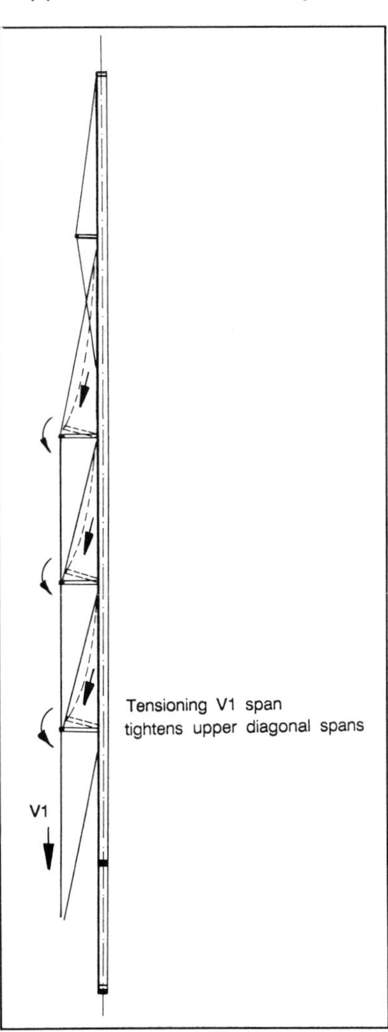

Spreader tip movement with tensioning

12) The next stage involves being hoisted aloft to adjust the remaining diagonals. Therefore the V1 shrouds should be reasonably tight but not as tight as the D1s.

13) Begin with the D2 spans. These spans should be adjusted to the point that they are just slack, then release a few turns (typically 2 to 3 full turns). In most cases this means that the whole operation can be carried out by hand without the use of a spanner.

14) Now move on to the D3 spans (if you have them) and adjust in the same way as the D2s. Then adjust the D4s and so on until you have set up all the diagonals. Now come down for a rest!

15) Release the tension on the standing backstay.

16) Sight up the mast athwartships and fore and aft and make any necessary adjustments.

17) Replace the locking pins or similar securing device in each of the rigging screws.

18) Fit the mast chocks securely and fasten the mast coat.

19) Make sure that the mast heel is securely restrained from moving fore and aft. Ideally it should be bolted right through the heel and step to prevent the mast from lifting off the step altogether. (In a number of classes this is mandatory.)

Fine tuning

The process of fine tuning a racing spar can be best described as continual! There are many factors which influence the way in which the rigging should be tensioned. These include areas such as:

a) Sail shape
b) Sail area
c) Sail configuration

d) Number of crew and hence effective righting moment

As these variables change so the rig may need to be tuned to match these adjustments. As a result the process of fine tuning may continue throughout the racing season.

One of the most important aspects is sail shape. Modern day racing masts are bent whilst sailing to achieve a particular sail shape for a given set of conditions. Fore and aft bend generally affects the camber ratio of the mainsail whilst athwartships bend influences the shape of the leech. (See Fall Off section).

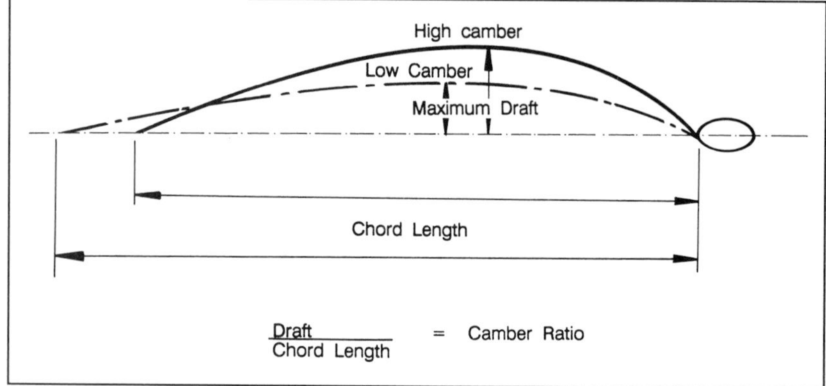

Camber ratio

In order to achieve the desired amount of bend in both directions the mast must be fine tuned under sail. This must be carried out during sailing trials as opposed to during a race.

Extreme care must be exercised when tuning under sail with all rigs but in particular for discontinuous type rigs. Some of the most important points to remember are:

a) Do not attempt to fine tune the rig in rough weather or choppy seas. Pick a day where you can comfortably sail upwind under full sail in flat water.

b) You may need to have a crew member up the mast from time to time to adjust the diagonal spans. In addition to the normal precautions with a person aloft remember that relatively small movements at deck level can be much more severe as one moves up the mast. This not only affects the person who is up the mast but also the boat's behaviour and the additional loads imposed on the mast and rigging.

c) When adjusting the rigging whilst under sail only adjust the *leeward* shrouds. If you attempt to move the windward rigging screws whilst under sail you will most probably damage them.

d) Unless the rigging is excessively slack only adjust the rigging screws two turns at a time, maximum.

e) When tightening the leeward shrouds be careful not to overtighten as this can impose unnecessarily high loads on the mast which could damage the rig.

f) Take particular care not to leave rigging screws unlocked whilst you are not adjusting them. They may shake loose and alter your tuning or even come undone altogether with disastrous consequences.

Fine tuning under sail

Describing exactly how to set up a rig to achieve optimum performance in a book of this size would of course be impossible but the following are some guidelines:

1) Select a day where the weather is such that you can sail upwind comfortably under full sail in flat sea conditions. (Typically 10-12 kts wind speed).

2) Before you begin, make a note of the rigging settings, rake and pre-bend as these will not only help you decide how much to adjust the rigging, but allow you to return to where you started should you decide that the previous settings were more effective. These notes should ideally be kept on board and updated as changes occur.

3) Having set sail, allow yourself plenty of sea room and sail close hauled under normal racing trim (ie crew on weather rail).

4) Sight up the mast, noting your position relative to the mast, and assess the amount of bend both athwartships and fore and aft and the relative tensions of the individual spans.

5) Now go onto the opposite tack and repeat 3).

6) As a rule of thumb, at approximately 15 to 20 degrees of heel the V1s should just be slack. If they are very slack gradually tighten the rigging screws no more than two turns at a time on each tack whilst sighting up the mast to check its straightness. The D1's should still be tight.

7) IMPORTANT – Make sure that the diagonal spans are not being over-tightened as the spreader tips move downwards as this may cause overloading. If this is the case it will be necessary to slacken off the diagonals before any further tuning takes place.

8) Having achieved the correct tension in the verticals adjust the diagonal spans so that they just have sufficient tension to hold the mast straight athwartships. DO NOT OVER-TIGHTEN.

9) On fractional rigs the topmast section will bend athwartships and 'de-power' the mainsail by opening the leech and 'spilling wind'. This can be used to the boat's advantage and on rigs with jumper stays can be controlled by either tightening or slackening these stays.

10) Fore and aft bend of the mast is mainly dependent on the desired camber shape of the mainsail and is usually adjusted

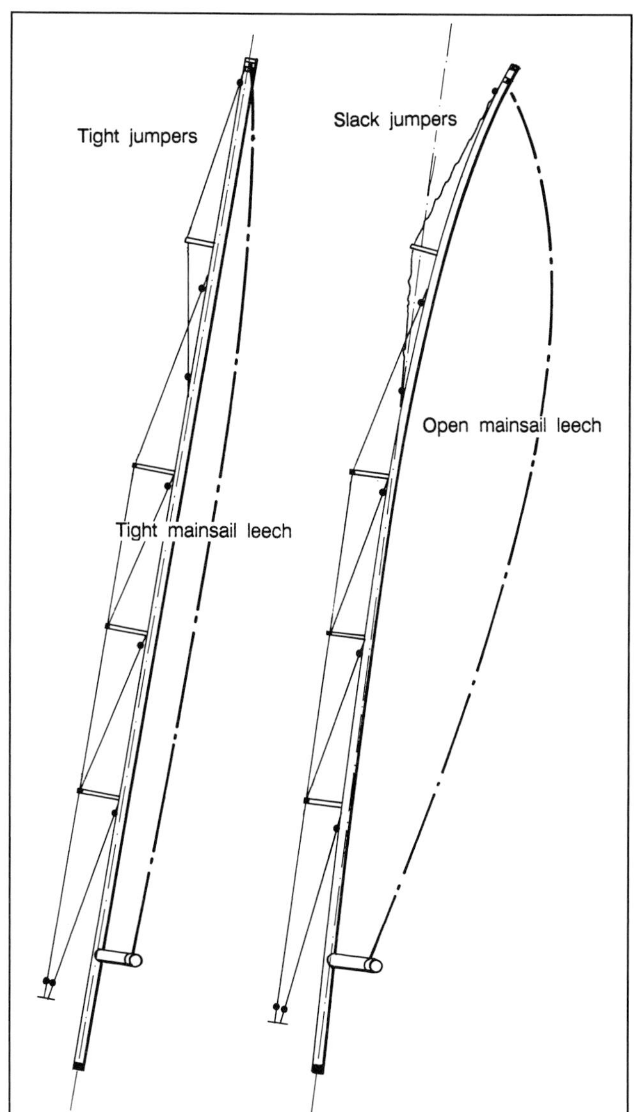

Left: Effect of jumpers on mainsail leech

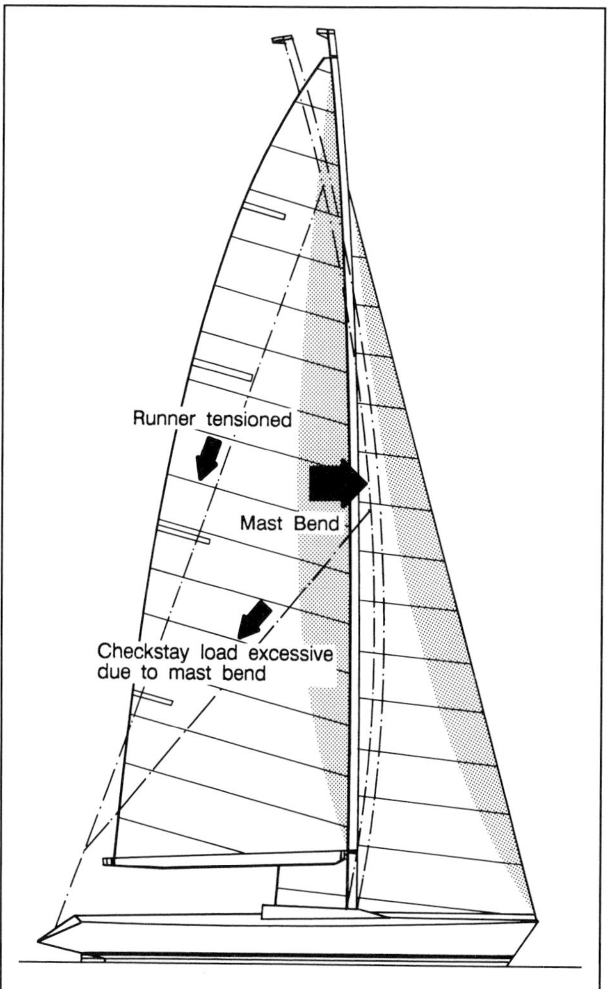

Above: Excessive runner load can overload checkstays

by means of the checkstays. However it is important to remember that pre-bend may also be present and when the mast needs to be straight the checkstays will have to work against this. Coupled with the fore and aft load imposed by the running backstays this can exert a very high load on the checkstays.

11) Over-bending in the fore and aft direction will reduce the effective height of the hounds and have similar effects as shown in the 'Fall Off' section.

12) IMPORTANT – When you have finished tuning make sure that all the rigging screw locking devices such as split pins and grub screws have been replaced.

A summary of the relative leeward rigging tensions at 20° heel:

D1 – Tight
V1 – Just going slack
D2 – Slack
D3 – Slack
D4* – Slack (* If fitted)

The following are common problems experienced when tuning rigs, if you are encountering one or more of these problems, STOP.

a) The shrouds have been tightened continuously for some time without any apparent effect.

STOP – Heave-to, lower the sails and check the tension in the rigging. If the shrouds seem excessively tight then there is a good chance that the boat is bending or the chainplates are moving. If this is the case slacken off the rigging and investigate the yacht's structure and chainplates.

b) The mast falls off to leeward excessively and cannot be controlled with additional cap shroud tension.

STOP – This is an indication that the mast is severely overloaded as a result of too much tension and is buckling under compression. The rigging must be fully slackened and the tuning process must begin again. This time you will have to watch carefully to prevent over-tensioning. Do not attempt to re-tune the mast by progressively slackening the rigging, you MUST start again from the beginning. (See fall off section.)

Having set up the rig in the athwartships plane, the balance of the helm can now be adjusted if necessary. As described earlier, this balance is mainly a function of mast rake.

Mark the head of the rudder stock or the wheel and set up the boat with the following conditions:

a) Full sail ie. Full main and no 1 genoa
b) Sail close hauled with crew in position
c) Flat water
d) 10 – 15° heel
Thus: Weather helm angle = 2 to 5 degrees

Jumper struts

Originally developed and termed as "diamond struts" this arrangement is almost exclusive to the fractionally rigged yacht. The diamond struts project out athwartships at about hounds height. Over these struts run diamond stays, the effect being to increase the stiffness of the top mast in the lateral plane.

Nowadays jumper struts are more common. In principle they are the same as diamond struts but instead of being exactly athwartships they are angled forward. This not only increases the stiffness of the mast athwartships but also increases it in the fore and aft direction. The angle at which the struts project depends on the amount of additional stiffness that is required in the fore and aft plane.

The use of such struts allows the top mast to have a more slender taper (ie reducing the moments of inertia further) thus reducing the weight at a point on the mast where it is most critical.

One can argue however that the jumper struts, stays and associated fittings increase the weight at the top of the mast. In recent years there has been a tendency to attempt to do away with the jumper arrangement altogether to try to reduce weight to a minimum. It has however been shown that it is:

a) Still lighter in most cases than a top mast of the same stiffness without jumper struts and,
b) almost impossible to achieve the same ability to vary the stiffness of the top mast in the same way that is possible with jumper stays and rigging screws. As a result the jumper struts are now commonplace on most fractionally rigged racing yachts.

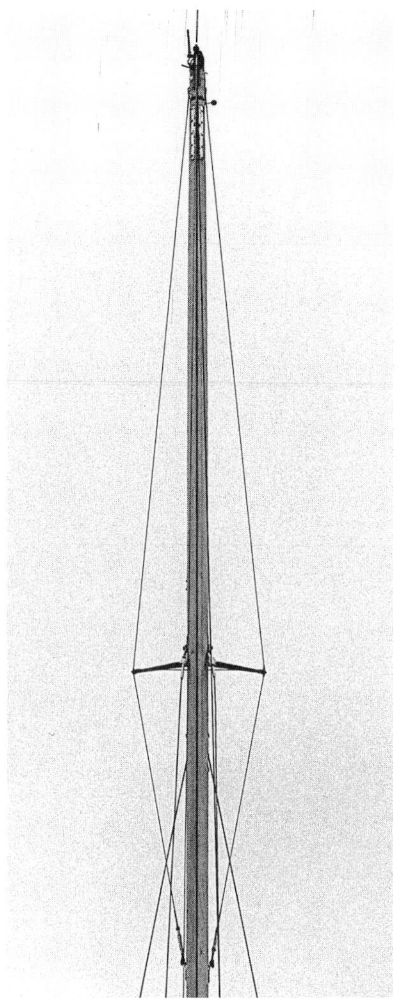

Jumper struts

As the jumpers control the top of the mast their primary effect is on the mainsail. Tight jumper stays will stiffen the top mast and hold the leech of the sail tight; whereas slack jumper stays will allow a more flexible top mast and hence a more open leech to the mainsail. (These tuning details will be discussed in more depth in the High Performance Tuning section of this chapter.)

You should find that from time to time you will have cause to alter the settings of the jumper stays to suit the prevailing conditions. While adjustment during the race is prohibited in some classes, it is not usually against the rules to alter the tensions before the race. However in order to know what settings to use you will have had to experiment beforehand. For this reason it is impossible to put down on paper perfect settings for particular rigs. Therefore the following are guide notes for setting up jumper struts initially.

1) The most important point as with any rig tuning is to note down the settings and what you have done to alter them.
2) The jumper struts should be slack when the mast is stepped in the boat. In this way the bend of the mast below the hounds is not affected whilst the main rigging is being set up.
3) Once the main rigging has been tensioned it is time to go aloft to tension the jumpers. Before you do, check to see if

Typical jumper strut sizes

Boat (m)	LOA (ft)	Strut section size (mm)	Strut length (mm)
7.50	24.6	35	170 – 190
9.00	29.5	46	200 – 240
10.00	32.8	46	230 – 260
12.0	39.4	64	230 – 385
14.00	46.0	64	250 – 385

the top mast is straight athwartships and fore and aft. If it is not make a note of both the amount and which way the topmast leans.
4) You will need someone to remain on deck to sight up from the backstay to ensure that the top mast is standing straight in the athwartships plane.
5) Take the slack out of the jumper stays by tensioning the rigging screws by hand.
6) Check the top mast for straightness athwartships.
7) If the jumper stays require adjustment to bring the top mast straight, do this by hand if possible.
8) Making a note of which side you have started, tension the rigging screws no more than two turns at a time to start with.
9) You will probably find that the rigging begins to tension quite quickly and therefore a reduction to one turn at a time will be necessary.
10) As a guide it is generally better to set up the top mast so that it errs on the side of too soft (so long as you correct this as soon as it becomes apparent). Therefore tension the stays until you feel that they are just beginning to have an effect on the stiffness of the top mast.
11) An over-stiff top mast may affect the lower sections of the mast which could be confused with the setting up of the main rigging. Therefore before attempting to fine tune the jumpers make sure that the main part of the mast is behaving satisfactorily.
12) Make sure that all locking pins or similar devices are replaced in the rigging screws.
13) Sight up the mast from below in both directions and adjust as necessary.
14) The rig should now be taken for sailing trials and the behaviour of the top mast studied.
15) In some cases where the top mast is very slender the forward angle of the jumper struts and tension in the stays may cause the top mast to angle forwards when at rest. As long as this forward rake is not so extreme as to affect the light airs setting of the mainsail this is OK.

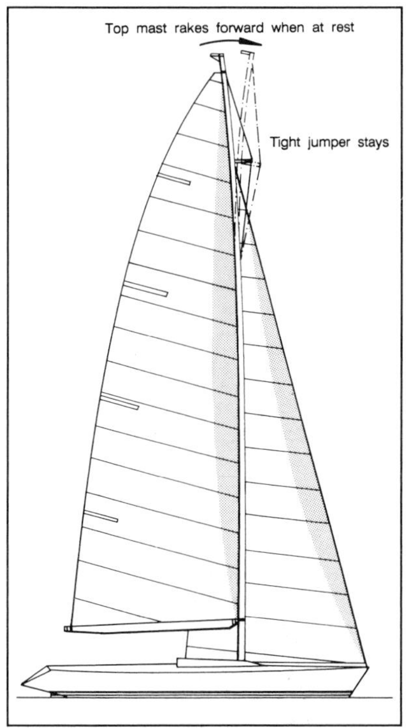

Fore and aft effect of very tight jumpers

Because the precise sizes and settings of these struts and their associated stays depends on a wide range of factors it is virtually impossible to develop a definitive table for the required settings. However the following table is intended as an initial guide and can be used as a starting point if firm requirements are not known. For more specific information your mast maker should be contacted.

Fall off and lateral support

One of the most significant factors resulting in poor performance of a rig is that of athwartships 'fall off'. By 'fall off' is meant a general tendency to deflect to leeward. Most masts display a degree of fall off under normal sailing conditions and this is most apparent when sailing close hauled. The question is how much should be tolerated. Unfortunately the answer is not a simple one, and can only be approached as a result of careful observation and tuning. However the following are guide lines which will help in achieving the best performance.

The mast begins to display fall off beyond an acceptable limit, if the sails start becoming difficult to trim correctly. This is often a result of over-compression. As the compression increases so the force required to deflect the mast out of column decreases. A common error when trying to reduce the amount of fall off is to tighten the rigging further when it is already too tight. As the mast is out of column this will very often only serve to make matters worse. This is not to say that if your rig is experiencing fall off you should immediately slacken off all the rigging! But there is an optimum and you should consider carefully whether your rig is over or under tensioned.

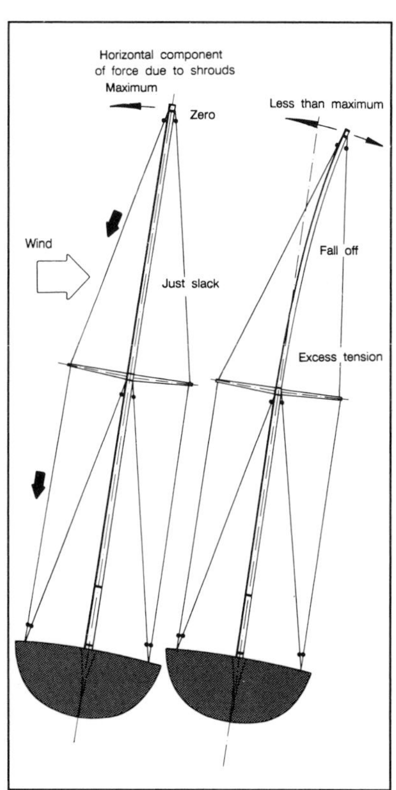

Effect of excess leeward shroud tension

Assuming that the mast section is of sufficient size to carry a given sail plan, the two main types of fall off are:
a) Topmast fall off to leeward.

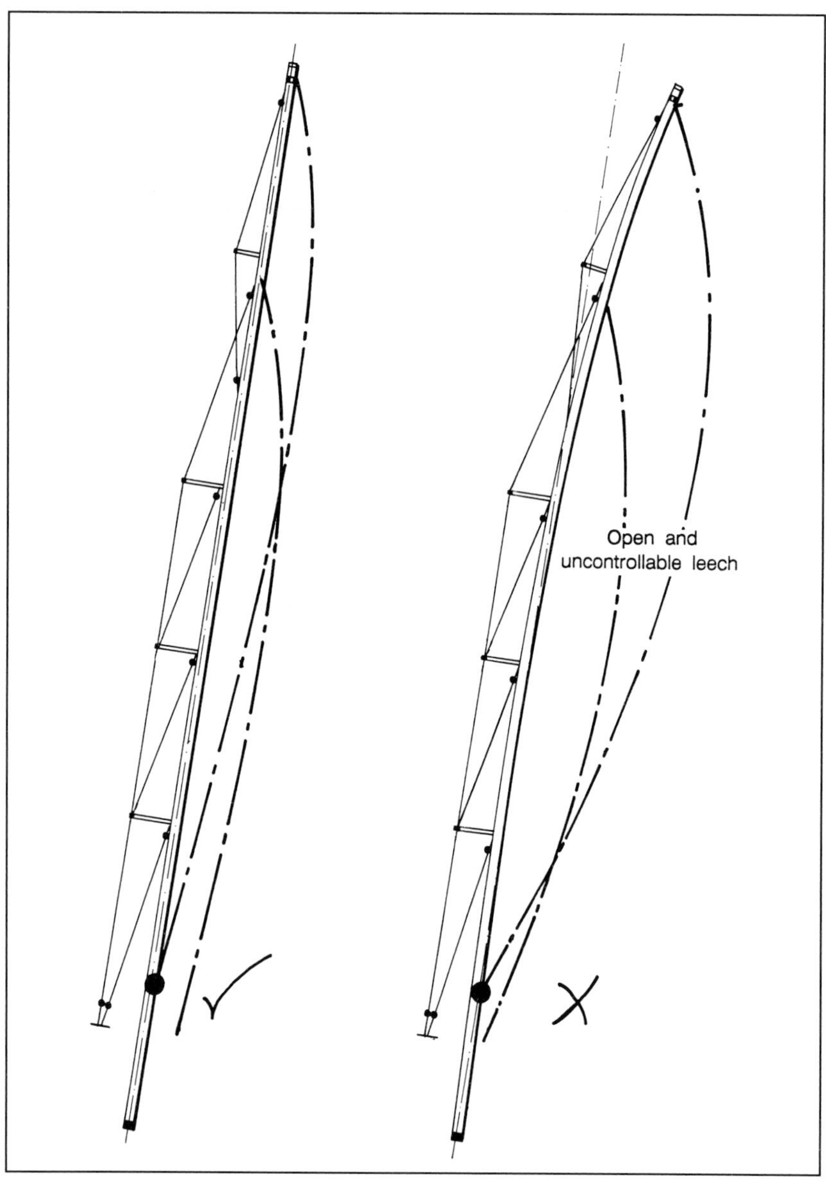

Top mast influence on leech tension

This causes the mainsail leech to open and de-powers the mainsail by letting the air spill out to leeward. It also slightly reduces the centre of effort of the sailplan thus reducing the heeling moment. The genoa is also affected as the foretriangle height reduces opening the leech (and hence the slot between main and genoa) and sagging the forestay. This effect can be both beneficial and detrimental depending on whether you need to de-power your sail plan for a given set of conditions or not.

b) Middle of mast falls away to leeward

This effect is always detrimental as not only does the foretriangle height reduce, but the slot between main and genoa closes.

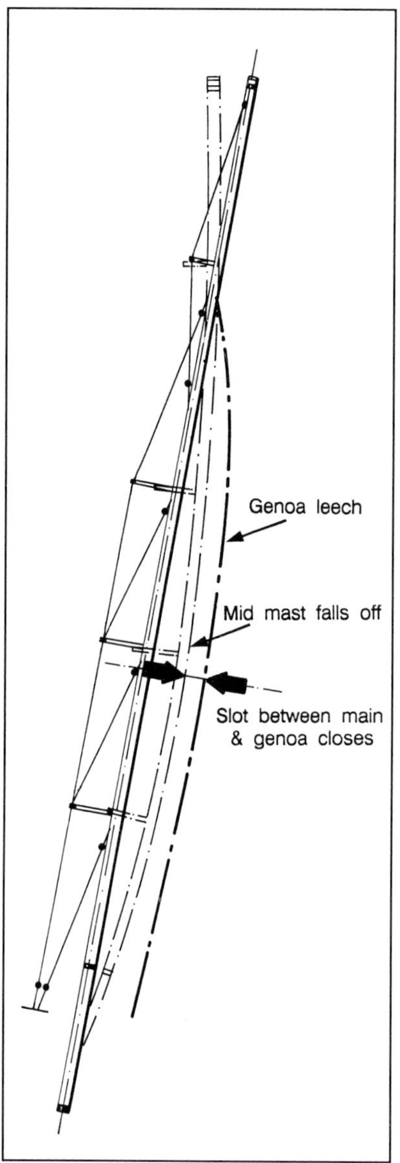

Mid mast fall off closes slot

Factors that induce top mast fall off include:
a) Over compression causing the mast to buckle which will force the middle of the mast up to weather. Remedy: Back off rigging tension and/or reduce running backstay load.
b) Insufficient shroud angle at the hounds to give support. Remedy: Increase spreader lengths and/or increase shroud tension with care. (see diagram overleaf)
c) Over-tensioned diagonal or intermediate stays. Remedy: Slacken diagonal or intermediate stays.
d) Slack leeward lower shrouds allowing the mast to 'pop' to weather. Remedy: Tighten the leeward shroud(s). (see diagram overleaf)

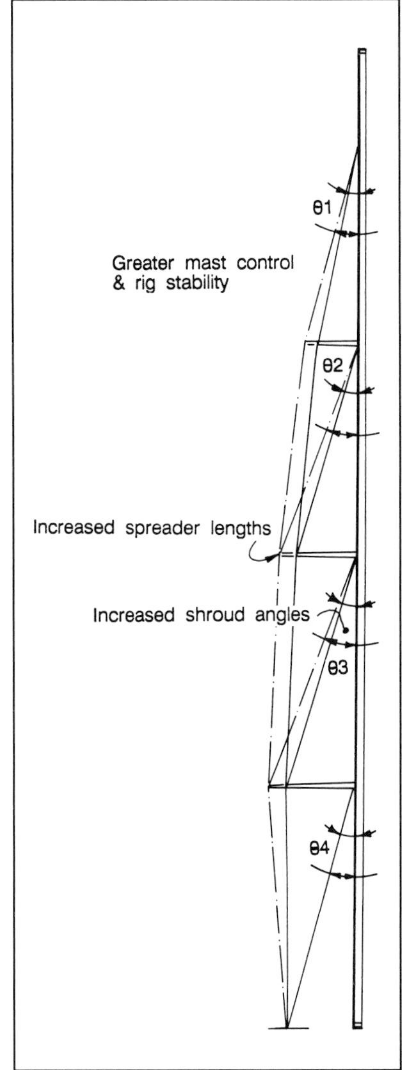

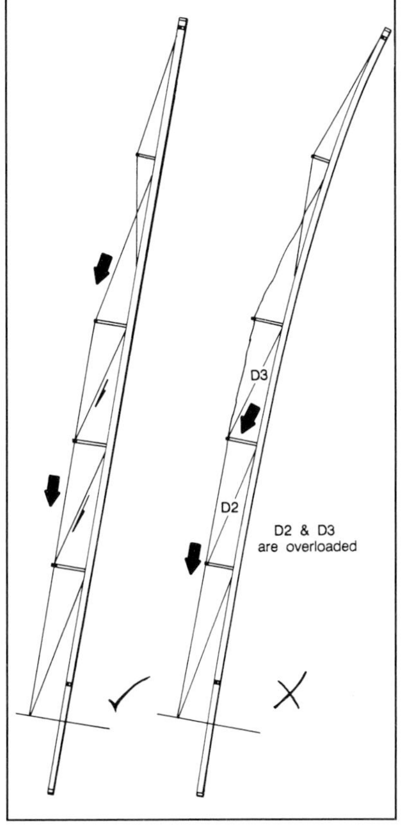

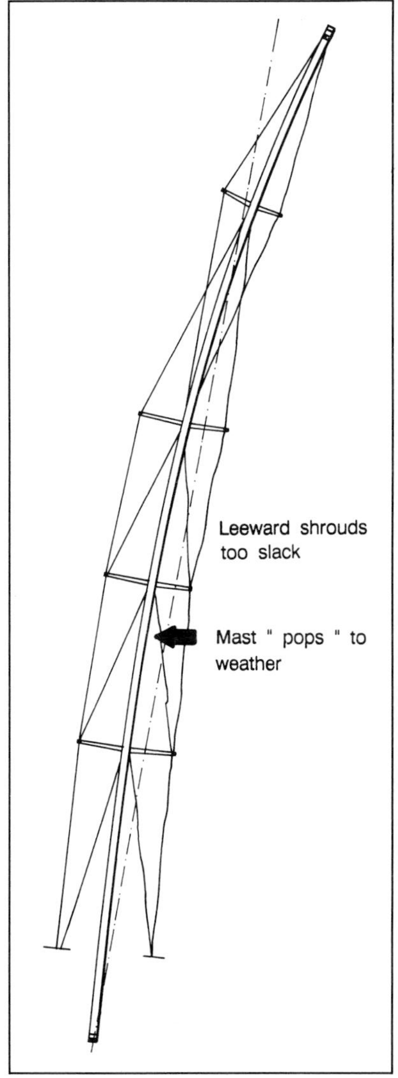

Above: Over-tensioned diagonals

Left: Increasing spreader lengths

Right: Over-slack leeward shrouds

Factors that induce mid mast fall off include:

a) Running backstay deck attachment is off centreline and to weather thus pulling the topmast up to weather. Remedy: Slacken running backstay and/or move running backstay deck attachment to centreline.

b) Spreaders are too long thus forcing the mast to leeward. Remedy: Reduce cap shroud

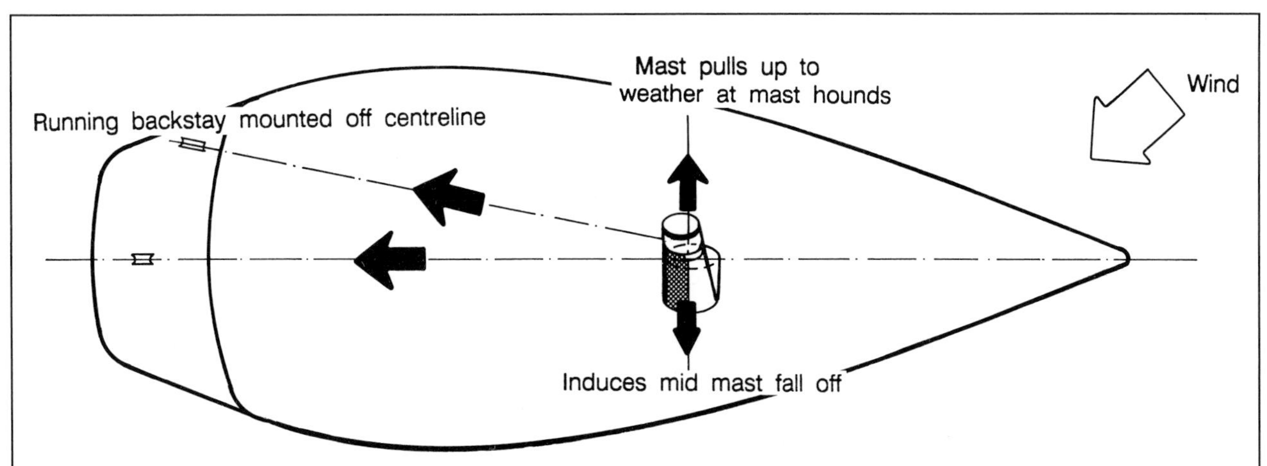

Running backstay deck mounting

tension and/or shorten spreader length.

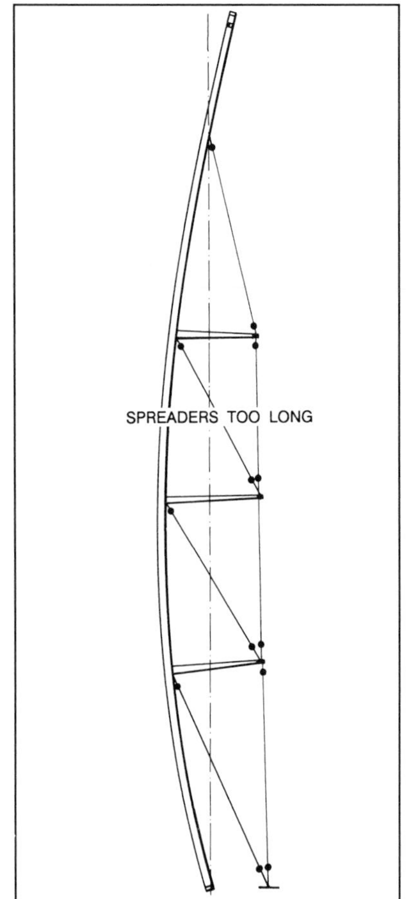

Over-length spreaders

Additional points:
a) Aft swept rigs with running backstays are particularly susceptible to problems with fall off. The reason is that as the windward running backstay is tensioned so the mast is raked aft slightly further thus reducing the load on the windward cap shroud. The load on the mainsail remains the same and the mast falls off to leeward to balance the loading. The more the tension on the windward running backstay is increased, the greater the fall off effect.
b) It is very difficult to achieve a good balance between the shrouds and the effect of the running backstays and it can only be assessed by observation in different sailing conditions.
c) The mast should be well supported and not allowed to twist at the deck area. The twisting is particularly detrimental on an aft swept spreader rig.

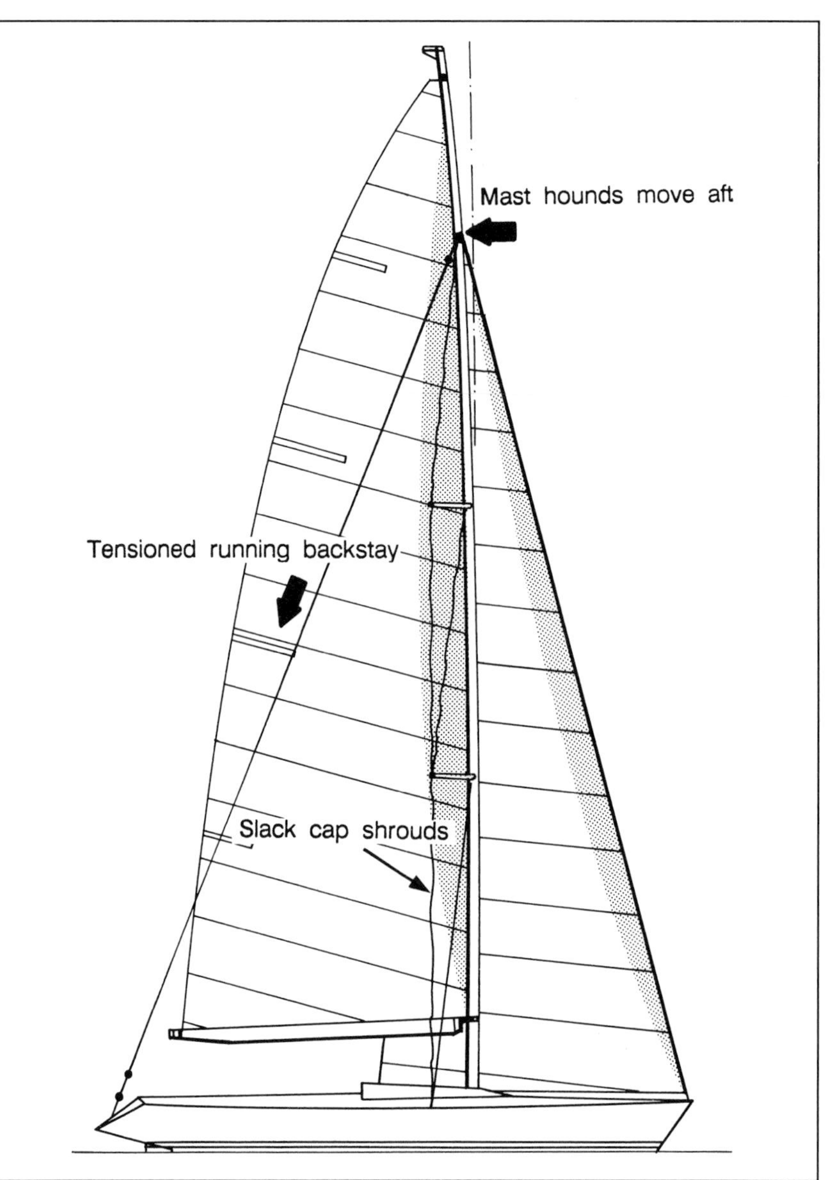

Running backstays on aft swept rigs

High performance tuning
In the previous sections initial, basic and fine tuning have been discussed. For most general applications these descriptions will be more than adequate to achieve a well balanced boat. For the racing crew the tuning process continues not only in this book, but right through the season. Following each race the various rig settings should be noted along with the weather conditions and how the boat performed. Such a tuning log will accumulate during the season to the extent that for a given set of conditions repeatable performance can be achieved!!!

High performance tuning is more about the feel of the boat and the behaviour of the rig. However before you can assess the feel of the boat there are some important ground rules that will act as both guidelines and the basis for a better understanding of what is happening, where and why. There are certain primary rig controls.

Primary rig controls

	Masthead		Fractional In line		Fractional ft/swept	
Forestay Backstay	+ + Tight forestay.	– – Slack forestay.	+ + Bend top Open m/s leech. F/a lower	– – Straight mast. Tight leech.	+ + Tight forestay. Open m/s leech.	– – Slack forestay. Tight leech.
Genoa luff	Fine	Full	Fine	Full	Fine	Full
Genoa leech			Open	Tight	V. Open	Tight
Runners	+ Straight mast. Prevents panting.	– F/a bend. Depowers m/s.	+ Tight forestay. Flattens m/s* Increase mast rake.	– Slack forestay Full m/s. higher CE.	+ Tight forestay. Slacken cap shrouds Induce fall off.	– Slack forestay.
Checkstays	Straight mast. Prevents panting.	F/a bend. Depowers m/s.	Straight mast. Full m/s. Prevents panting.	Bend mast Flat m/s. Use with +babystay	As In-Line but not very common	
Main luff	Full	Fine	Fine	Full	Fine	Full
Kicker	+ Increases f/a bend low down.	– Allows twist in m/s	+ Increase f/a bend low down.	– Allows twist in m/s.	+ Increase f/a bend low down.	– Allows twist in m/s.
Mainsheet	+ Tight forestay. Increase bend.	– Slack forestay. Reduce bend.	+ Increase bend.	– Reduce bend.	+ Tight forestay. Increase bend.	– Slack forestay. Reduce bend.

* Mast rake increased therefore backstay slackens closing leech of mainsail. Therefore increase backstay tension to maintain twist.

Helm balance – CLR vs CE
Earlier in this chapter helm balance was briefly discussed. Weather helm, or the lack of, greatly affects the performance of the boat. Too little and the boat lacks pointing ability, too much and the large rudder angle induces high drag thus slowing the boat. A balance therefore has to be struck. There are several factors that affect weather helm.

Weather helm – influencing factors

CLR Hull	CE sail plan
Keel position.	Mast rake
Shape of underwater profile.	Mast heel position
Crew position.	Sail plan combination
Heel angle.	Genoa tack position
	Sail shape

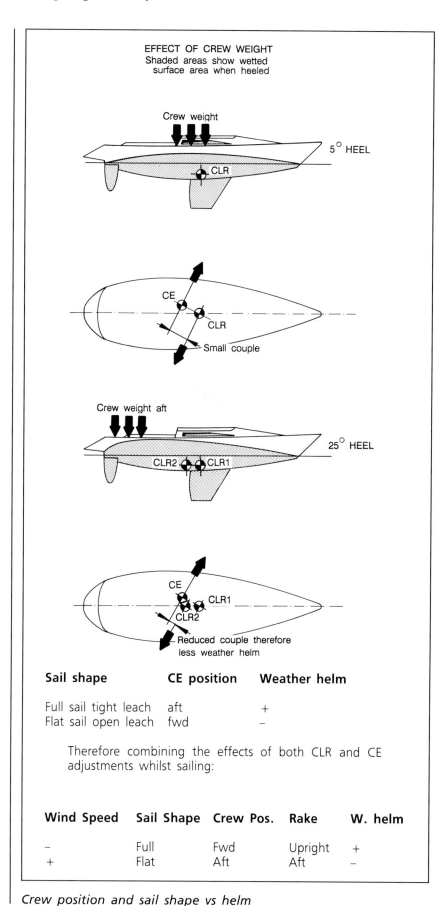

EFFECT OF CREW WEIGHT
Shaded areas show wetted surface area when heeled

Crew weight

5° HEEL

CLR

CE

CLR

Small couple

Crew weight aft

25° HEEL

CLR2 CLR1

CE

CLR1

CLR2

Reduced couple therefore less weather helm

Sail shape	CE position	Weather helm
Full sail tight leach	aft	+
Flat sail open leach	fwd	–

Therefore combining the effects of both CLR and CE adjustments whilst sailing:

Wind Speed	Sail Shape	Crew Pos.	Rake	W. helm
–	Full	Fwd	Upright	+
+	Flat	Aft	Aft	–

Crew position and sail shape vs helm

a) Crew weight. Crew weight and heel angle affect the CLR. As the boat heels so the CLR moves forward thus increasing the 'lead' and therefore weather helm making the boat progressively more unstable. A typical situation when broaching!

From this it can be seen that it is always important to sail the boat as upright as possible in all but extremely light airs.

b) Mast rake.

c) Sail plan combination. In order to obtain the resultant CE of the complete sail plan each sail must be considered separately. Then the relevant individual CE for each sail are balanced to give the resultant CE. Therefore the final CE depends on which sails are up at a given time.

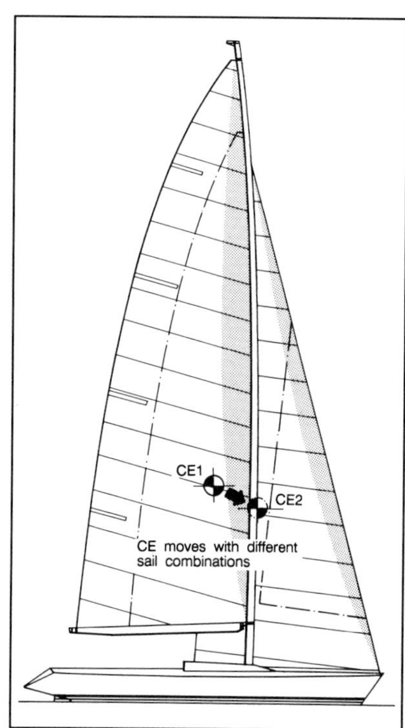

Effect of sail plan on CE

d) Sail shape. The shape of a sail alters its CE and therefore the total resultant CE varies with full sail moving it aft and flat sail positioning it forward.

As this sail shape has an effect on helm balance, and overall performance, it is useful that

Mast bend vs wind strength – in-line spreader rig

Wind Speed	**+**	–
Requirements	Flat sail Open leech de-power sail	Full sail Tight leech or twist
Mast bend	+	–
Optimum draft	fwd	aft
Cunningham	–	+
Back-winding	–	+
Masthead Rig	+ backstay – twist + sheet tension + runner tension + checkstay	– backstay + twist + pre-bend – runner tension – checkstay
Fractional Rig	– twist + runners – checks + backstay + sheet tension + rake *	+ twist – runners + checks – backstay

* Increasing the rake in this case helps to reduce the height of the sail plans CE and therefore the heeling moment is reduced

Where: + = increased
– = decreased

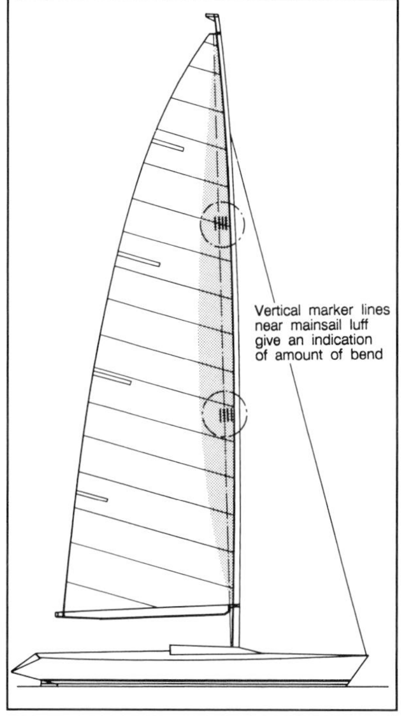
Vertical marker lines near mainsail luff give an indication of amount of bend

Vertical marker lines on mainsail

Before you can attempt to assess and adjust the fore and aft bend in the spar you must have some means of measuring the degree of bend present for a given set of conditions. The simplest way to assess the bend in the mast is to attach a light line from the

there are ways in which the mast can be used to alter balance.

Mast bend
An earlier part of this chapter described how and why pre-bend is induced into the spar. Whilst sailing the fore and aft bend can be altered to adjust the shape of both the mainsail and the genoa. There are two ways in which the mast achieves this:
a) The mast forms the leading edge of the mainsail and therefore any bend will affect the luff shape and draft of the sail.
b) As the mast bends so the vertical height of the foretriangle reduces. This can cause the genoa leech to open and in some cases the forestay to slacken.

Forestay tension versus luff entry shape

Forestay tension	Luff entry	Effect
+	Fine	High pointing ability. Prone to stalling. In light airs use only for high pointing in flat waters
–	Full	Reluctant to stall at large angles of attack. Particularly effective in fickle wind directions.

Where: + = increased tension
– = decreased tension

masthead to the gooseneck on each side of the mainsail. Marker lines can be put onto the mainsail so that the line can be read against the calibration points.
On fractionally rigged boats one of the most frequently asked questions and perhaps one of the most difficult to answer numerically is "How much runner tension?" The only way to answer this is to look at the genoa as it is the running backstay that is altering the shape of the luff entry. (If at all possible a forestay load cell should be fitted to the forestay so that readings for given conditions can be monitored see Chapter 12.)

Typical forestay loads

	Forestay load	
Boat size	**lbs**	**kg**
¼ Ton	1000	454
½ Ton	2000	909
¾ Ton	3500	1590
1 Ton	6000	2727
2 Ton	8000	3636
50′ IOR	12000	5454

Courtesy Riggama

Mast bend vs wind strength; aft swept spreader rig
On these types of rig, and in particular the single spreader version the forestay tension is a problem as it is derived from a combination of controls. (In the case of the in-line version whilst some of the following controls may also affect forestay tension they can, to a certain extent, be

Sail setting aft swept rigs

Wind speed	+	–
Requirements	Flat sail	Full sail
	Open leech de-power sail	Tight leech or twist
Mast bend	+	–
Optimum draft	fwd	aft
Cunningham	+	–
Back-winding	+	–
Lowers	–	+
Cap shrouds	+	–
Backstay	+	–
Spreader angle	Increase angle aft	Decrease angle aft
Mainsheet bales	fwd	aft *

* If possible move the mainsheet bale(s) on the boom. This will have the effect of reducing the compression on the gooseneck in strong winds and increasing the compression, thus inducing prebend, in light airs.

Where + = Tighten
– = Slacken

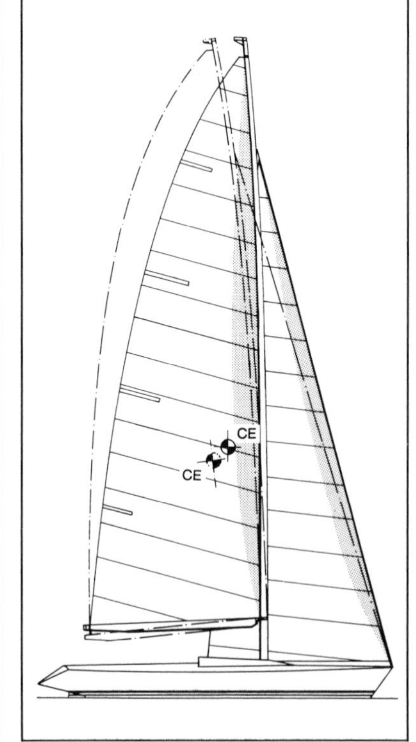

CE shift with rake

Forestay tension – fault finding

Forestay tension	**too +**	**too –**
Mainsail shape	Ok	Ok
Spreaders	Too forward	Too aft
Lower shrouds	Too tight	Too slack
Result	Mast too stiff fore & aft	Mast too soft fore & aft
Remedy	Spdrs aft Slacken lowers	Spdrs fwd Tighten lowers

Where + = tight
– = slack

overridden by the running backstays.)
Forestay tension controlled by:
a) Backstay
b) Cap shrouds
c) Lower shrouds
d) Mast stiffness
e) Main sheet
It is therefore necessary to strike a delicate balance between these factors to achieve the optimum sail setting for a given set of conditions.
If it is possible to move the mainsheet bale(s) on the boom, it will have the effect of reducing the compression on the gooseneck in strong winds and increasing the compression, thus inducing pre-bend, in light airs.

Racing spar additional tuning tips
The following notes are general guide lines for most types of rig and are very important if the best performance is required.
a) The spreaders should be fitted and checked to make sure that they are exactly the same length and aligned symmetrically in all planes. If the mast is already stepped measure from the spreader tip down to the deck to check the height of the outboard end.

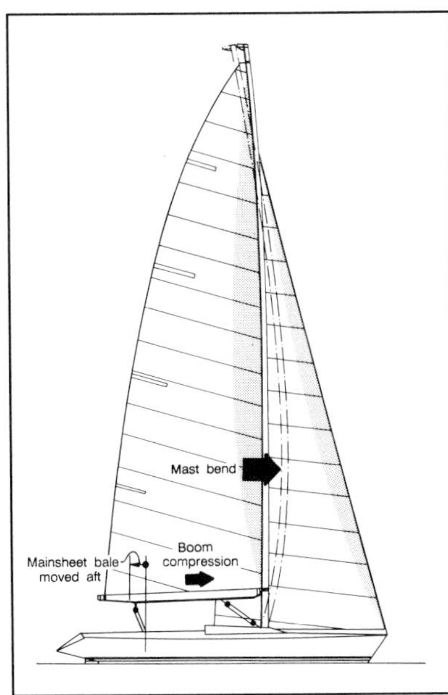

Inducing bend with mainsheet and kicker

Fall off summary

Span	Area of 'fall off' Mid mast	Top mast
Cap shrouds	Too tight	Too slack
Lower shrouds	Too slack	Too tight
Spreaders	Too long	Too short

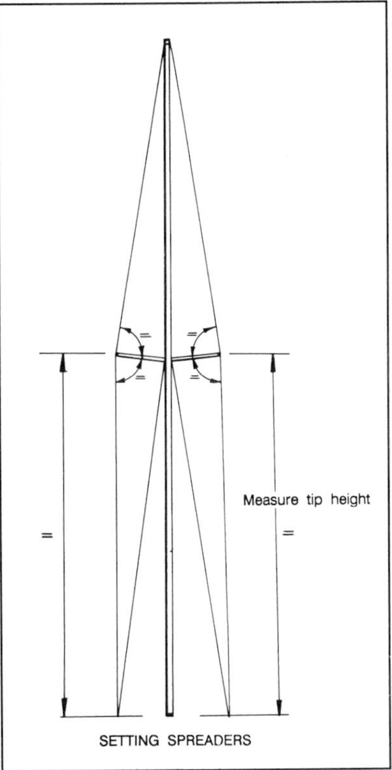

Setting spreaders symmetrically

b) If the fore and aft bend is different on each tack first check the spreader angles. If these are correct then check the lengths of the shrouds and running backstays.
c) If fall off is a serious problem that cannot be cured by retuning the mast, check the diameter of the shrouds (if possible check them against the rigging of a boat in the same class.) Too small a diameter shroud will stretch and it may be necessary to increase their size.
d) To prevent over-hoisting the main sail above the black band, drill and tap a machine screw into the bolt rope groove in such a position that the headboard cannot be hoisted past the black band. It is important to also mark the halyard to make sure that it is not forced so high that it damages the mast track where the bolt is situated.
e) On fractional rigs a weak link at the bottom attachment of the permanent backstay will prevent the topmast from damage in the event of over-tensioning.
f) Be careful when setting up the genoa halyard on the downwind leg when the forestay is slack. Once the boat has rounded the leeward mark tension comes onto the rig from the backstay, running backstays and mainsheet and may overload the luff of the sail. To prevent this, mark the halyards whilst on the wind for typical settings.
g) Beware of excessive fore and aft mast bend as it can cause twisting of the mast.

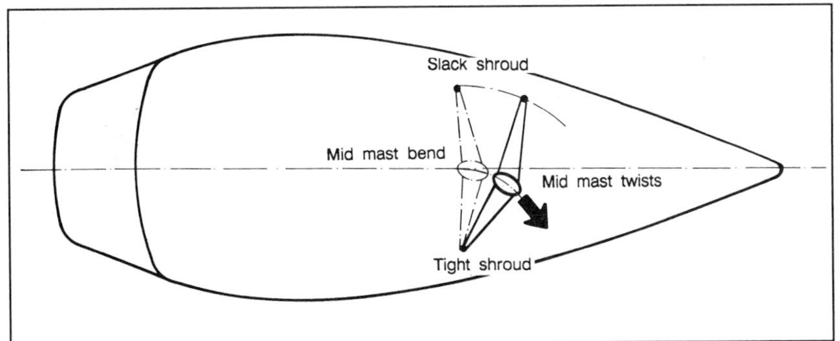

Excess bend can twist mast

7: Booms, spinnaker poles and other spars

Main booms
Main booms are subjected to a higher bending load and a lower compression load than the masts on which they are attached. The bending load is generally a result of the kicking strap (boom vang in USA), which is opposing the vertical load imposed by the leach of the mainsail at the outboard end of the boom. The bending load may be further increased on the mainsheet when its attachment is forward of the leech position. The effect of vertical bend on the boom as a result of the mainsheet increases as the attachment position is moved further forward.

Under normal circumstances,

Below and right: Loads on booms

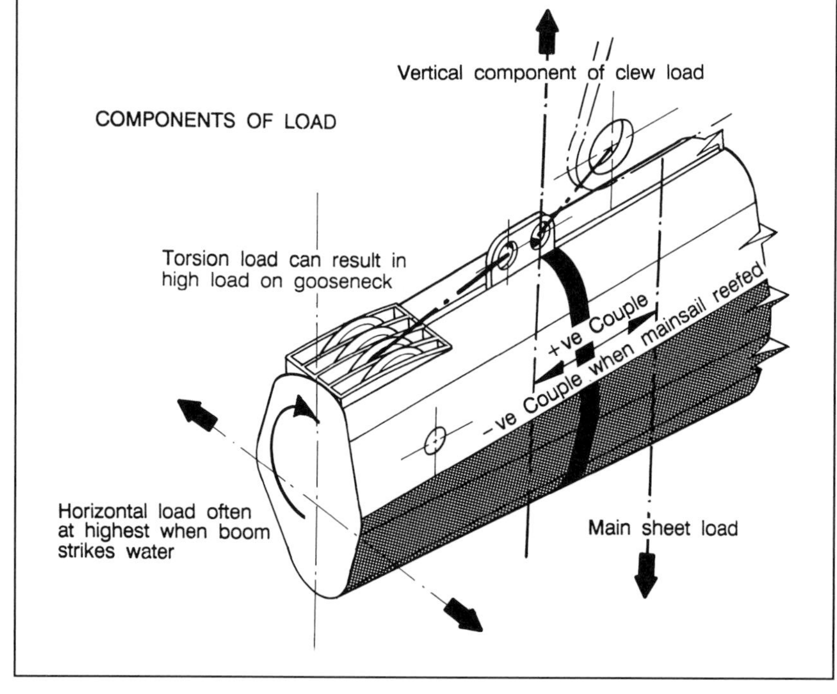

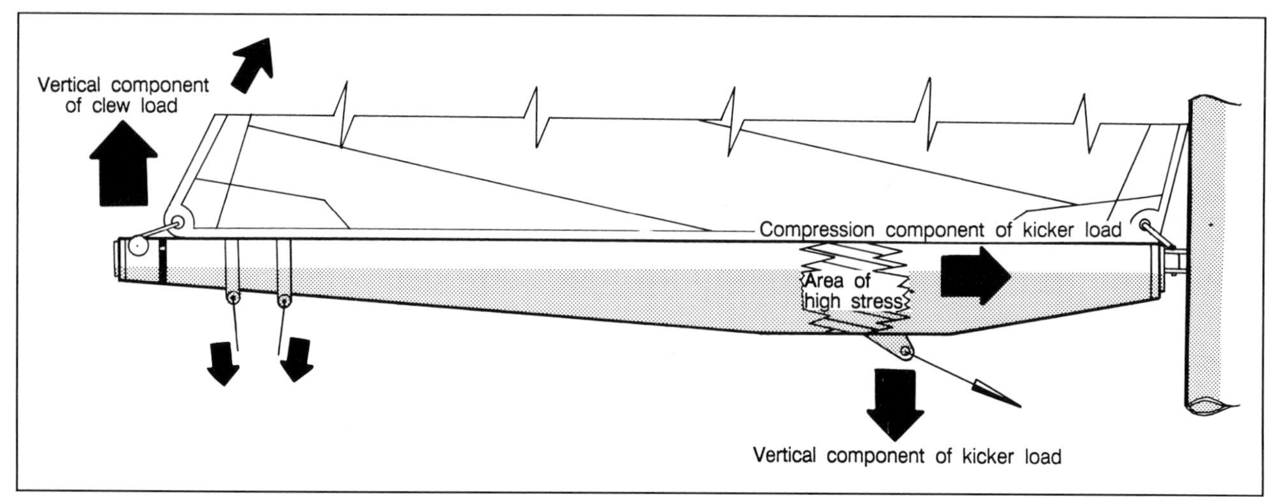

the horizontal loading on the boom is considerably less than the vertical loading as there are smaller components of horizontal force. However having said that, the horizontal loads in the boom can be considerably increased, especially when reaching, when the outboard end of the boom is allowed to strike the water. The boom is then forced back in towards the boat whilst the wind load on the mainsail forces the boom away from the boat. This can often result in the boom breaking.

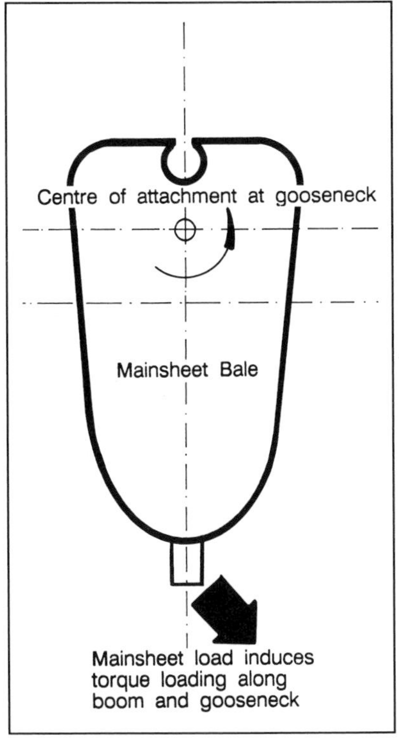

Torque loading on boom

Whilst the compression on the boom is less than that found on the mast it is all too easy to underestimate this load. If a kicking strap is fitted to the boom it will produce not only a vertical load, holding the boom down, but also a compression load. When the boom is close to the centre line i.e. in a close hauled position, the loading along the boom results in the compression on the gooseneck fitting on the aft side of the mast. Apart from the sheer load imposed on the gooseneck pin mountings a compression load is spread over the area of the gooseneck attachment on the mast. It is unusual for this type of loading to cause any problems or damage. However when the mainsail is freed off, the compression loads are transferred at an angle across the back of the mast thus imposing sheer and bending loads on the gooseneck and its fastenings. It is at this time when these fittings are most at risk. With fractional rigs, and hence larger mainsails, becoming increasingly popular, gooseneck backing plates are more commonly found which wrap around the aft face of the mast, thus distributing the loads.

The third component of loading on the boom is that of torque. On slab reefing booms this is usually a result of the mainsheet attachment being on the under-side of the boom and at a horizontal position below that of the gooseneck attachment. This becomes more of a problem on deep section racing booms where the mainsheet bail is even further below the gooseneck pins.

On roller reefing booms the torque loading is a result of the mainsail leading off one side of the boom. Some ways in which these loads can be relieved will be described later.

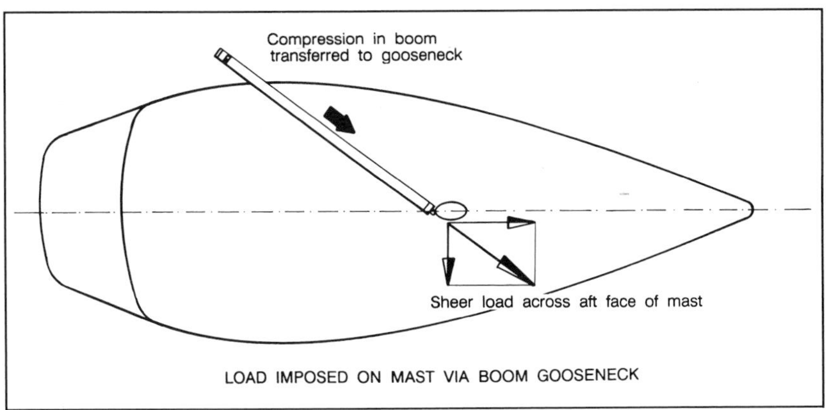

Sheer load across aft face of mast at gooseneck

Roller reefing boom

In order to shorten sails on this system, the boom is rotated and the mainsail is furled onto the spar. There are two distinct advantages of this system, the first being that there are few limitations as to the amount of mainsail that can be reefed and the second is that the sail can be simply and effectively stowed on the boom when not in use. However the disadvantages of this system have resulted in the declining use of roller reefing.

One of the most significant problems is that of sail shape. With this type of system it is very difficult to maintain a good sail shape when the mainsail is reefed because of the camber in

Roller reefing boom – outboard end

Roller reefing boom – Inboard end

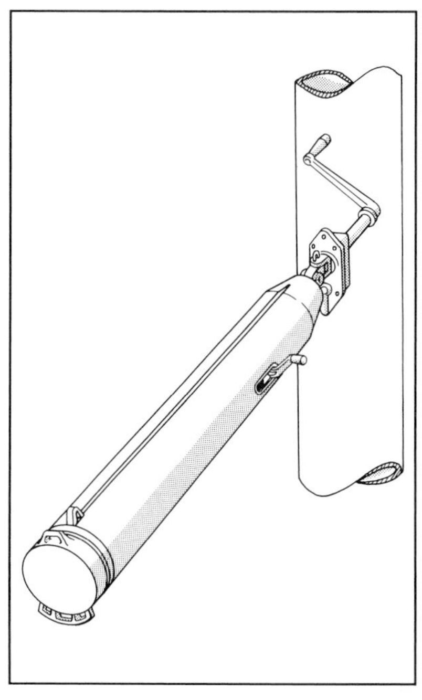

Roller reefing boom

the sail. When under full sail, the under-side of the boom is clear for a kicking strap attachment but as soon as the mainsail needs to be reefed, these attachments must be removed so as not to distort the sail as it is wrapped around the boom. This means that an alternative method of kicking strap attachment needs to be used. There are two ways that this can be achieved. The first is by using a claw ring system (see diagram) or secondly by using a strop that is sewn into the mainsail and wrapped around the boom as the sail is furled, leaving one end for the kicking strap attachment.

An additional problem with this type of rigging system, especially for short-handed crews, is that the operation needs to take place at the mast and the controls can not usually be led back to the cockpit.

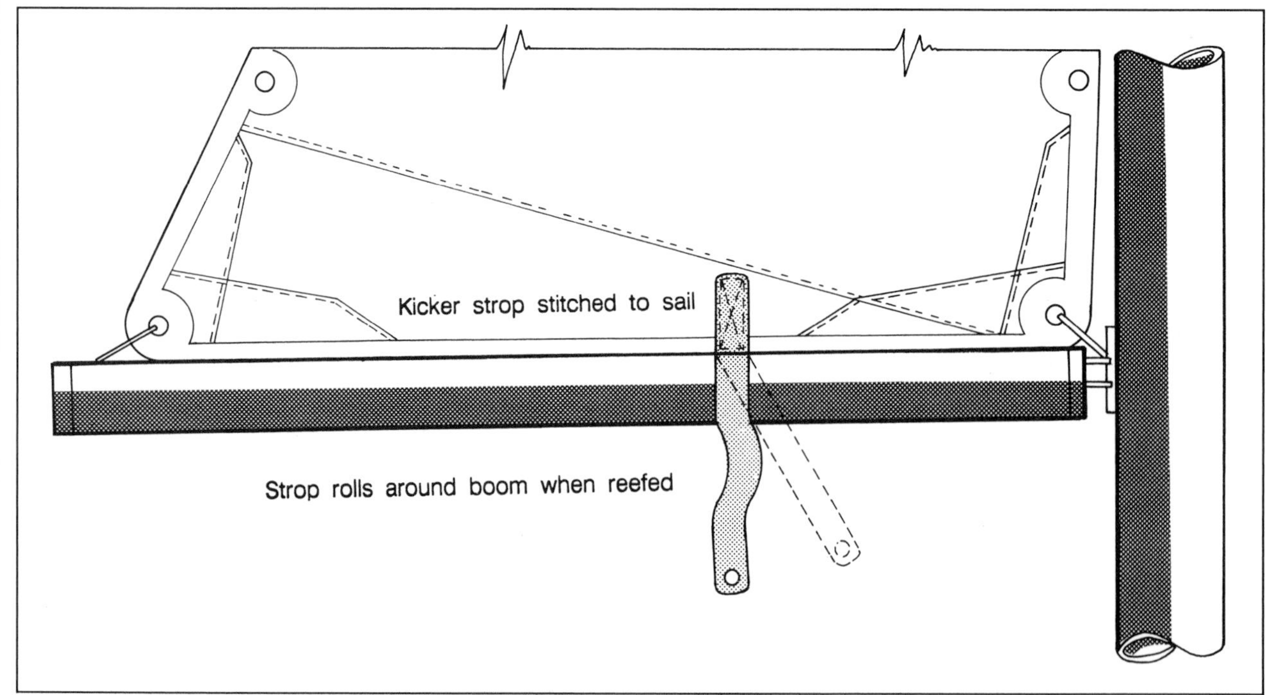

Kicker strop in mainsail

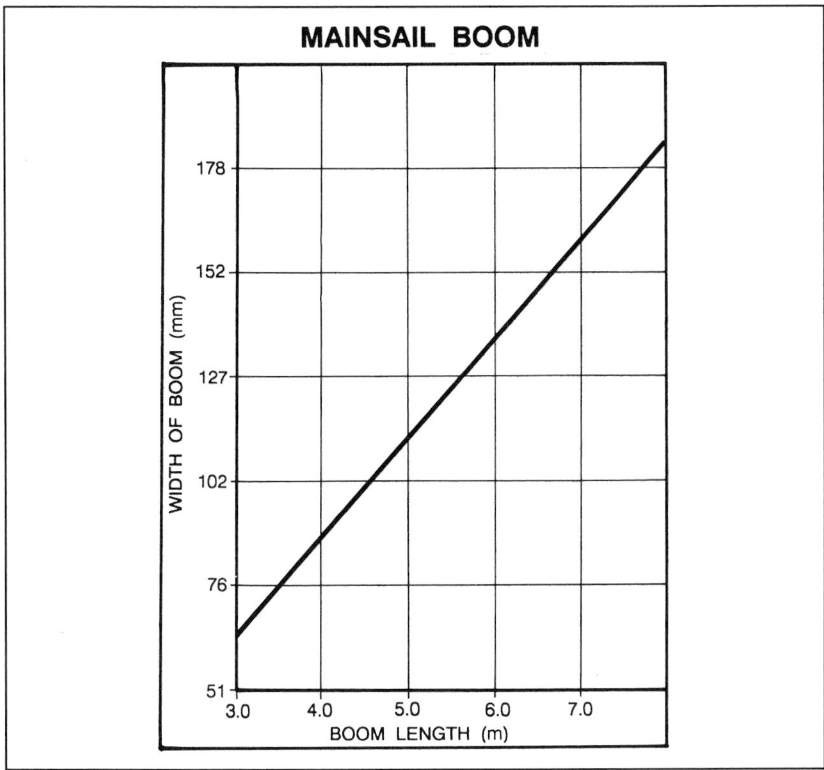

Boom section size guide

Slab reefing
This type of reefing system is by far the most popular and as the term suggests consists of reefing the mainsail to pre-set points as ''slabs'' of sail area. This reefing system has a number of advantages which are as follows:
a) a better sail shape can be achieved, as the system allows the foot tension to be adjusted as necessary.

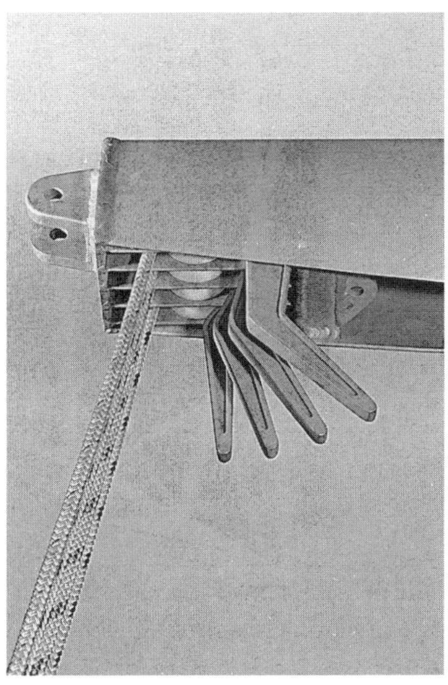

Slab reefing boom – inboard end
(Courtesy Proctor Masts)

b) the operation of reefing can, if required, be carried out from the safety of the cockpit.
c) the system is cheap to install and easy to maintain especially on large boats where there is no necessity for complicated worm drives or rotating fittings.
d) the system works equally well with both mainsails fitted with bolt ropes or sail slides. The latter which do not necessarily have to be removed from the track in order to reef.
e) the kicking strap attachment on the boom does not have to be removed and can be permanent.
The disadvantages of this system over a roller reefing are that:
a) a smaller range of different reefed positions is available.
b) the reefed part of the mainsail will require rolling up and tying to the boom to prevent it flogging and getting in the way.
c) during the process of taking in a reef the mainsail tends to

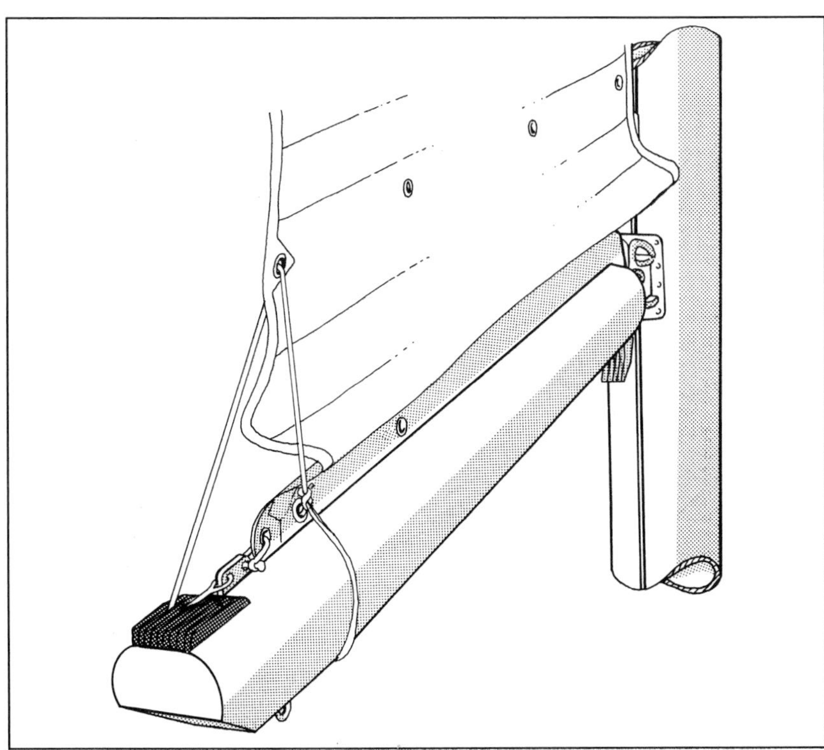

Slab reefing boom – (Courtesy Proctor Masts)

flog, and the boom threaten the crew which sometimes makes the operation more difficult, especially if the control lines are not led aft to the cockpit.
There are three versions of the slab reefing boom system which are as follows:

Tack hooks for slab reefing

a) Basic systems with tack hooks – the number of control lines for reefs and outhauls will depend not only on the specific requirement for the boat but also on the space available for a given boom section. The most common arrangement for boats up to about 55ft l.o.a. (16.8m) is to have one outhaul control and three reef lines. The sheave box on the outboard end is usually fitted as four abreast, but may on some slender boom sections be arranged with the outhaul sheave on the centre line with the three reef lines mounted directly aft. If a flattening reef is fitted then one of the reef lines can be used for this purpose. The remaining two reef lines can be used for reef no: 1 and reef no: 2, with further reef positions being achieved by using the now lazy flattening line. In order to make reeving of the third reef line easier, the mouse (messenger) line in the form of a loop can be tied between the second and third reef so that the flattening reef can be attached to this mouse line and drawn through when the second reef has been pulled in (see diagram).

Outboard end sheave box arrangements
(Courtesy Proctor Masts)

From the outboard end of the boom, the reef lines then travel inside the section to the inboard end where they usually pass over a set of cam jammers and sheaves where they are then led down the aft base of the mast either to a winch mounted on the mast or back to the cockpit. The reef tack positions should consist of either cringles in the sail or rings which can be hooked over a set of tack hooks mounted on the gooseneck.

The procedure for taking in a slab reef is as follows:
1) Ease the mainsheet and kicking strap to take out the load in the sail and then lower the main halyard sufficiently for the tack reef eye to be positioned over the tack hooks. As the main halyard is released, the boom will of course lower at the outboard end and this can cause problems with the boom either getting caught in the pipelines or striking deck and crew. To prevent this happening it is worth considering the use of either a boom topping lift or a rod type kicker arrangement which will hold the boom above the lifelines and the deck during the operation. It will also help if the main halyard has been marked

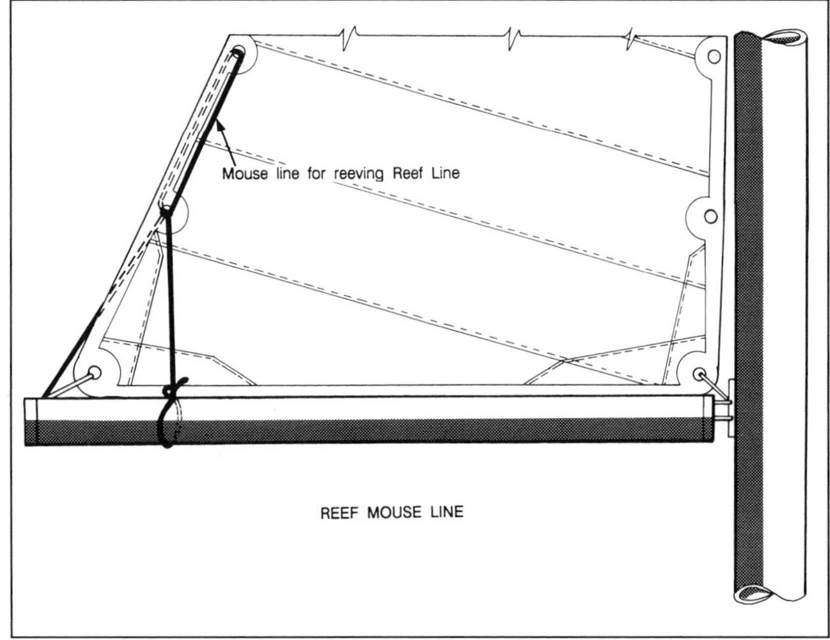

Mouse reef line system

at a position relative to the cleating arrangement to show where it has to be let off to, to allow the tack eye to fit over the tack hooks.

2) With the tack cringle firmly on the hooks, tension the main halyard and cleat off. Permanent shock cord to stop the cringle falling off the hook, before tension is taken up, is useful.

3) Take up the slack in the outboard end reefing line and tighten until the leach cringle is touching the top surface of the boom. Small amounts of further tightening may be necessary to obtain the correct sail shape. Ideally, the slack on this reefing line should be taken as the main halyard is lowered to prevent the loose reefing line flogging and becoming entangled with other control lines or fittings.

4) It is important that the main halyard is tensioned before the leech reefing line is tensioned otherwise the bolt rope of the mainsail on the luff may be pulled aft and out of the sail feeder thus damaging the sail.

5) With the reef firmly in place, sheet in the mainsail and continue to sail.

Cam jammers fitted in the boom at the inboard end are usually only sufficient to hold the reef line for short periods of time and a more permanent cleating arrangement should be fitted on deck for large yachts.

If the main halyard winch is mounted on the mast, it is worth considering mounting the reefing line winch on the aft face of the mast so that the whole reefing operation may be carried out from one position. This is particularly important if the boat is to be sailed short-handed. However if the main halyard winch and cleat are mounted within easy reach from the cockpit then the reefing lines should also be cleated at that position so that it is only necessary to go forward to the mast to put the luff cringle on the hooks, an operation that if it is set up correctly should only take a few seconds.

b) Slab reefing with fly-away tack lines is a development of the basic slab reefing system and only differs in so far as the attachment of the luff of the mainsail. Instead of having a set of hooks mounted on the gooseneck, this system uses tack lines that are led down through blocks on or near the aft face of the mast and are then either cleated near the mast or more usually led back to the cockpit.

Flyaway tack line system

The procedure for taking in a reef is exactly the same as for the above system with the exception that it is not necessary to go forward to hook the sail onto the tack hooks but instead the fly-away tack line is pulled down and securely cleated. There are usually only two fly-away tack lines fitted as each of them has a hook on its top end allowing the lazy tack line to be removed and hooked into the next available reef position.

One important point to bear in mind is to make sure that the angle of the cleated fly-away tack line is sufficient to hold the luff of the sail close to the aft face of the mast. If this is not done, the luff of the mainsail may come aft from the back of the mast and put a high load on the bolt rope with the risk of damaging it and/or the sail.

c) Single line slab reefing boom. This is a further development of the basic slab reefing system and is most commonly found on fully battened mainsail systems although it can be used on conventional mainsails quite successfully. This system differs from the above two in that it has a single line per reef which pulls down both the tack and the clew of the sail simultaneously. This vastly simplifies the operation in that only two controls need to be adjusted, that is the main halyard and the reef line.

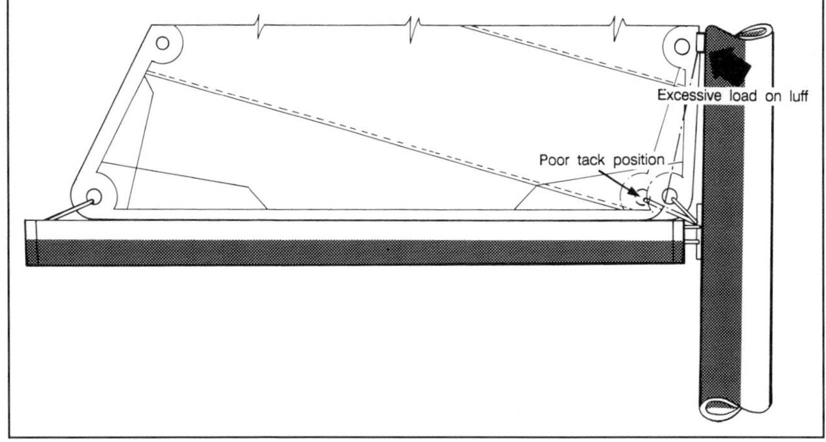

Mainsail tack must be in the correct position when reefed to prevent load on the bolt rope

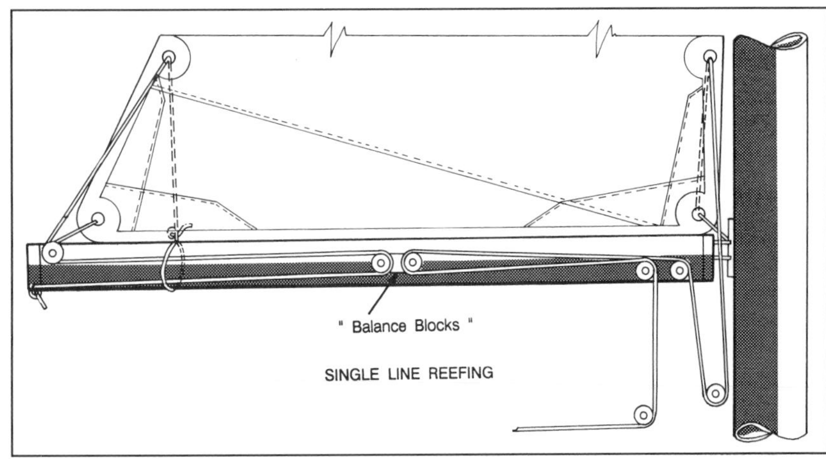

Single line reefing system

As a result, this system is extremely beneficial to short-handed crews as the whole operation can be carried out quickly and efficiently by one person. In addition to the correct boom, this system ideally needs two self-tailing winches to be mounted on deck, one for the main halyard and the other for the reef line. The procedure is as follows:

1) Ease the mainsheet to relieve the load in the mainsail.
2) Place the desired reef line on the self-tailing winch and place a handle in the winch.
3) Put sufficient turns comfortably to hold the main halyard on the other winch and release the cleat.
4) Lower the main halyard to the correct position for the desired reef (again if the main halyard is marked for this position it will greatly help the operation).
5) Pull the slack out of the reefing line and tension until both the tack and clew are firmly in position with their cringles touching the top surface of the boom.
6) Tension the main halyard.
7) Sheet in the mainsail and continue sailing.

Usually these types of booms are fitted with one outhaul line, two single line reefing systems and one flattening reef. If a set of tack hooks or similar attachment fitting is present at the gooseneck, the flattening reef, if it is long enough, can be used as a spare reefing line. In order to reduce the mainsail to the third reef position, assuming that the first two reefs are already in place, the first reef can be untied and re-reeved through the third reef cringles. As with the conventional slab reefing system it will make the operation considerably easier if mouse lines are in place in the mainsail. Alternatively, and assuming there is sufficient space inside the boom, a third single line reefing system can be fitted.

So far we have mentioned reef positions one, two, three etc. but an additional control line in the form of the flattening reef has also been mentioned. This is a cringle in the leach of the mainsail positioned a small distance above the clew of the sail. It does not have a corresponding cringle at the luff of the mainsail and therefore when it is tightened the boom is raised slightly above its original position. The purpose of the flattening reef is, as the name suggests, to flatten the shape of the mainsail without the need for a reef. It is also very useful. However, for lifting the end of the boom to prevent it touching the water when the boat is reaching and the mainsail eased. This significantly reduces the chances of the boom being damaged as a result of it being trapped between the wind and the sea! Of course the flattening reef is no guarantee that the boom will not strike the water and if there is a chance of this on a regular basis then the kicking strap should be close to hand so that it may be released momentarily to allow the boom to lift clear of the water. On most racing boats, one of the crew will be assigned this as all or part of his responsibility as not only is the boom at risk but even if it is not damaged it can certainly cause the boat to broach in an uncontrollable manner.

Unless class rules detail otherwise, most racing yachts use the slab reefing system. Cruiser racer types use conventional slab reefing booms as described

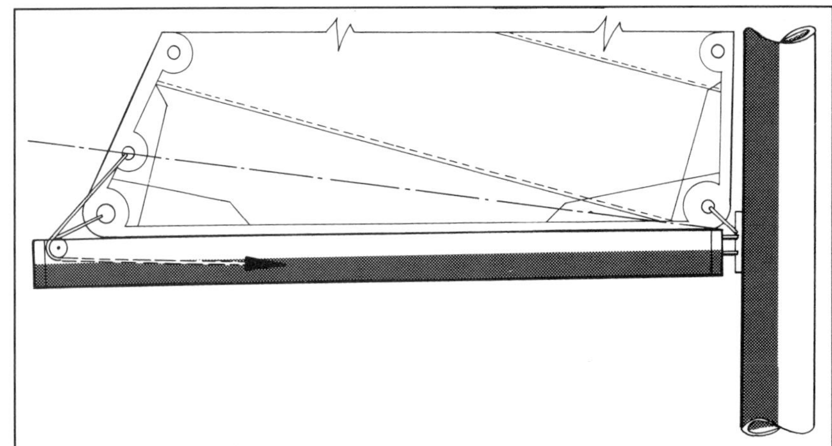

Flattening reef

previously. Grand-Prix yachts, however, normally use specialized versions of the slab reefing system. Sometimes it is necessary to achieve a tight leech on the mainsail and with the low stretch properties of many of the current sail materials, the vertical loads imposed on the boom can be higher than those resulting from sail material which is less rigid and therefore able to absorb some of the shock loads. Therefore in order to obtain consistent control over the mainsail leech, it is necessary to reduce the bend in the boom. The basic principles for achieving a stiffer boom section are the same as for the mast and there are two options. Either the boom section can have a thicker wall thus increasing the moments of inertia or the overall section size can be increased whilst the wall thickness is reduced which also increases the inertia. The latter is generally the preferred method in that, as for the mast, a lighter weight section can be achieved for the same moments of inertia. However, there is quite often a restriction on the overall size of the boom section, for example, under the IOR rule, the maximum boom depth cannot exceed 5% of the foot dimension of the mainsail known as the 'E' measurement. These types of booms are generally termed as 'maxi-depth' booms and are the most common of the high-performance boom sections. They are usually produced from conventional mast sections with the difference being that they are cut in the athwartships plane with the front and back of the section being re-joined with side panels to achieve a deeper overall section. The side panel material is usually light-weight thin gauge plate; this allows the thicker walled mast section to be displaced further away from the neutral axis of the section, thus providing a more efficient use of the material. As the section material is used in a more efficient way i.e. further away from the neutral axis, a smaller initial section can often be used than the equivalent standard boom section. Even with the additional side panels and their fastenings, these types of booms should be lighter than the standard slab reefing equivalent.

To reduce the weight further still, the boom can be tapered along its length. The highest loaded area of the boom is at the kicking strap attachment and therefore this is the area in which the highest section inertias are required. As one moves from this position aft, the vertical loads gradually reduce therefore enabling the section to be tapered. The same is also true of the area forward of the kicking strap although the taper is not usually quite so dramatic as there are high compression loads involved and the section must be sufficient to withstand buckling.

In recent years there have been many attempts to reduce the overall weight of the boom for a given yacht. One of the disadvantages from the weight point of view of the 'maxi-depth' boom is that there are four joins to produce the section which means that the material needs to overlap at the join thus increasing the weight. The most recent and successful development of the 'maxi-depth' boom is the Proctor 'egg-boom', which is constructed from very light-weight aluminium sheets which is carefully folded with the use of a special press to form an elaborate box section. As with the conventional 'maxi-depth' boom, the section is as deep as is allowable by the rules in order to maximize the efficiency of the material. On a large number of booms it is possible to achieve this box section with only one join along the top of the section. However sometimes this is not possible as the overall section size is too deep and a join top and bottom is necessary. This is still a significant improvement over the 'maxi-depth' boom. The basic principle of the boom section is similar to that of an egg in that it achieves its high strength properties, even though it has a very thin wall, from the fact that it is a completely rigid section. Because of the very thin walls, all bending, compression and torsion loads must be reduced to an absolute minimum by "designing out" these loads by careful investigation into the loads anticipated on each fitting. For example, we have already seen how the mainsheet bale, when it is mounted on the under-side of the section, induces a torsion load on the boom. Therefore, to reduce this on the 'egg-boom' the mainsheet is attached to a continuous strop hung around the section which allows the mainsheet load to be transferred to the top of the boom section. This has the result of reducing the torsion load to an absolute minimum. In addition to this, it also spreads the load over a wider area of the boom section.

Another version of high-performance boom is the 'lattice' boom which is a combination of light-weight tubes and rigging wires which attempt to provide the required stiffness whilst reducing the overall weight to an absolute minimum. These types of booms have been experimented with by many mast manufacturers but have not yet achieved the weight savings that are necessary.

Lattice boom example – Inboard end

The number and types of control lines travelling down the inside of the boom and emerging at the outboard end are usually the same as for the conventional slab reefing system. The types of rope used may of course be different in order to minimize stretch and weight by using material such as Kevlar or Spectra. The number of control lines necessary would normally consist of: one outhaul, one flattening, two reef lines. On some Grand-Prix racing yachts the control lines can be reduced to as few as two by combining the outhaul and flattening reef system in one control line and 'leap-frogging' this control line and the spare reef line up the leach of the sail as each reef is required.

Simple cam jammers are rarely found on modern racing yachts as most of the reef lines are led back to the cockpit to enable the reef to be controlled without moving crew weight forward on the boat. If the reef lines are to be jammed off in the boom very often a bank of high-load rope clutches will be fitted allowing a secure jamming method without damaging the ropes.

On yachts of 30ft l.o.a (9.1m) and less, where it is very important not to add weight forward unnecessarily, fly-away tack lines are used to haul the luff of the mainsail. This system is also used on short-handed racing yachts where the whole operation needs to be controlled from the safety of the cockpit.

Outhaul cars.

On most racing yachts of all sizes and cruising yachts of over 35ft l.o.a. (10.7m) the high leech loads imposed on the boom make it very difficult to adjust the outhaul whilst under sail. In some cases, especially on racing craft, the loads imposed on the conventional slug in bolt rope groove section exceeds the strength of the bolt rope groove. In these cases, it is necessary to fit an outhaul car system in order to spread the load imposed by the leach and the mainsheet. There are many different types of system ranging from profiled wheels to lever systems.

When considering an outhaul car system it is very important to bear in mind the nature of the loading on the boom and the frequency of adjustment that is necessary. When one considers this it can be seen that as the loading is often very high it is important to spread the load over as great an area as possible. From an adjustment point of view, the frequency by which the outhaul is adjusted is a great deal less than say, the number of times the genoa sheet/car position is adjusted and trimmed. Therefore, the primary consideration for these two should be that the system be capable of supporting higher loads without distortion to the fittings. It is for this reason that ball race type systems should be avoided. The high loads involved in an outhaul car system are carried by a number of small ball-bearings, each of which has a point load on the car and the track. With excessive and prolonged loading these balls tend to develop flat surfaces which make them difficult to operate smoothly. The preferred system should include sliders of some form that distribute the load more evenly and are not so prone to distortion. In fact, even if distortion is to occur it is less likely to restrict the movement of the bearing as it does not have to rotate.

Combined outhaul/flattener control line(s). This control line can range from simple fixed clew position to the more complicated hydraulic combined flattener/outhaul system. A range of set-ups is best described in pictures. For cruising yachts it is usually sufficient to have the outhaul line exiting on the boom where it is cleated. Inside will be fitted a simple purchase arrangement depending on the size of the yacht.

On racing yachts where, due to weight restriction, the number of sheaves on the outboard end of the boom needs to be reduced to the minimum, a combined flattener/outhaul system is sometimes used. In order to make this system work effectively, a high power adjustment mechanism will be required.

Goosenecks

The gooseneck area of the boom is the connection between the boom and the mast and is a highly loaded and a much abused fitting. Most of the loads that are imposed on the boom are in some way transferred to the gooseneck which in turn transfers the load to the mast at a point where it is already highly loaded due to the mast compression. As a result, much time is spent by manufacturers designing gooseneck that will provide long and trouble free service. There are three main types.

a) Sliding gooseneck. This type of gooseneck is very rarely seen on modern masts. Its purpose

Sliding boom gooseneck

was primarily to tension the luff of the mainsail but this is now achieved with the use of the "cunningham", a cringle a few inches up the luff, thus simplifying the gooseneck arrangement.
b) Fixed. This system is by far the most common and is the successor to the sliding gooseneck detailed above. As its name suggests, it is fixed to the aft face of the mast and on racing yachts it is aligned so as the mainsail can suit the specified black band dimension. The most common arrangement is for the part of the fitting to be attached to the mast to have a toggle arrangement which fits snugly between the two jaws permanently fixed to the inboard end of the boom.

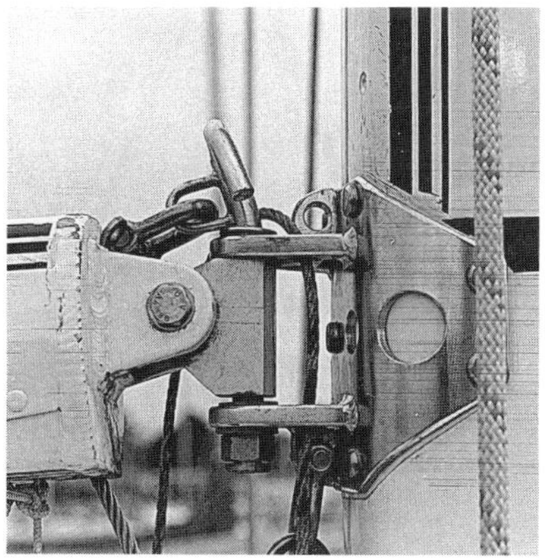

Fixed boom gooseneck

There are however some other arrangements where the toggle is in the form of a set of jaws which fit outside a single lug on the inboard end of the boom. The latter arrangement is not as desirable as the loads imposed along the boom are transferred through a single lug.
c) Rotating. As we have described earlier, on some booms especially deep section types, the torsion loads can be very high which can in turn lead to excessive wear on the gooseneck fitting and boom jaws. This is a particularly significant consideration on large long-distance cruising yachts that may be many miles from specialist facilities and therefore require the torsion loads to be reduced to an absolute minimum. There are two ways of achieving this the first being to alter the method of attachment of the mainsheet. This involves moving the point of attachment as close as is possible to the horizontal position of the gooseneck and can be achieved with the use of mainsheet bales which help to transfer the loads away from the bottom of the section. The second method of reducing these loads is to allow the boom to rotate. In order to do this, the inboard end mountings of the boom be they either a set of jaws or a lug, need to allow limited rotation.

Lightening holes.
Over the years the methods of

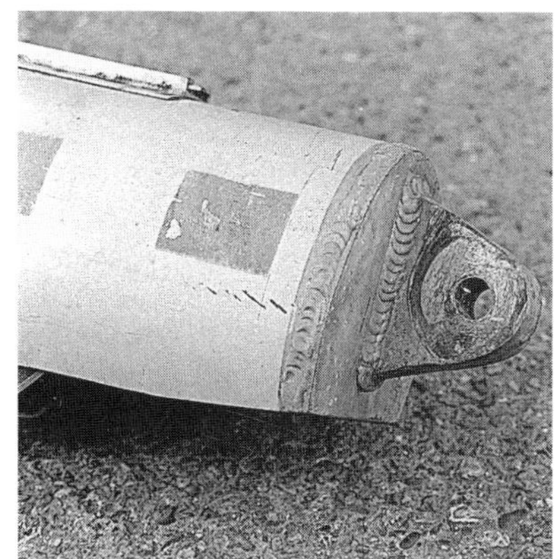

Single lug on inboard end of boom

Rotating gooseneck relieves torsional loads on boom

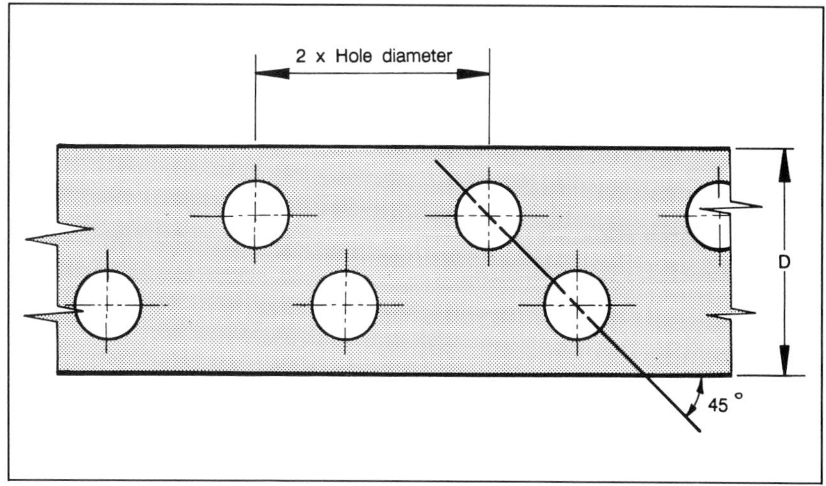

Recommendations for cutting lightening holes in boom sections

calculating section sizes for booms on racing yachts has become significantly better and as a result the need for lightening holes in booms has thankfully reduced. Any hole in a section on any spar can be the source of an inherent weakness. In most cases, any overloading in the vicinity of the hole will usually manifest itself in the form of a crack extending from a part of the hole. There are occasions where a boom needs to be lightened and provided it is carried in the correct way, lightening holes can be a relatively cheap and efficient way of achieving a saving in weight.

Mainsheet attachments
The position of the mainsheet attachment relative to the leach of the mainsail can change depending on the amount of sail that is up at a given time. The greater the horizontal distance between the mainsheet attachment and the leach of the mainsail the greater the bending moment. A boom that has its mainsheet attachment positioned at a distance forward of the outboard end of the boom will, under full sail, allow the outboard end of the boom to try to move in a vertical direction. However, with sufficient reef the clew position may come forward of the mainsheet attachment in which case the bending may be reversed and the outboard end of the boom tries to dip downwards.

Reef

Reef

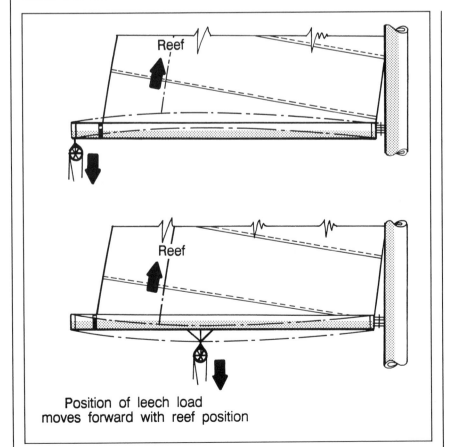

Position of leech load moves forward with reef position

Bending loads vs mainsheet position

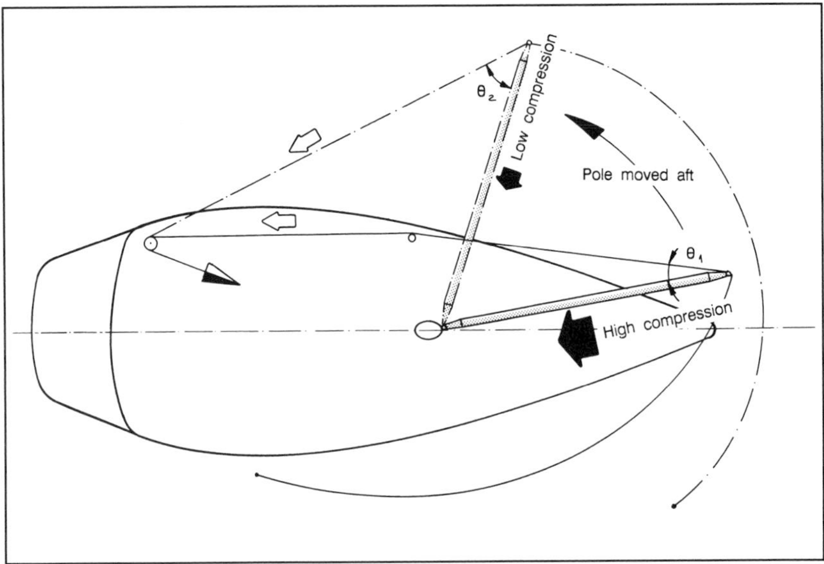

Spinnaker pole loading conditions

Spinnaker Poles
There are two main forms of loading that a spinnaker pole is subjected to under normal sailing conditions. First and by far the most significant is compression. This loading is at its highest when the boat is close reaching and the spinnaker pole is parallel to the centre line of the boat. As the boat bears off and the spinnaker pole is brought aft, the compression loading reduces to a minimum when the spinnaker pole is at right angles to the centre line of the boat. The critical factor that influences compression in the spinnaker pole, is the angle between the guy and the end of the pole. As with the shroud to mast connection, the smaller the angle the higher the component of compression. On some yachts with very narrow beams, the angle between the spinnaker guy and the pole, when close reaching, is too small to gain proper

control over the pole position. In this case it is necessary to use a jockey pole (reaching strut in USA) which increases that angle thus also reducing the compression.

The second loading that the pole is subjected to is bending. In view of the relatively high compression loading, bending should be avoided as far as is practically possible, as the relatively thin wall section is susceptible to failure through buckling. It is usually a result of either incorrect positioning of topping lift and downhaul attachments or the imbalance of the loading between the two control lines.

Another cause of buckling is an attempt to dip-pole gybe without first removing the babystay.

Whilst mentioning the loads of the spinnaker pole especially when close reaching, it should be noted that care should be taken when the spinnaker pole is set close to the forestay to prevent it from bearing on the forestay. This can not only damage the spinnaker pole tube but also the forestay and/or luff groove track that may be fitted especially if it is of the aluminium type. In addition to this, the point loading towards the outboard end of the pole due to the forestay, creates a bending moment on the outboard end of the spinnaker pole which may result in damage of the fitting or the pole.

Spinnaker pole sections may be tapered or untapered. The untapered poles are as the name suggests, parallel tubes into which fit the spinnaker pole end fittings. In some cases, the diameter of the end fitting may be smaller than that of the tube in which case a cone type adapter needs to be used. The main reason for using this type of pole is that it is cheaper and simpler to repair as the tube can be cut back in the event of damage to the ends. However, this type of pole is relatively heavy especially on section diameters of 4 in (100 mm) and above. In addition to this, the large diameters at the ends often make the pole difficult to handle.

Tapered poles are generally lighter as a result of having both less tube weight as well as not requiring end adapters on larger poles. The tapered ends also make the poles easier to handle.

Whilst most spinnaker poles are of a set length for a particular boat which is usually related to the horizontal distance between the forward face of the mast and the forestay fitting at deck, known as the 'J' measurement, a large number of cruising yachts require such poles for a number of different uses. E.g. spinnaker pole, headsail booming out pole. The result is that a combination of different length poles are required for which there is very little deck space to accommodate these different lengths. The popular answer to this problem

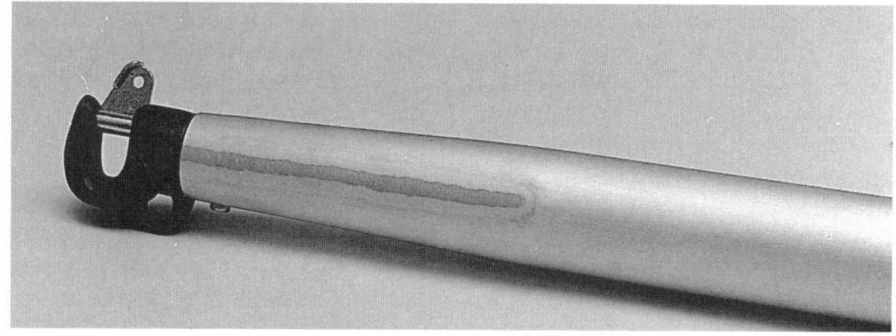

Tapered (above) and untapered (below) spinnaker poles
(Courtesy Proctor Masts)

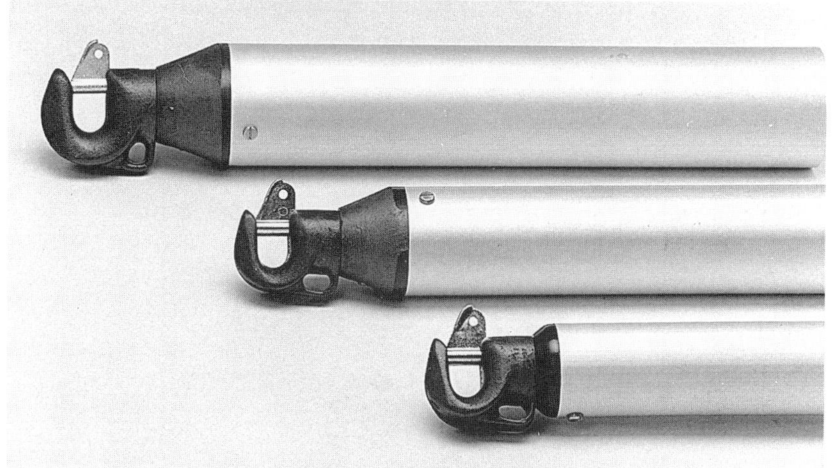

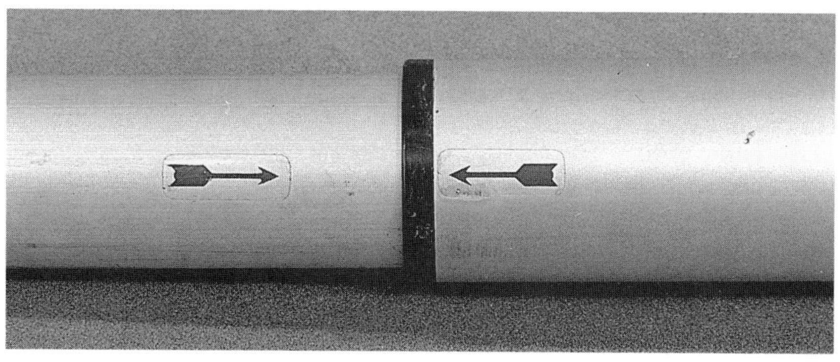

Telescopic spinnaker pole centre posiiton

is to use a telescopic spinnaker pole that has a number of settings depending on its required use. They usually consist of a parallel tube section with simple spring clips to alter the length. Another advantage of these types of poles especially for cruising yachts is that they can be fully retracted and stowed at a shorter overall length than the more conventional fixed type.

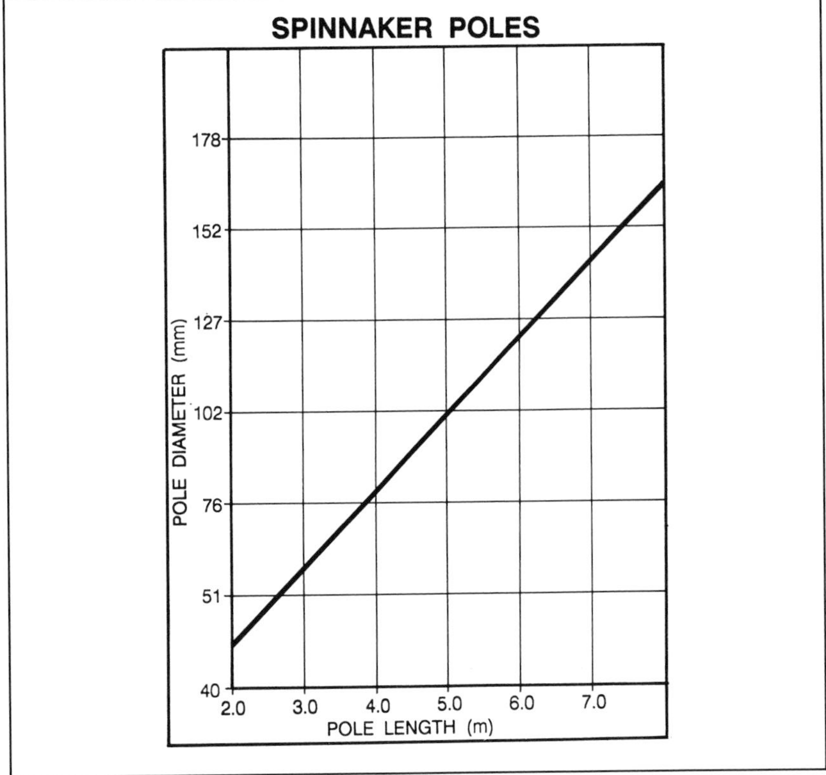

Spinnaker pole section size guide

Fittings and specifications

As with any spar the specification in terms of fittings depends entirely on the pole's use. In the case of the spinnaker pole, its use is usually determined by the method in which the spinnaker is gybed. There are three common ways in which this is achieved and are briefly described as follows:

a) 'End for end'. This type of system can be comfortably used on boats up to about 30ft l.o.a. (9.1m) and is perhaps the simplest form of gybing requiring the fewest control lines and crew to carry out the procedure. It involves removing the inboard end of the spinnaker pole from the mast and attaching it to the spinnaker sheet so that the spinnaker pole is suspended between the spinnaker sheet on the leeward side and the spinnaker guy on the windward side. The boat is then gybed and the old spinnaker guy, (now the spinnaker sheet) is unclipped from the pole and then connected to the mast fitting thus completing the gybe procedure.

As the wind strength increases the removal of the pole from the mast becomes more difficult as a result of the high compression loads. There are two ways of making the procedure easier to handle:

i) The use of twin sheets and guys (see diagram).

ii) Tripping the outboard end of the pole and thus releasing the guy allowing the spinnaker to fly free before removing the inboard end from the mast. Whilst this takes all the load out of the spinnaker pole it does allow the spinnaker to fly virtually uncontrolled and therefore speed is of the essence when reconnecting the pole on the new side.

The important point in terms of specification of this type of pole is that it should be

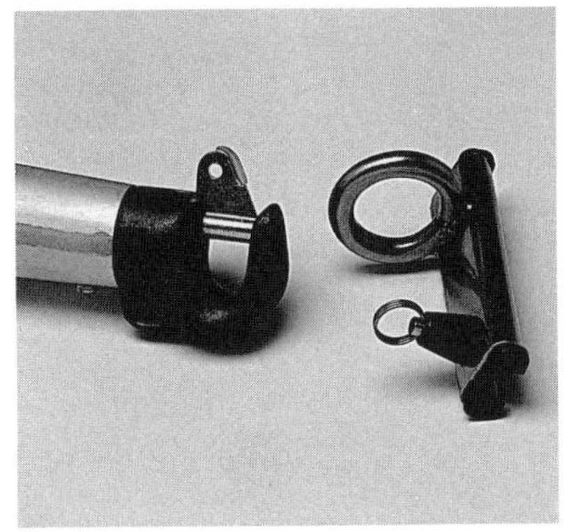

'End for end' spinnaker pole end fitting – note striker plate on plunger helps in attaching the pole end onto the ring (Courtesy Proctor Masts)

Spinnaker pole specification guide

Boat size LOA (ft)	20	30	40	50	60
Untapered	+	+			
Tapered		+	+	+	+
'End for end'	+	+			
'Dip pole'			+	+	+
'Twin pole'			+	+	+
Ring slider on mast	+	+			
'Dummy' and cup			+	+	+
Bayonet and socket				+	+
Trigger end			+	+	+
Internal trip			+	+	+

symmetrical about its centre. i.e. the topping lift and downhaul attachment need to be at the centre of the length of the pole so that it can be used on either side. On small boats of up to approximately 25ft l.o.a. (7.6m) the spinnaker pole topping lift and downhaul can be attached to eyes fitted at the centre of the pole. However, on larger boats or racing yachts where the loads are higher, bridles should be used top and bottom in order to transfer the load to the ends of the pole. It is important to make sure that either one system or the other is used and not a combination of the two as the latter could easily result in failure of the pole. (see diagram).

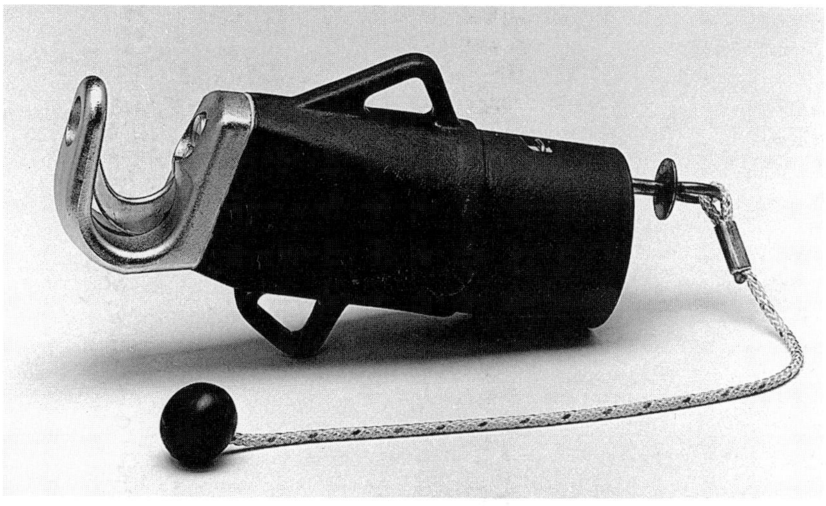

'Dip pole' spinnaker pole end fitting – 'Snapper'

b) 'Dip pole' gybing. This procedure is used on yachts of 30ft l.o.a. (9.1m) and above and consists of swinging the outboard end of the pole through the fore triangle. Firstly, the inboard end of the pole needs to be raised to a point such that the inboard end can be comfortably swung inside the forestay when dipped. (It is best to mark this position on the mast and on the heel hoist line). Next, trip the outboard end of the pole thus releasing the guy and lower the spinnaker pole topping lift (also to a marked position) so that the outboard end can swing down towards the forestay fitting. The new 'lazy guy' can then be attached and the topping lift be hauled up. Before the spinnaker pole takes any load, lower the inboard end to the correct position. The new guy may now be tensioned and the procedure is complete.

The main requirement for this type of system is that the outboard end fitting should be of the trigger type. This allows the plunger to be held open once the guy has been released until the new guy is placed in the fitting which automatically trips the plunger thus securing a new guy. In terms of layout, this type of pole is asymmetrical with a piston end fitting on the out board end and some form of universal attachment on the inboard end. The topping lift and downhaul lines are attached to the outboard end of the pole to give the best control and reduce the bending loads on the pole.

c) Twin pole gybing. This system uses two spinnaker poles and the process involves setting the spare spinnaker pole on the leeward side just before the gybe takes place. The boat is then gybed and the new leeward spinnaker pole (i.e the old pole) is lowered and stowed on the deck. This system has the advantage that the spinnaker is under rigid control throughout the gybe procedure. The disadvantage of the system is that duplicate controls are required on each side of the boat i.e. two spinnaker sheets, two spinnaker guys, two topping lifts, two downhauls etc. The position for the spinnaker pole topping lift and downhaul attachments are the same as for dip-pole systems. It is not necessary to use a trigger type end fitting for this system although it does help the operation.

Topping lift arrangements.

a) Bridle. This system is used for end for end gybing and is an effective means of transferring the loads to the ends of the pole. The disadvantage of this system is that the additional wires can get in the way.

b) Centre eyes. A simple eye fitting is attached top and bottom at the centre of the pole for topping lift and downhaul attachments. This is the simplest form of connection, but tends to induce bending in the pole. Care must be taken with the fixing of these eyes in that the section is weakened with the fastening holes at a point where the pole can be potentially highly loaded.

Topping lift attachments – Simple eye at centre of pole

Topping lift attachments – Bridle (above) and outboard end attachment (below)

d) Outboard end attachment. The spinnaker pole topping lift and downhaul attachments are positioned at the outboard end of the pole often incorporated in the pole end fitting itself. This system offers the lowest relative loads in the control line and fittings, but does mean that the pole cannot be reversed in its use. On some poles, the spinnaker pole topping lift and downhaul can be almost permanently attached with a self-stowing shock-cord arrangement.

e) Parallel pole hoist. This system is used almost exclusively on racing yachts where fast settings of the spinnaker pole are required. It consists of a split topping lift, one end of which is attached to the spinnaker pole, the other part is attached to the slider on the forward face of the mast. The lengths of these two lines are set so that when the topping lift is raised the pole is hoisted in a parallel fashion. Two downhaul lines are however required for this system, one for the spinnaker pole and the other being for the car. This type of system can only be used in end-for-end gybing as it is not possible to dip the pole end and swing through the fore triangle.

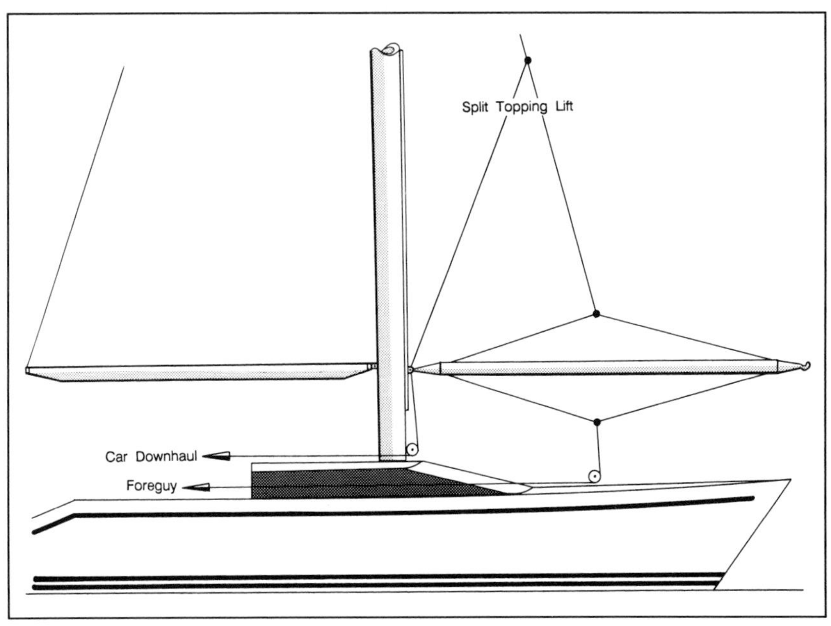

Parallel pole hoist system

Outboard end fittings

A vast majority of these fittings consist of a basic piston system. There are many different makes of this type of end fitting and whilst they all may seem very similar they should be checked carefully for their ease of operation. In particular it should be checked as to whether the piston itself has a striker plate which automatically retracts the piston when it is pressed against either a ring or a sheet. This feature is very important as it will allow a one-handed operation. (You may need the other hand to hold on!) The bearing surface for the spinnaker guy should be studied carefully to make sure it is well radiused and does not possess sharp edges which could easily and quickly chafe the guy.

The trigger outboard end fitting is a development of the

piston fitting with the difference that once the piston has been retracted it is locked in the open position. Pressure applied to the bottom surface of the jaw, or in some cases a hand operated trigger lever, will release the piston thus closing the device. Again, the fitting should be checked for smoothness and large radii on bearing surfaces to minimize chafe.

Inboard end fittings
On boats of up to approximately 30ft l.o.a. (7.6m) the spinnaker pole end fittings will be relatively simple and will be the same as the outboard end mainly as a result of the fact that the spinnaker pole is end for end gybed. A mast fitting will consist of either a simple fixed ring on the forward face of the mast of which there may be three in total to allow different pole heights or a ring slider arrangement fitted to the track on the forward face of the mast. The ring slider arrangement will usually have a sprung plunger with a range of stop positions drilled into the track.

Boats of 30-55ft l.o.a. (9.1–16.8m) will normally be fitted with a dummy or socket end. These fittings attach into a cup or bayonet respectively which is mounted on a slider travelling on a track fitted on the forward face of the mast. This slider can either have a sprung plunger or a heel hoist control line. In the case of the latter, a simple jammer arrangement may be used or a more specialised heel hoist winch which can be locked off at a number of positions.

The majority of spinnaker tracks and car systems are fitted with low friction plastic slider inserts. Some of the more specialized racing yachts do however use re-circulating ball systems on the cars in order to reduce friction to an absolute minimum and ease the operation. However, it must be stressed that this type of system is generally undesirable for all but the most specialized racing craft as already explained.

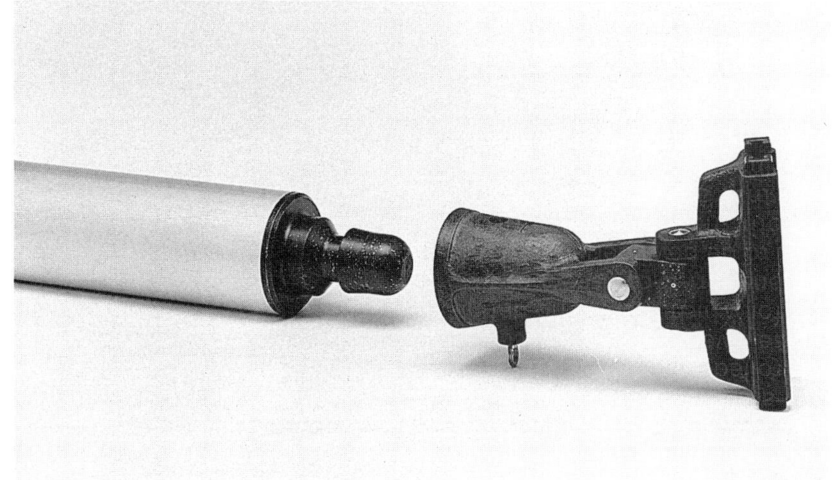

Dummy and cup inboard end fittings (Courtesy Proctor Masts)

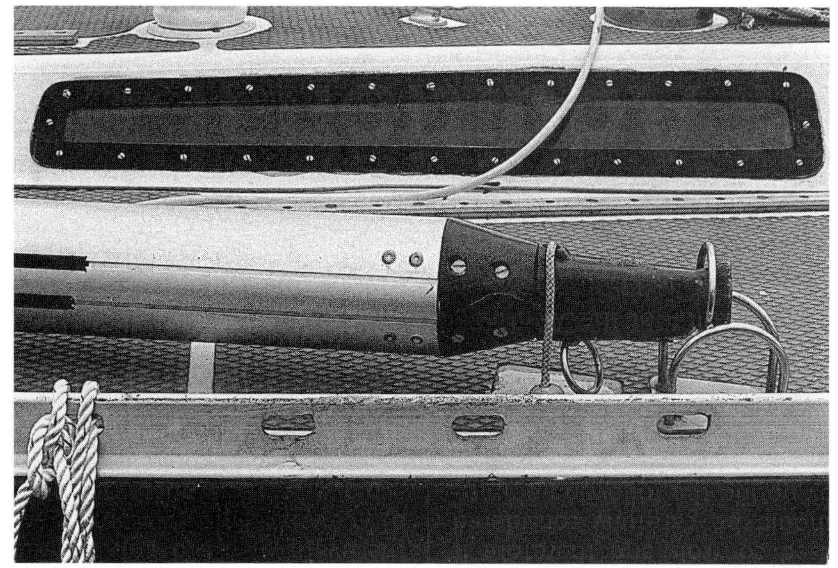

Spinnaker pole stowages

Pole stowage
The most common form of stowage is with the use of deck chocks. These must be non-fouling. However if twin poles are used and especially on cruising boats, the foredeck area may become cluttered and therefore pole stowage up the mast is preferable. This system requires extra long tracks on the forward face of the mast as well as a special toggle arrangement

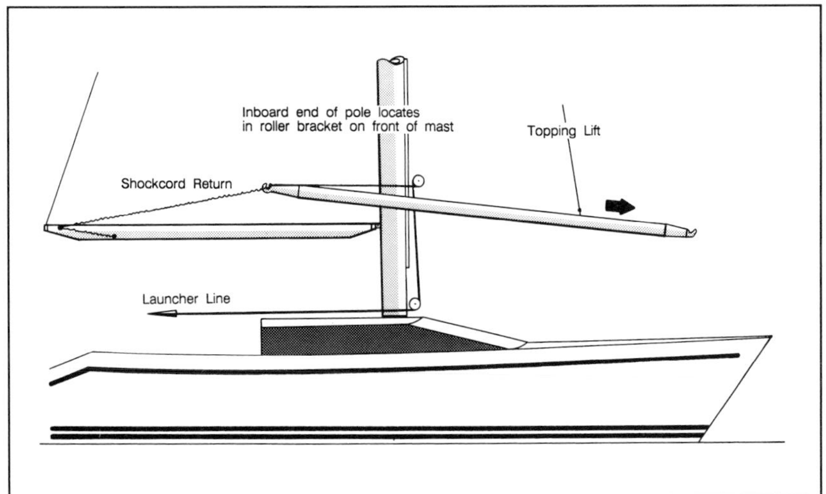

'Flyaway' pole system

on the slider. The car sliders are usually operated by means of a continuous line, heel hoist, which raise the inboard end to the correct height. The lower end of the spinnaker pole (i.e. the outboard end) can then be attached to a fitting which is fastened to the forward face of the mast at the deck area.

On racing yachts the spinnaker pole is generally left in position but lowered to the deck so that it is ready for quick use. Some of the smaller racing craft stow the spinnaker poles on the boom in much the same way as is seen on dinghies and incorporate a flyaway pole launcher system. (see diagram). This type of system can usually only be used on boats up to about 25ft l.o.a. (7.6m).

Jockey poles and reaching struts

The spinnaker pole is stowed on the mainsail boom in a similar way to that seen on a lot of racing dinghies. The inboard end of the pole has a simple plug with a line attached to it. This line travels forwards along the boom to a roller mounted on the forward face of the mast around which it turns and descends down to the deck level. From here it then travels back to the cockpit. Also from the inboard end of the pole is a length of shock-cord which is attached to the outboard end of the boom. (This shock-cord retrieves the pole when not in use.) When the flyaway line is pulled, the spinnaker pole is forced forwards until the socket on the inboard end of the pole locates on the roller mounted on the forward face of the mast.

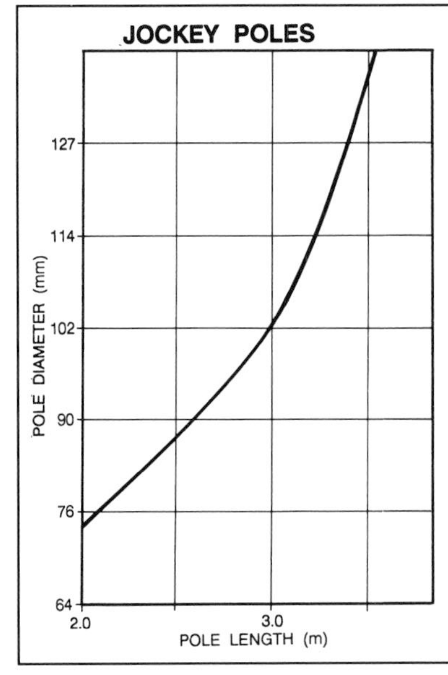

Jockey pole section size guide

When a spinnaker is set and the boat is close reaching the spinnaker pole is close to parallel to the centre line of the boat. This means that the component of compression in the spinnaker pole is very high. Conversely, the component of force in the athwartships plane is low making it difficult to control the pole end. The relation between these two components of force is directly proportional to the angle that the spinnaker guy makes with the outboard end of the pole. In order to reduce the compression load and increase the athwartships load, the angle between the guy and the spinnaker pole needs to be increased. In certain cases this may be achieved by careful repositioning of the spinnaker guy lead blocks but in most cases these have already been placed at their optimum positions. The most popular solution is to use a jockey pole (reaching strut) which increases the critical angle of the spinnaker guy. The inboard end of such a pole usually consists of a simple piston fitting which connects on to a ring mounted on the side of the mast. The outboard end is usually a large diameter sheave mounted in a special cage. In order to prevent the jockey pole from moving in the fore and aft plane it is usually lashed to either the shrouds or the guard wires by means of a sail tyer or similar.

Running sail booms

These poles are used in particular on long distance cruising yachts that sail for long periods of time with boomed out headsails set. A conventional spinnaker type system is usually undesirable for this type of craft due to the high risk of chafe combined with the different angles of loading involved. The basic system of mast attachment usually consists of a track and slider arrangement much the same as for conventional spinnaker pole. However, because downhaul control lines are not normally used on these poles they need to be set so that the inboard end is higher than the outboard end. The action of the genoa sheet and the tension in the foot of the sail combined with this sloping attitude of the pole prevent the outboard end from lifting. As a result any compression load that is transferred along the pole needs to be allowed for at the universal joint fitting on the slider. Therefore the lug parts of the slider need to be angled downwards in order to align better with the direction of loading (see diagram).

Even some of the best outboard pole end fittings can chafe sheets on long passage sailing. Therefore in order to reduce chafe to an absolute minimum special fittings such as the triangular end plate system should be used. This fitting can then take block arrangement through which the genoa sheet can run while also providing attachments for downhauls and additional control lines to stay the pole as required. As this type of system usually requires two poles they are usually stowed up the mast.

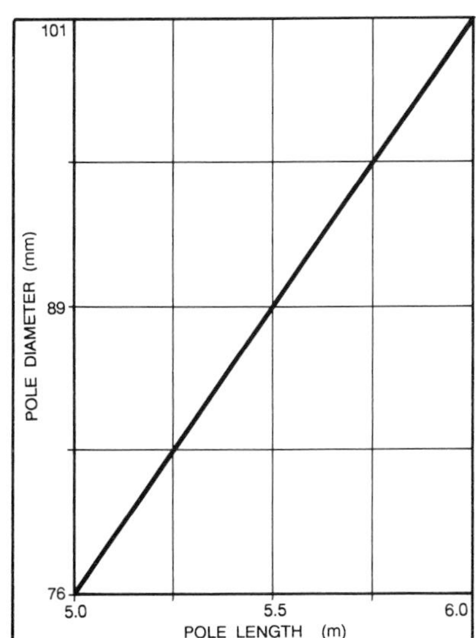

Running sail boom section size guide

Staysail booms

Cutter rigs with self-tacking staysails will generally require a staysail boom. The tack arrangement is usually clamped around the inner forestay where

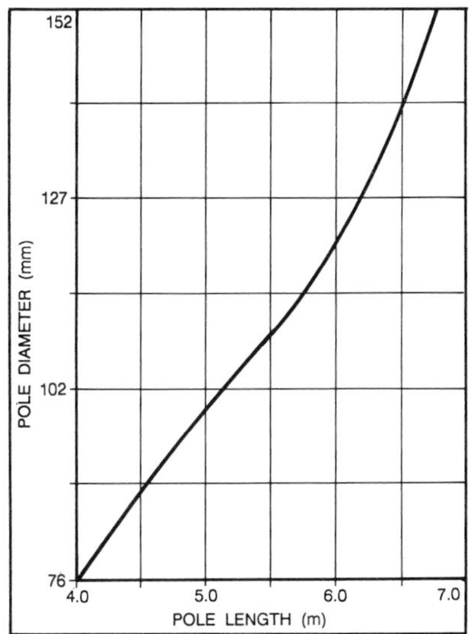

Staysail boom section size guide

it can rotate around the stay. The fitting is prevented from sliding up the stay by means of a set length downhaul strop. Some arrangements on larger yachts may use a separate post onto which the staysail boom gooseneck is attached. The outboard end of the staysail boom should usually have provision for both the clew attachment of the staysail (sometimes including some form of adjustment) and a staysail boom topping lift attachment. On the underside of this boom at the outboard end will be an attachment for a staysail sheet.

Additional stays

Whilst we have mentioned most of the stays and control lines involved with spinnaker poles etc. there is a set of stays which can prove invaluable in saving the mast should the boat be involved in a broach. These are known as 'Chicken stays'. Their attachments on the mast are around the usual height position for the spinnaker pole inboard end fitting. When the stays are in place they travel forwards to a point on the gunwale approximately mid-way between the mast and the forestay attachment and their purpose is to oppose high compression loads transferred by the spinnaker pole on to the mast. In the case of a windward roll which results perhaps in a serious broach the spinnaker pole may strike the water and transfer very high compression loads back to the mast thus running a high risk of seriously damaging if not breaking the mast. The 'Chicken stays' can go some way towards dissipating these loads away from the mast. There are restrictions on such stays under IOR and other rules to discourage thin masts.

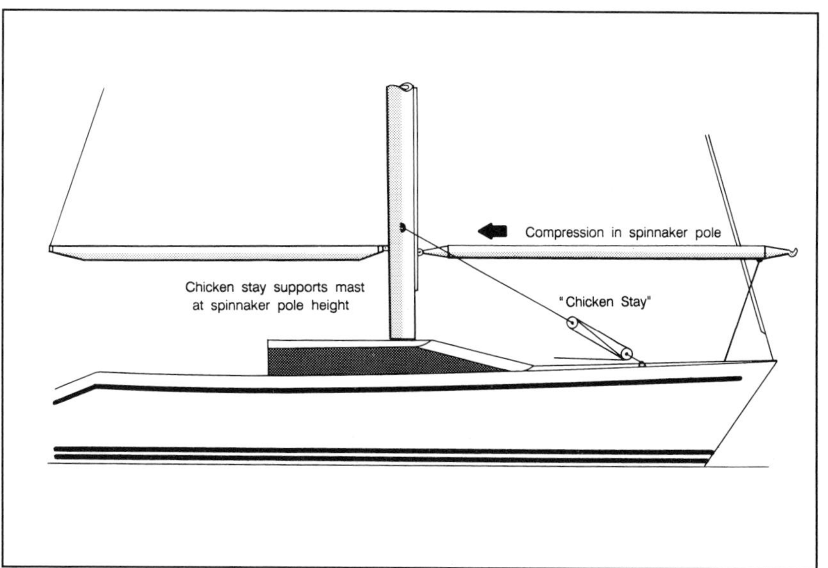

Chicken stays

8: Additional equipment

Having specified a particular set of spars for a yacht it would then be necessary to develop specification for the control systems i.e. the method in which sails are sheeted and spars are controlled and stayed. This is of course a very varied subject and one for which there is no definitive answer. It can seem at first sight to be bewildering in terms of both sheer numbers of controls that are required and the way in which reasonable purchases are achieved. The aim of this section of the book is not to list every combination of option available, but to highlight some of the main areas and suggest some popular solutions. Probably the most important point to remember is that in general the simpler the system the better, so long as it satisfies the needs for a particular boat.

Mainsheet arrangements

Boat LOA (ft)	Minimum purchase ratio	Breaking load (kg)	Rope diameter (mm)
20-25	4:1	950	10
25-27	4:1	1220	13
27-32	6:1	1220	13
32-35	6:1	1820	14
35-36	6:1	1820	14
36-39	6:1	1820	14
39-41	6:1 + winch	4100	14
41-48	6:1 + winch	4100	14
48-60	6:1 + winch	6360	19
60-70	3:1 + winch	8200	19
70-80	4:1 + winch x2	10910	19

Mainsheet

Along with the genoa sheet this is one of the most commonly used controls and therefore it should be carefully considered by noting the following points:-

a) Boat size
b) Position of the mainsheet on the boom
c) Deck attachment methods
d) Purchase required
e) Application of the yacht e.g. racing or cruising

Kicking strap (boom vang) systems

a) Block and tackle. This is the simplest purchase arrangement for a kicker and is most efficiently achieved by means of a cascade system. This allows a high purchase to be gained with the minimum of blocks and is quick to tension (and release in the event of a broach).

b) Lever. This system also achieves a high purchase ratio but only allows a small degree of travel. One of the limiting factors with lever kickers is usually the space available in which the lever can swing. The system is borrowed from dinghies, where there is proportionately more space. If this is not a problem the lever system would be ideal in terms of simplicity. As can be seen from the diagrams the purchase ratio of this system can be dramatically increased with the additional use of a block and tackle system and /or a winch.

c) Rod kicker. There are a number of different types of rod kicker available on the market most of which are very similar in their operation. They consist primarily of two tubes that form a telescopic strut. Fitted inside the tubes and holding the ends apart is a large spring. This provides upward thrust on the boom thus dispensing with the

Kicking strap systems – block and tackle above and cascade below

Kicking strap systems – Lever above and solid strut below

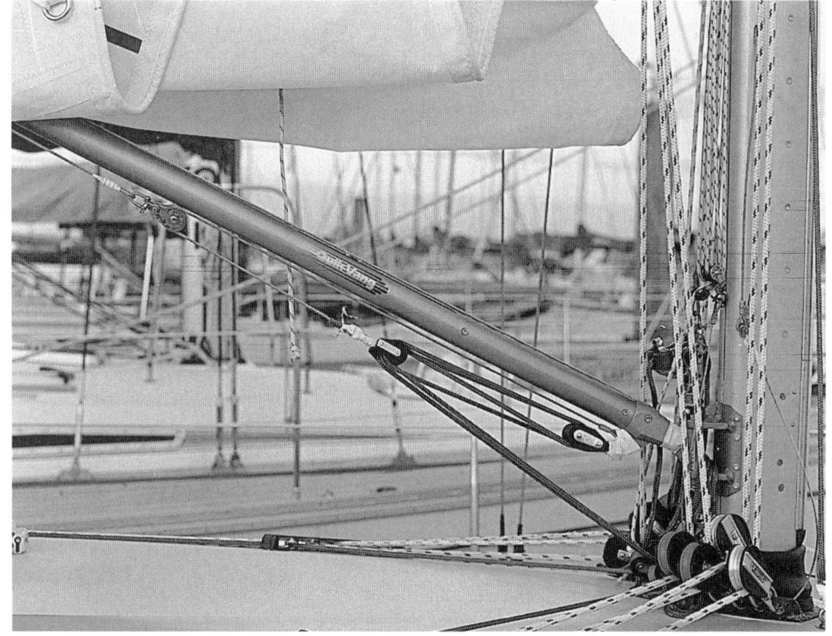

need for a topping lift. Most good systems have a spring adjuster in order that the degree of upward thrust can be adjusted. This is quite important as whilst the rod kicker may be quite capable of supporting the boom on its own, it also needs to support the boom when the mainsail is stowed on it.

Another reason why this system has gained popularity is that because it holds the boom up it makes slab reefing a lot easier to carry out and prevents The boom from being caught in the guardwires or damaging the deck.

d) Hydraulic. The high power capabilities make this type of system popular on large yachts. Typically they are used on cruising yachts of 35ft l.o.a. (9.1m) and above and racing yachts of 44ft l.o.a (13.4m) and above. They are very simple to operate and have similar advantages to that of the rod kickers in that they can hold up the boom when reefing and when the sail is stowed. However, there are a number of disadvantages which normally mean that these types of system are only found on larger yachts. These factors are: high cost compared to rod kicker systems, weight on racing craft – this is usually a prime consideration, speed of operation – again on racing craft the kicker may need to be released quickly and hydraulic controls do not generally lend themselves to this.

There are two main types of hydraulic kicking strap which are as follows:

i) The integral kicking strap – this is a self contained unit consisting of the ram and a pump. This is most commonly found on cruising boats where there is no other form of hydraulics on the boat. The vertical thrust of the ram is achieved by air pressure and can be varied depending on the weight of the boom and the sails. The integral pump has a valve which when shut and the pump handle is operated, shortens the length of the kicking strap thus pulling the boom end down. To release the kicking strap and thus allow the outboard end of the boom to rise the valve is opened and the air pressure in the kicking strap forces the boom upwards.

ii) Remote ram – the kicker ram for this system works in the same way as for the integral kicking strap but in this case the control panel is set at a remote location usually at some point in the cockpit. This system is used generally where there are a number of other hydraulic controls and the valves for which are grouped on a hydraulic control panel.

e) Drum and axle. This type of system is mainly seen on dinghies, but can be successfully adapted for racing yachts. The system consists of an axle with a drum mounted on one end of this axle. The wire kicker is attached to the axle and the

Typical hydraulic integral vang sizes

Mainsail area (sq.m)	Pin diam. (in)	(mm)	Upward thrust (kg)	Max. tension (kg)	Approx weight (kg)
18-22	$\frac{7}{16}$	11.1	160	1350	6.4
22-26	$\frac{1}{2}$	12.7	230	2200	9.1
26-35	$\frac{5}{8}$	15.9	430	3800	13.2
35-50	$\frac{3}{4}$	19.0	640	5300	15.5
50-85	$\frac{7}{8}$	22.2	850	7000	24.2
85-120	1	25.4	1000	9100	27.7
120-180	$1\frac{1}{4}$	31.8	1100	10400	31.5

(Courtesy Seaway Products Ltd.)

rope control line is attached to the drum. This system could be advantageous for racing yachts as it reduces the weight above deck to a minimum in that it should consist only of a single wire, and the drum and axle unit can be kept low in the boat with the control lines being led aft to the cockpit. Large purchases can be achieved with large drums. Another advantage is that the degree of travel is only restricted by the wire and rope carrying capacity of the axle and drum. It is a simple and cheap arrangement and whilst it is not yet universally popular, it should be seriously considered by any racing yacht owner.

Spinnaker pole topping lift

A relatively simple arrangement consisting of a one to one control line from the pole being led up over a sheave, down the mast and to a small winch (depending on the size of the yacht). On a cruising yacht this is generally all that is required. However for racing yachts more elaborate systems are sometimes employed. However before one gets too carried away with designing a complicated system, it is important to remember that the topping lift generally carries very little load. Therefore high purchase systems are rarely required.

There are two primary conations when choosing a topping

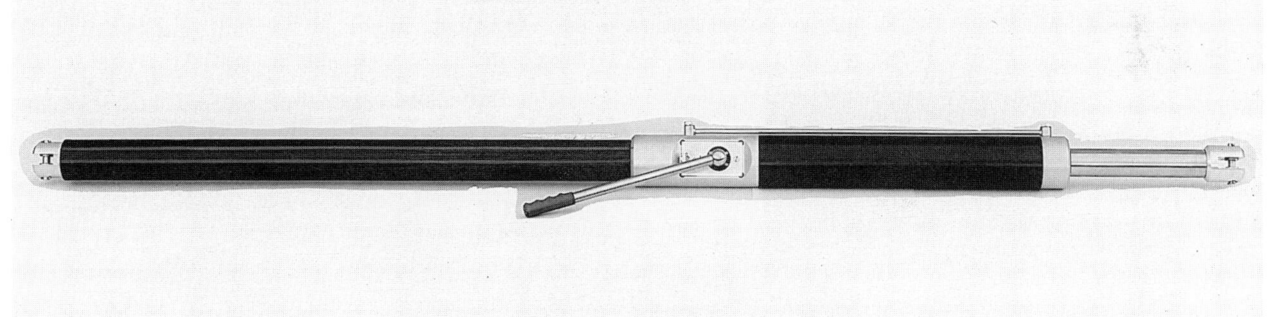

Integral hydraulic kicker system (Courtesy Seaway Products Ltd.)

Remote ram hydraulic kicker system (Courtesy Seaway Products Ltd.)

lift system:
a) The position of the topping lift sheave.
b) The manner in which the pole is hoisted.

Normally the spinnaker pole topping lift sheave in the mast is fitted at a position somewhere approximately halfway between the forestay fitting, however in recent years the trend has been to fit this sheave close to the hounds position. As the topping lift on the pole needs to be attached before the gybe and run outside the genoa, a high sheave allows this.

The single line topping lift system is the most popular due to its simplicity.

The parallel pole hoist system is almost exclusively a racing type topping lift with the advantage that the pole can be lifted in a parallel fashion from its stowed position on the deck up into position ready for the spinnaker hoist. This is achieved by splitting the topping lift as it emerges from the topping lift sheave into parts. One part travels down to the spinnaker pole bridle and the other is attached to the car slider on the front of the mast. The relative length of these two parts is critical in order to keep the pole parallel, but once set, it should not need to be altered. This system does however require an additional downhaul to hold down the free-running car slider.

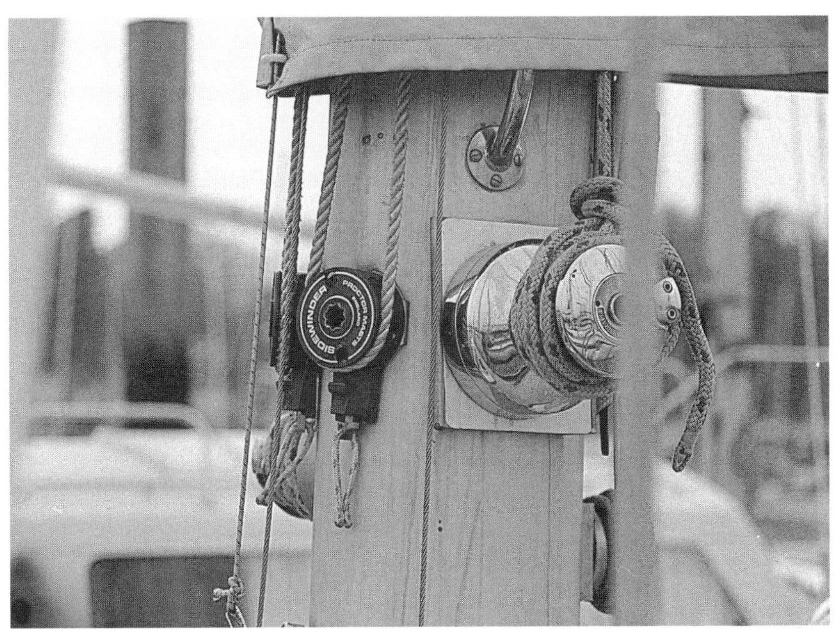

Spinnaker pole heel hoist system – Chain drive above sidewinder rope type below

Spinnaker pole heel systems.
If the car is not fitted with a sprung piston that locates into holes up the track, a control line system will be required in order to adjust the height of the slider. This takes the form of a continuous line, or an uphaul and a downhaul, depending on the size of the yacht.

Cruising yachts generally use a line driver type of winch, most of which accept the standard winch handle. Probably the most popular winch of this type is the Proctor Masts 'Sidewinder' winch which incorporates a four-position control system allowing: 1) ratchet clockwise 2) ratchet anticlockwise 3) lock 4) free.

This type of system is suitable for yachts of up to approximately 60ft l.o.a. (18.3m). For larger cruising yachts a geared heel hoist winch is required. The 'chain hoist' system is a popular choice for yachts of above 60ft l.o.a. (18.3m).

Racing yacht pole hoist systems are again continuous, but are usually operated by hand without the use of a winch. The line is again continuous but is cleated by means of a pair of cam jammers fitted to the side of the mast. A one to one system is generally suitable for hts of up to 38ft l.o.a. (11.6m) and above this purchase systems are necessary.

Spinnaker pole downhaul (or fore-guy). This control line holds down the outboard end of the

Racing heel hoist systems for the spinnaker pole often use free running ball race cars and tracks

spinnaker pole and can, at times, be very highly loaded and therefore each individual component should be carefully selected to ensure that there is no risk of it failing whilst under sail. If any part of this system does fail then there is a strong likelihood of an exciting broach! On cruising yachts a one to one downhaul, with the use of a winch on yachts of approximately 30ft l.o.a. (9.1m) and above, is normally sufficient. On racing yachts, a common system is a purchase arrangement, usually two to one, with the control lines led back to the cockpit on either side for easy adjustment. Normally the deck attachment is positioned at some distance between the forward face of the mast and the forestay fitting thus achieving an effective downward pull on the pole without increasing the compression in the pole too much. However it does have a disadvantage in that the downhaul needs to be released slightly each time the pole is brought aft. On yachts of 30ft l.o.a. (9.1m) and below it is sometimes possible to bring the deck attachment for the downhaul aft to a position just forward of the front face of the mast thus allowing the pole to be brought aft without the need for the downhaul to be eased. (Beware all foredeck crew, this system does require some degree of agility when gybing!)

Another method employed by some of the racing yachts, is to dispense with the downhaul line altogether and instead use a pair of guy tweaker lines fitted on the gunwale in a well forward position. The 'triangle of forces' means that the spinnaker pole guy also acts as the downhaul.

Reef lines fall into three categories:

a) Standard. Consisting of hooks for tack attachment and reef line for clew attachment. This is the most popular system at present and is certainly the simplest.

b) Flyaway system. This system dispenses with the need for tack hook and instead uses a pair of tack downhaul lines similar to the cunningham.

c) Single line reefing system which is as the name suggests a single line which simultaneously tensions both the luff and the leech in a single reefing process. This system greatly simplifies the reefing procedure and allows it to be carried out from the safety of the cockpit.

Cunningham. This is a simple control line that can be either one to one or two to one depending on the size of the yacht. This control line is usually only found on racing yachts. Rarely seen on cruising yachts, it can however significantly contribute to the effective control of the mainsail and thus improve performance quite significantly.

Checkstays. In recent years these

have become more common especially on racing yachts with the advent of fractional rigs. Their method of adjustment normally falls into one of two categories:

a) Adjustment at running backstay/checkstay connection. This is the simplest and most effective means of adjusting the checkstays and a number of different types of arrangement are shown in the accompanying diagram. The importance of checkstays on a racing mast is often overlooked and it is often assumed that the checkstays are of little consequence and carry low loads. This is quite simply not the case, they are very important stays and contribute significantly to the safety of the rig. As a result the purchase arrangement and method of adjustment should be considered very carefully.

The main advantages of this type of system are that a) it is simple, cheap and light, b) at a quick glance it is easy to see at what position the checkstay is set (not so easy when looking up at the mast from the aft quarter of the boat), c) the checkstay can be freed easily due to the low friction of the system.

Internal deflection type checkstay consist of a fixed length checkstay with a deflector wire which travels down the inside of the mast usually exiting below deck.

This system is generally only recommended for large yachts whose checkstay positions would be too high to reach if fitted in the manner described above. In addition to this it is sometimes also considered safer in as far as the checkstay itself is a fixed length, and it is assumed that the deflector part of the system is most likely to break; should it do so the mast will still be supported. (This is a very debatable point!) Whilst the system can be made to work well, it does suffer from two distinct problems:

a) It is difficult to assess quickly the mast bend present as a result of the checkstay setting. This is a very important consideration as over-tensioning of the checkstays is a common cause of mast failure due to it inverting the mast whilst it is under high compression.

b) whilst it is very neat to lead checkstay control lines aft to the cockpit the resultant number of blocks and turning sheaves required significantly increase the friction in the system and make it difficult in some conditions to release checkstay line. This can, in some cases, have catastrophic results. It is therefore important to reduce the friction in the system to a minimum.

Checkstay arrangements – Deflection type above, Block and tackle below

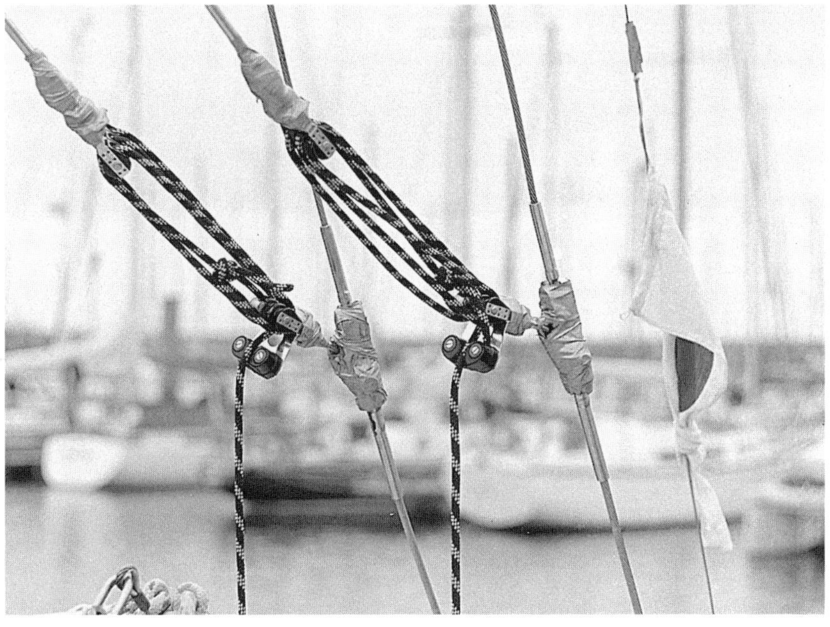

Running backstays. These systems are generally simple and consist of a 2:1 purchase which is then led to a winch. A self tailing winch is most commonly used so that the stay may be easily adjusted whilst under sail.

Small racing yachts of 30ft l.o.a. (9.1m) and less sometimes achieve tension in the running backstays without the need for winches.

Cruising yacht running backstays tend to be a simpler affair, a one to one line leading on to a winch. On large cruising yachts hydraulic running backstays may be used but due to their relatively short travel, they are normally only used for final tensioning.

Backstays. There are many backstay tensioning arrangements some of which have already been covered. The important point to bear in mind when considering any type of backstay arrangement is whether the rig is masthead or fractional type. If

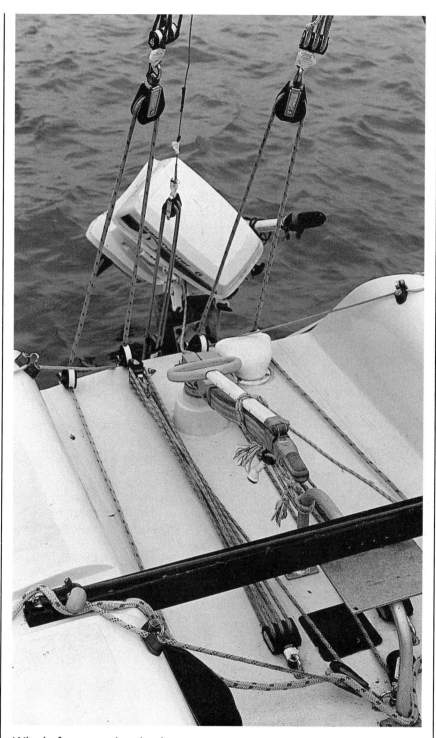

Winch free running backstay system

it is a masthead rig the backstay will be a primary support and therefore the fittings should be if anything over specified in size. In the case of fractional rigs backstays are generally more of a tuning device than primary support. However it is important to remember that this is not always the case and one should look very carefully at the specific use of the backstay. In other words carefully establish what you are trying to achieve with the backstay and match a system to suit.

Hydraulic running backstay tensioning

Hydraulic systems

As with many other applications, the flexibility in terms of remote control that hydraulic power offers can easily be seen as an advantage on a yacht. Rig tensioning is probably the most popular use of hydraulics on sailing yachts and simple backstay rams being the most common of the stays adjusted. With the exception of the integral rams, simple hydraulic hand pumps sited in the cockpit enables the rig tension to be controlled from a position remote from the ram. Many yachts include other units such as kicking straps, baby stays, rams in order to provide greater control of the rig from a single position. Some yachts, such as the maxi racers have very complex systems with multiple pumps mounted in the side decks, a rotary hand pump driven by a grinder 'pedestal' and rams for every conceivable

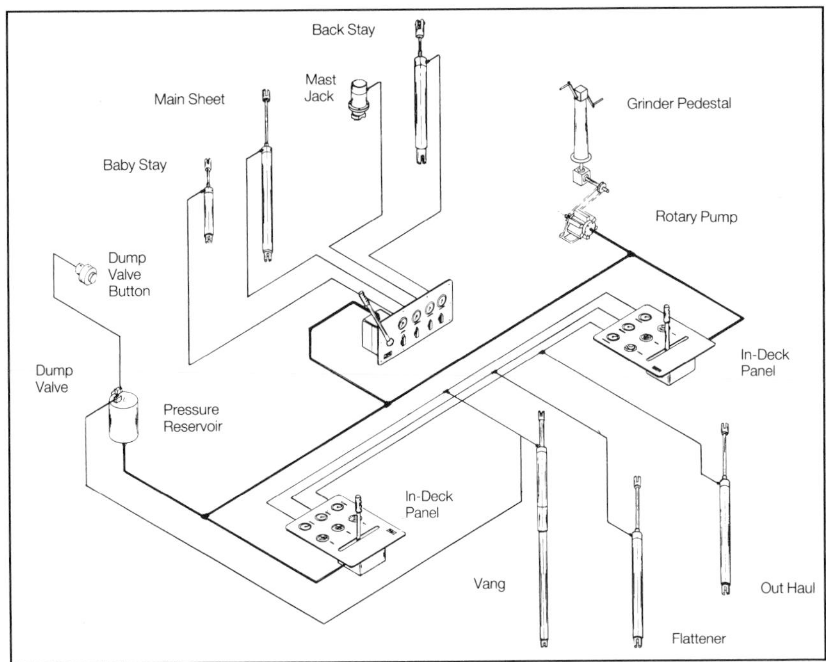

Typical hydraulic circuit (Courtesy Seaway Products)

application including mast jack, runners and genoa car positioners in addition to the common applications. In most cases an emergency 'dump valve' is fitted to allow for almost instantaneous release of the kicking strap in the event of imminent knock-down.

One important point to note about remote multiple systems is that a number of units can be operated by a single person, thus ensuring a co-ordinated rig control. Remote systems also allow for the pumps and panels to be situated so that the weight of the units and operator can be best positioned.

Hydraulic rams are usually available in three different types:

a) Stainless steel rams are usually fitted to luxury cruising yachts where strength and extended low maintenance is required. Due to their high corrosion resistance they are also ideal for keel lift rams and indeed any adjustment that is necessary in a poor environment.

b) Aluminium rams are the most popular type and are used by both racing and cruising yachts alike. The cylindrical body of the ram is manufactured from aluminium with the rod part of the ram being made from stainless steel.

c) Titanium rams are the lightest versions, their use being almost exclusively on Grand Prix racing yachts due to their high cost.

Mast jacks.

These fittings are primarily used for racing yachts where regular adjustment of the rigging is necessary. Whichever of the two systems is employed it is usually only incorporated on yachts of 40ft l.o.a (12.2m) and above. The system allows the mast to be jacked vertically over a sufficient distance (usually up to about 80mm) (3.25in) in order to pre-tension the rigging and offers the following advantages:

a) rigging tension can be adjusted quickly and simply by lowering the mast off the jack. Some rating rules do not allow the height of the mast to be altered after measurement.

b) removal of the mast and thus disconnecting the rigging is simplified and can be carried out in a very short space of time as the rigging is slackened by simply lowering the mast of the jack.

c) the tension can be backed off the rigging quickly and easily in order to move the heel fore and aft.

d) shorter threaded and hence lighter rigging screws can be used.

e) the tension in the rigging can be relieved between races in order to minimize the 'creep' in the rigging. The most important point when considering either of the two mast jack systems is that the heel MUST be shimmed and the load on the rams relieved so that ALL of the compression load down the mast is carried in pure compression by the shims and not the rams. Failure to do this, and 'sailing on the ram' seriously risks the safety of the mast. If for any reason there was a hydraulic failure, the mast could lower with the result that the standing rigging would be slackened, offering little or no support for the mast. The two main types are as follows:

Integral Mast Jack. For this system the ram is fitted internally in the bottom part of the section and is usually part of the integrated hydraulic system aboard the yacht. It is very simple to operate and requires very little in the way of setting up. However it is very important to ensure that the controls are not too easily accessible especially when under sail to ensure that the ram is not inadvertently operated whilst in motion.

Tommy Bar System. This system is often used on very light weight racing yachts where leaving hydraulic equipment ashore is considered to give a weight advantage. It consists of a removable bar which is fitted in either the fore and aft or athwartships plane under which a bottle jack is positioned on each side. A portable hydraulic pump provides the power to jack up each side of the 'Tommy Bar' thus lifting the heel of the mast. At the desired position the mast is then shimmed and the pressure released from the bottle jacks. The jacks and the portable

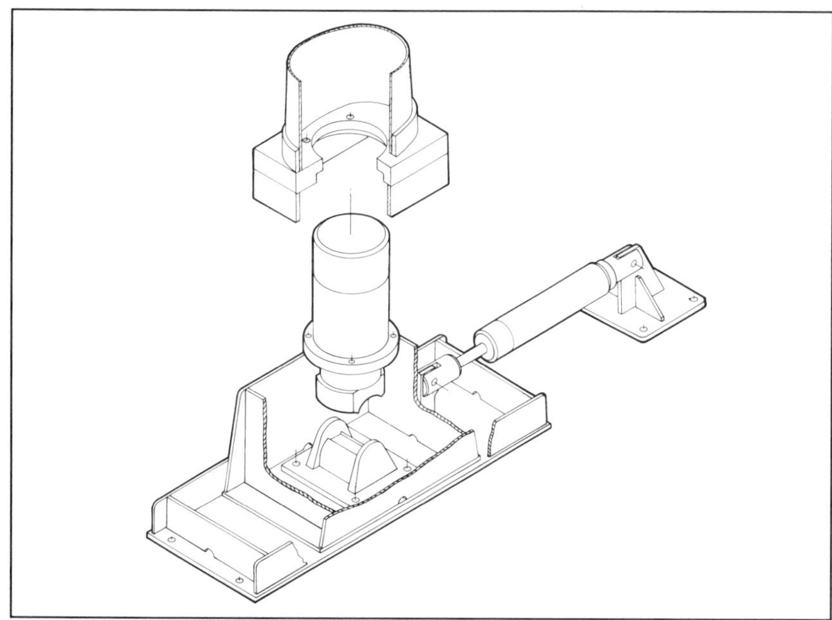

Integral mast jack (Courtesy Seaway Products Ltd.)

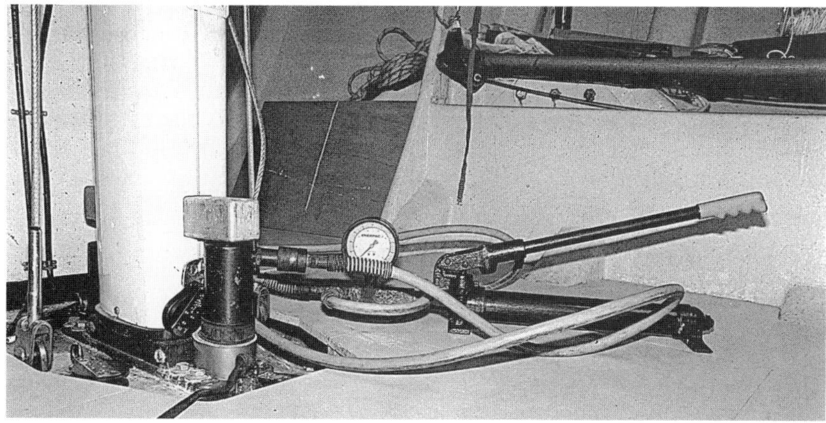

Tommy bar mast jack system

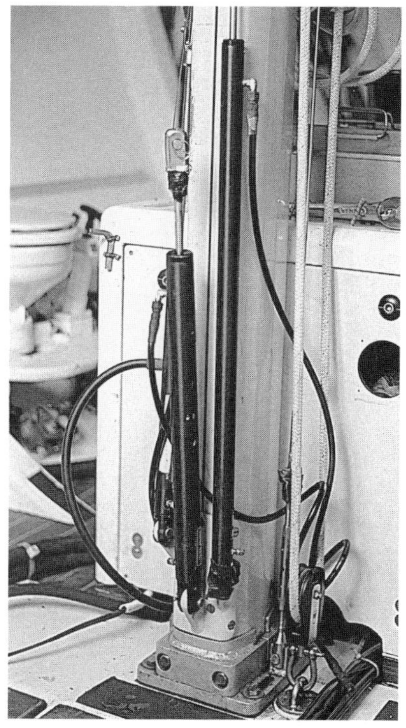

Hydraulics mounted below deck

pump are then removed, stowed ashore and the yacht is now ready to go sailing. This system is often used on yachts where no other form of hydraulic power is available or desired.

As well as being used for standing rigging adjustments, hydraulic rams are also used for adjustment for highly loaded control lines that need to be frequently adjusted. E.g. checkstays, flattener, outhaul etc. A popular way of mounting the rams whilst keeping the weight low down in the boat is to lead the control lines below decks via the mast. Rams can be mounted close to the mast heel in a vertical manner to control items such as those already mentioned.

Cruising yachts' hydraulic systems, when they are used, tend to cover a much wider range of applications and whilst this section of the book will not go into specific details on hydraulic power systems, it is interesting to note the equipment that a typically 53ft cruising yacht may require.

e.g. 53ft (16.2 m) LOA cruising yacht specification.

2 off primary winches hydraulic drive/manual override
1 off secondary winches hydraulic drive/manual override
1 off mainsheet winch hydraulic drive/manual override
1 off backstay ram pin size 19mm stroke 300mm
1 off remote kicker pin size 19mm stroke 300mm
1 off dinghy hoist complete with davits

Tension measurement.
The relative tensions in any yacht be it racing or cruising are important (albeit different degrees of importance) in order to obtain both the best efficiency of the rig and the safest distribution of loading. In order to achieve this optimum balance it is necessary to somehow judge the relative tensions in the rigging. In fact, in practical terms on most cruising boats the rigging is set up in a fashion that 'feels right'. However, this is a very subjective way of setting up one of the most important features on the yacht. There is little need for the setting up of the rig to be biased towards guesswork as there are some fundamental factors that act as guides to show whether the mast is set up correctly or not. These are detailed in the setting

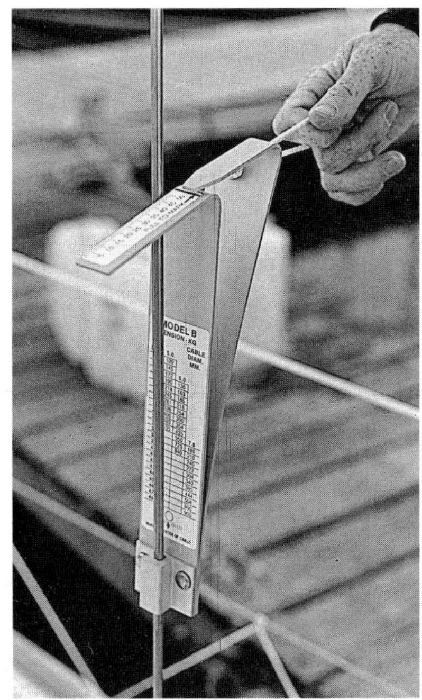

'Loos' gauge for tension measurement

up section of this book which describes the relative tensions in terms of effects that can be seen on the rigging. If one wishes to measure actual tension in the rigging, some form of loading measurement will be required. Right from the start one must carefully consider whether an actual load measurement is required or in fact whether the RELATIVE tensions of the rigging spans are sufficient (this is often the case).

Measuring the relative rigging tensions can normally be considered to be a cheaper operation in terms of equipment than measuring the actual loads on the rigging.

There are three types of load measurements commonly used which are:

a) Wire deflection type gauge. This is a simple instrument which consists of two bend plates joined together at their lower end which deflect away from each other a certain amount for a given load. Whilst this device is actually calibrated to measure actual loads it is in fact more useful in determining relative shroud tensions. Whilst this is a simple, effective and cheap tool its main limitation is however that it is only really suitable for wire rigging. The gauge is used as follows:

1) Measure the wire diameter.
2) Clip the gauge on to the wire
3) Pull the lanyard until the pointer is positioned at the black calibration mark on the inner end of the scale.
4) With the pointer at the black calibration mark read the scale at the exact point where the middle of the cable touches the scale. For best accuracy the gauge should be held so that the scale barely touches the cable thus eliminating friction.
5) Be careful not pull the lanyard excessively as it may permanently bend the plate and damage the gauge.
6) For relative readings, simply note the number on the scale.
7) To convert the scale reading to actual tension, see the conversion table mounted on the gauge.

b) The 'Tension Meter'. This is a more elaborate measurement device and again works on the principle of deflecting the stay in order to measure the load being carried by it. It is designed for measuring loads in static and moving ropes and strands and the principle can also be adapted to measure the loads in single wire steel rod, fibre rope, webbing, cable etc. The item in which the load or tension is to be measured is deflected by an eccentric arrangement between the two outer wheels or shoes which subject the main frame to a horizontal component of the rope load causing the frame to bend. This is measured and translated in to the load in the rigging span. The advantage of this system is that it can be adapted to measure the various types of load, within close tolerances, whatever the cross-sectional area of the item.

Whilst the above two methods are useful tools for establishing static loads in rigging their common limitation is that it is

Tension gauge – portable deflection type

Electronic load cell

Electronic load pin

not easy to continually assess a change in loading whilst sailing. The following instrument is the third and most popular form of rig tension measurement.

c) Electronic Load Cell. This form of measurement for yachts is the successor to the previous hydraulic form of measurement. The load cell unit consists of a sealed unit in which are mounted a series of electronic strain gauges. The unit is fitted in the line of the load i.e. close to the deck fitting. In some cases the load cell actually takes the form of the forestay clevis pin at the lower end. Cables then run back through the yacht to an amplifier unit and then on to a simple LCD display unit. Tension or compression loadings can be constantly displayed on the LCD units with very little battery power being required. These load cells are ideal for forestay load measurement on racing yachts. In fact for any serious racing yacht, this type of equipment is essential particularly on fractional rig boats with running backstays so that the running backstay tension can be carefully adjusted to suit the conditions.

If such a system is to be used on a yacht that does not already possess it, it must be borne in mind that it may well be necessary to shorten the forestay if the existing rack is to be maintained. Alternatively, the load pin type of load cell should be used which requires no alteration of the forestay length.

Track systems

There is a wide range of track types available for many different applications. There are a number which are commonly used on the spars and their sections' shape depends upon the required application.

Luff Groove Tracks. These fall into two categories the first having a circular type section which is suitable for bolt ropes on sails and circular section slug slides. These are commonly used where a mast section with a rectangular section track taking sail slides, needs to be converted to a mast section that will take a bolt rope. The tracks are normally in the form of aluminium extrusions, typically 4.8 metres in length. The critical factors when choosing a section are that a) the correct internal diameter to accept a given bolt rope diameter is achieved and b) that the flanges of the track sit correctly on the aft face of the section. These types of tracks are usually side fastened with pop rivets.

Another type of externally fastened track is the sail slide track which accepts flat section

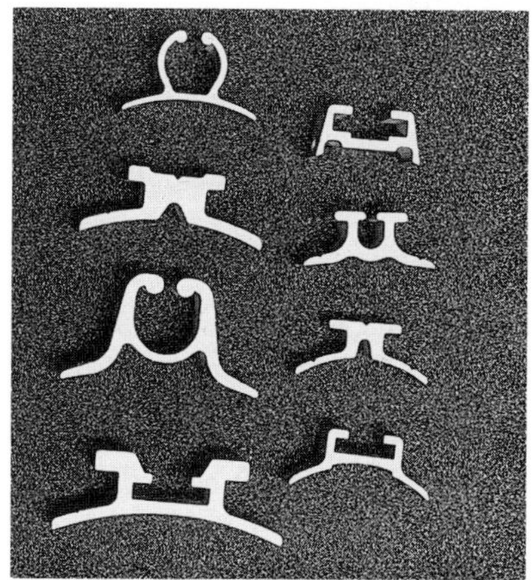

Luff groove track examples

sail slides. The groove is generally rectangular in shape and is side fastened in the same way as for the bolt rope track.

Tri-sail tracks are often fitted as an additional luff attachment system on larger cruising yachts. The section is normally rectangular in shape but differs from the conventional luff groove section in that it is centre fastened with countersunk fastenings in order to allow the track to be positioned as close to the centre line as possible. These tracks often extend down to the deck so that the sail slides can be loaded at a safe height and also that the sail may be stowed on the deck ready for quick hoisting if required. An additional advan-

Genoa luff groove

tage is that the mainsail does not have to be taken off the mast in the event of having to hoist a tri-sail, it may however be necessary for the track to be bent around fittings such as gooseneck and winch pads.

Genoa headfoil grooves are popular ways of attaching the luff of the genoa and are used on both racing yachts to achieve a better aerodynamic flow over the leading edge of the sail and also cruising yachts on headsail furling gears.

Some of the most popular racing luff groove systems are produced as plastic extrusions with a double groove in order to allow efficient headsail changes.

Furling headsail systems generally use aluminium extrusions for their luff groove systems. These may also have twin grooves as some of the systems can also be used for cruiser/racing. The best versions allow the drum arrangement to be removed in racing in order to both improve the airflow over the luff of the sail and allow the luff of the genoa to extend right down to the deck level.

When considering a luff groove system it is important to bear in mind the nature of sailing that will take place. Whilst twin luff groove extrusions are ideal for racing yachts with large crew and therefore plenty of manpower to man-handle the sails, short-handed sailors could find the luff groove system to be a disadvantage in terms of handling. The reason is that as the sail is lowered the genoa luff emerges from the track and is not restrained from being dragged overboard. The conventional hank system however ensures that as the sail is lowered the luff is kept securely in place on the lower part of the forestay and is prevented from falling overboard. Of course, from a handling point of view, the luff groove system that is part of the headsail furling equipment is ideal. However if the yacht is to be used for competitive long-distance short-handed work a compromise will have to be made in terms of performance when the sail is partly furled.

Spinnaker pole tracks. These types of tracks are required to take much higher loading's than the luff tracks for sails and at a range of angles. As a result, their shapes may differ a great deal from the luff groove types and some of the high performance tracks are specifically designed to allow the spinnaker pole car to be moved freely even when the track and car are subject to high transverse compression loads. The main versions are as follows:

a) 'T-type', the most popular version and certainly the simplest. It is designed to carry simple cars with nylon sliders and is commonly available in inch and inch and a quarter widths.

b) 'Ball-race' tracks, these are the same as are used for genoa tracks and mainsheet tracks and are generally found on racing yachts. As a general rule, their use is not recommended for conventional yachts due to their poor load distribution. They are however very free running.

c) 'X-Type' tracks, these tracks are specifically designed to take high transverse loads and yet still run freely. The tracks are designed to accept cars with wheel bearings which tend to be more durable than the ball-race system even though the point loading is greater.

Typical genoa luff groove system sizes

Max. forestay diam.		Width A		Length B		Weight/length	
(mm)	(in)	(mm)	(in)	(mm)	(in)	(gm/m)	(oz/ft)
5	3/16	10	0.375	25	1.000	158	1.7
6	1/4	11	0.438	30	1.188	205	2.2
8	5/16	12	0.469	32	1.250	213	2.4
10	3/8	15	0.594	38	1.500	325	3.5
12	1/2	18	0.719	41	1.600	437	4.7

(Courtesy Victory Marine)

Headsail changing

Spinnaker pole track and sliding eye

Radar platforms

Where space on the deck is limited radars can be mounted at a position up the mast either on the main mast or on the mizzen if fitted. They should be mounted on a platform of which there are a number of types available. Consideration must be given to a number of points such as:

a) The radar manufacturer's recommended height.

b) The platform should be fitted in such a position that it does not foul additional stays such as inner forestays.

c) The radar must not be fitted in such a position that it can be damaged by the leach of the genoa when tacking or damage the leach of the sail as a result of constant chafing.

d) From a spar manufacturer's point of view and also from a stability point of view, the radar should be mounted as low as possible in order to reduce the additional heeling moment effect and thus loading on the mast and rigging as far as is practically possible.

When a radar is subsequently fitted to an existing mast, the relatively large diameter co-axial cable may not fit inside the existing cable conduit. There are two options in this case, the first being to fit an additional internal conduit. The second alternative is to fit the cable inside an externally mounted cable cover. This is often referred to as an external radar conduit. It is simple to fit, requiring only 'pop' rivet fastenings and is normally available in a range of colours.

Mast steps and climbing rungs

Mast steps are often used either up the entire length of the mast or at areas where it will help support a person carrying out work or maintenance inspection. Popular areas for fitting such steps are on large boats where the gooseneck height is out of easy reach and a few steps will allow a crew member to reach the head of the mainsail when it is lowered. A few steps are often fitted at the top of the mast on a masthead rig and/or in the vicinity of a radar bracket. The standard type of mast step is a triangular type fitting which is fixed. This type of fitting, whilst it is very simple and cheap, can sometimes spoil the aesthetics of the mast and if this is a concern then fold away type steps can be used. When fitting steps they should be staggered each side of the mast at approximately half metre spacing.

Another form of mast steps is the collapsible ladder type arrangement that is hoisted up the aft face of the mast once the mainsail has been lowered by using the main halyard. This is a very useful piece of equipment when maintenance or inspection work needs to be carried out but cannot be used whilst the yacht is under sail with the mainsail set.

Radar platform

Mast steps

Winch pads and mountings

On rigs that do not have their halyards led aft, the winches are sometimes mounted on the side and aft face of the mast which will require some form of mounting bracket. This bracket usually consists of a flat plate which forms a stable seating for the winch. The bolts that pass through the base of the winch to fasten it should be tapped into the mast wall to provide a secure mounting for the winch. Unless the pad has been specifically designed to do so, the winch should not be bolted directly onto the pad. The rivet fastenings on the pad are by no means sufficient to take the high halyard loads and will usually result in the pad tearing off the mast. Another important point to bear in mind is that there should be an insulating pad between the base of the winch and the surface of the winch pad. This prevents any corrosive action between the different metals.

Most manufacturers have a range of winch pad sizes to suit different winches which normally correspond to the maximum base diameter of the winch. Slab reefing winches may also be fitted to the aft face of the mast below the boom gooseneck. In order to prevent riding turns on the winch, this pad should be angled and specific pads are generally available for this purpose. Before fitting the pad, it is important to ensure that the winch is mounted at a height that a full swing of the handle can be achieved. Again the sizes of these pads depend on the maximum base diameter of the winch.

On luxury custom yachts, faired-in winch pads may be fitted and these are again purely a means of mounting the winch and not a method of securing it. As a result the winch securing bolts should be tapped into the mast wall and not the winch pad.

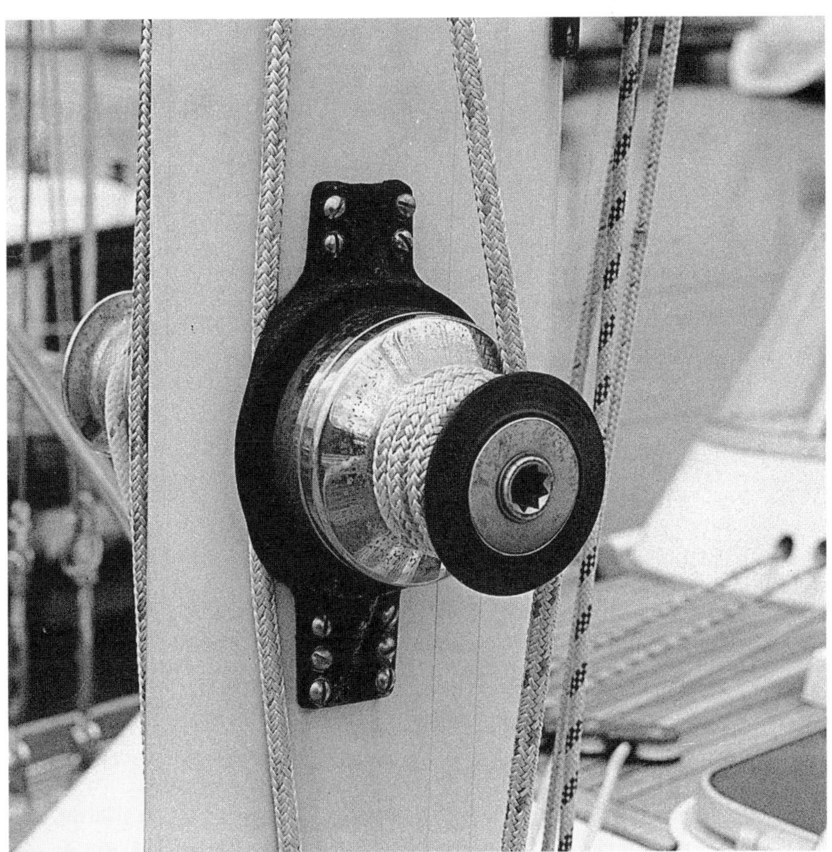

Winch pad examples

Winch pad sizes

Winch pad size (mm)	Winch Type		
	Lewmar	Harken/Barbarossa	Barient
95 x 95	6	B6	B, 10
105 x 105	7, 8	B8, B16.2	12,17, 18/24
115 x 115	16	B32.2	–
125 x 125	10, 25	B40.2	21/30
140 x 140	30, 40, 42	B42.2, B44.2	22/35, 24/41
175 x 175	43, 44	B46.2, B48.2	25, 27, 28

Sizes based on Proctor winch pads

Masthead equipment
A yacht will need to comply with regulations for the prevention of collisions at sea (COLREGS) and it is from these that the types of lights required are established. In terms of fitting such equipment, whilst it may seem obvious to fasten the equipment securely, it is all too easy to underestimate the loads imposed on navigation lights as a result of their being at the top of the mast. Unless this type of equipment is fastened securely, the constant motion of the masthead will result in the fastenings working loose and the equipment coming free. Care must also be taken to ensure that navigation lights are aligned correctly in accordance with the regulations. Various types of lights are available for a given purpose and as a general rule of thumb it is better to try to keep the weight aloft to a minimum.

When considering equipment of this type it is also important to bear in mind the conduit capacity (if one is fitted) and the number of cables that need to be fitted inside.

9: Maintenance

In a sense a large proportion of this book has been concerned with maintenance as keeping the rig operating in the boat requires regular checking of certain fittings. If one considers the analogy with motor cars, most people would not be surprised if after say three years of continual use without any form of maintenance or servicing the car broke down or developed a number of faults. Indeed, most cars are serviced on a regular basis in order to prevent serious failures occurring. Unfortunately in many cases yachts are left with their rigs standing without any form of inspection let alone being removed from the boat for a number of years. One only has to be familiar with a few marinas to see that this is the case.

The object of this chapter is to emphasize some of the key points and also include additional guide lines that cannot easily be incorporated into the previous chapters. The subject of maintenance has been divided into the following groups.

Beginning of season
Any maintenance required will only be established by thoroughly checking the spar and its associated fittings including the standing and running rigging. This area is covered in detail in Chapter 5 concerning the receiving of the mast through to stepping. An 'aide mémoire' at the end of this chapter suggests a checklist for the key areas.

End of season maintenance
Unless the spar is to be worked on immediately, the equipment will need to be laid up for the winter. There are two ways of doing this a) to leave the mast in the boat and b) to have the rig un-stepped and laid on trestles. The latter is always the most desirable from a point of view of being able to assess the condition of the spar and work on it where necessary. Ideally, the rig should be removed from the boat at the end of each season but this is not always a practical solution. Whilst there is no definitive maximum period for leaving the rig in the boat from a safety point it should be un-stepped and checked thoroughly at least every three years.

With the rig remaining in the boat during the winter layout period some of the following items will not apply. These are noted with an asterisk.

1) With the use of a number of trestles make sure that the mast is adequately supported and does not deflect significantly over its length. Failure to do this will result in the possibility of permanent bend in the spar making subsequent tuning difficult and possibly reducing the performance of the rig. The spars may be stored in a mast rack, but again it should be checked for adequate support.
2) Make sure that the mast is not in contact with a dissimilar metal by placing insulating pads at the support points, such material could be plastic, foam rubber, wood etc.
3) Lubricate all moving parts.
4) Where possible, remove all electrical equipment such as masthead transducers, VHF aerials, navigation lights etc. and store in a dry place.
5) Painted spars must not be stored in polythene or tubes as this may damage the paintwork.
6) Remove all standing rigging from the mast leaving the attachment pins on the mast. The rigging should then be coiled and stored in a dry place.
7) Remove all running rigging and replace with draw lines. The draw lines in comparison to the running rigging need only be light lines but do make sure that they are of adequate size to prevent breaking due to chafe. At least 3mm (0.11in) diameter. This is particularly important if the mast is to be left in the boat. Store all running rigging in a dry place.
8) Thoroughly wash all spars with fresh or soapy water.
9) The laying up period is often

Mast badly supported on trestles

Corrosion examples

a good time to check over the spars and associated fittings and rigging so that any necessary repairs can be carried out in good time over the winter period. Ideally, all aspects should be checked (see Chapters 3,4 & 5).

10) Ensure that your mast is not in contact with any other masts on racks or trestles as substantial corrosion can take place during the lay up period.

General maintenance

Corrosion. The aluminium alloy used for most spars has a high natural resistance to corrosion resulting from the formation of the tough impervious oxide film on the surface of the aluminium when exposed to air. This oxide film which is grey in colour is self-repairing if removed by chafing or scratching. It will protect the aluminium from further corrosion in the normal atmosphere provided no dissimilar metals are in contact with the aluminium to cause electrolytic corrosion. Whilst this oxide film is valuable in preventing the corrosion, it does however cause difficulties in painting or bonding as these materials do not adhere to the oxide without detailed preparation to the surface. While this is possible, the vast majority of spars are anodized.

Anodizing is an electrolytic process which causes thickening and toughening of the natural oxide film. The anodic film is approximately 0.03mm thick. It is very hard and provides excellent corrosion and abrasion resistance. Most spars have a silver anodized finish but it is possible to colour the anodizing by dipping the item into a dye bath immediately after anodizing. The porous anodizing film will then soak up the dye. Immediately following the anodizing process, the spar is then sealed chemically in order to set the colour and increase corrosion resistance.

Because of the natural oxide film that is formed when the anodizing surface is scratched it is not absolutely necessary to re-treat scratched or damaged anodized spars. However the appearance of the spars can be partially restored by cleaning the aluminium surface thoroughly with a fine emery cloth or sandpaper onto which is painted a suitable etch primer. The damaged area can be painted to match the anodized surface. Paint should not be applied to the anodized area of the spars, as it will not adhere.

Having said that, scratches and corrosion can be treated in the above manner, it is important to bear in mind that surface corrosion may be an indication of more substantial corrosion in other parts of the spar. While scratches will not usually seriously affect the strength of the spar, large areas that have corroded deep into the mast wall could seriously affect the structural properties of the spar and in this case the advice of a mast manufacturer should be sought.

Two of the most common areas where corrosion occurs on a mast is at deck level and/or in the bury area near to the heel plug. Damage to this area of the mast should be treated very seriously as it is a highly loaded part of the mast and a detailed examination of the extent and cause of the corrosion should be made. It is also important to check the rest of the mast for similar corrosion before considering a possible repair schedule.

Whilst the anodizing process in itself is relatively simple, it is not generally possible to re-anodize masts that have been scratched or where the anodizing has been worn. The reason for this is that in order to re-anodize the spar the existing anodizing has to be completely removed and this is achieved by chemically stripping the anodizing. In order to do this every single fitting and dissimilar metal must be removed from the spar before it is stripped. During the stripping process, any dissimilar metal contact with the aluminium will cause serious and rapid corrosion. In addition to this, the time taken to remove all of the old fittings which may have seized or become damaged coupled with the time that it would take to reassemble the spar makes this process unrealistic from a cost point of view.

Anodized spars that have become dull in their appearance can sometimes be cleaned up by using a mild abrasive liquid similar to the colour restoring products available on the automotive market. A wax polish can then be used to restore some of the original appearance of the spar.

Dents. The main load on a mast is generally compression and in order to ensure that the section can carry the often high loads involved, a spar relies totally on the structural integrity of the section. As a result, any dents that are found in a spar should be treated very seriously as they become weak points in the section and can lead to buckling. It is sometimes possible to dress such dents, but it is more common to fit some form of doubler over the area to restore strength. In order to restore the mechanical properties of the spar it is important that the doubler closely matches the section shape and as a result this repair should be carried out by a reputable mast manufacturer.

Cracks. As with any structural member, cracks can cause complete failure if left to develop. At beginning and end of season at least the spars should be checked thoroughly for cracks particularly in high stress areas such as around the deck close to shroud tangs, spreader areas and the masthead etc. Whilst there are a number of different ways of searching the spars for cracks possibly the simplest and most effective is to use a magnifying glass in the first instance. Any cracks that are subsequently found or where there is good reason to believe that a crack may exist further investigation may be made with the use of a dye penetrant. This dye when applied to the suspect area will show up cracks if they exist. Another method of crack detection is with the use of X-rays, but the cost is usually a prohibitive factor. It will then be necessary to contact your spar manufacturer for further advice.

Sometimes it is possible to anticipate an area which is likely to crack by searching for bulges around exit areas. This can be carried out quite simply by running ones fingers around the suspected area. On racing spars, in particular, bulging is sometimes found around exit slots. This is usually the result of the spar being over-bent, usually accidentally, and is the first sign of buckling in the mast wall.

Halyard sheaves. From time to time it may be necessary to replace worn or damaged halyard sheaves. Whilst it is, of course, easier to carry out this operation whilst the mast is lying on trestles this is not always possible. A common concern of many yachtsmen is how to remove the halyard sheaves without their dropping down the inside of the mast. The answer is:

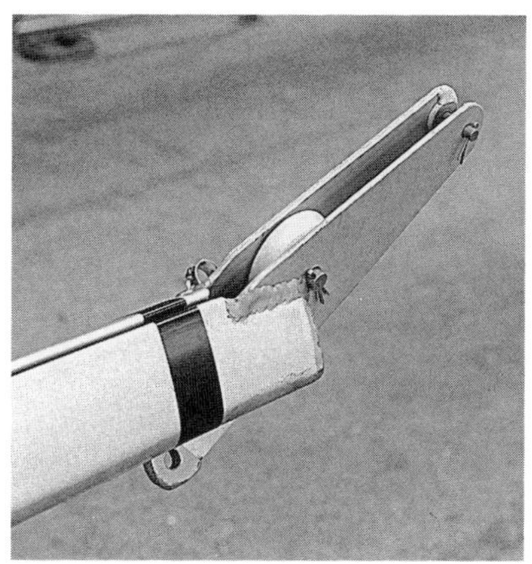

Removing halyard sheaves

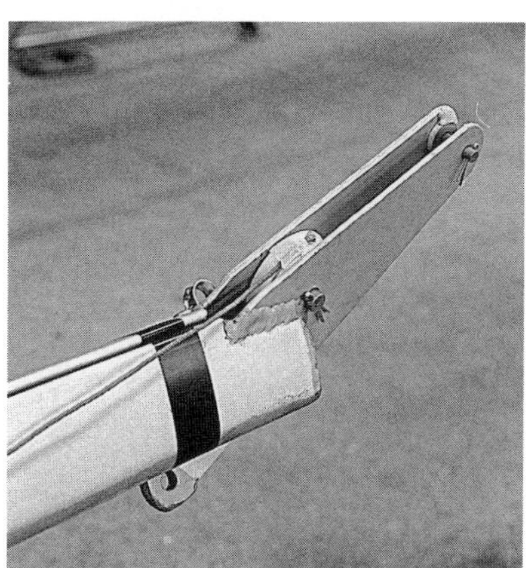

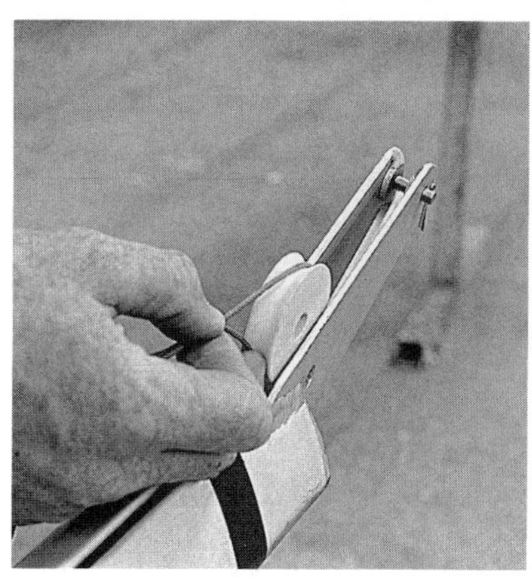

1) Remove the halyard concerned, whilst pulling through a draw line at the same time.
2) Attach a light line with a piece of tape or similar to a point on the halyard bearing surface of the sheave.
3) Rotate the sheave until the end of the line reappears at the exit position.
4) By holding both parts of the light line, the sheave may be

supported whilst the sheave pin is removed.
5) Replacement of halyard sheave is the reverse of this process.

There are many ways of mounting sheave pins and the pin area should be studied carefully to ascertain the way in which it is removed. Sheave pins are often manufactured from stainless steel and because they bear on the aluminium surface, they often present a problem with corrosion and are difficult to remove. It is therefore important to know the way in which the pin is removed, especially if the pin is corroded into the mast. Two of the most popular ways of securing sheave pins are with cover plates that have two small self-tapping screws to secure them into the mast. In order to remove the halyard sheave pin these screws should be removed and the cover plate lifted. One of the popular types of sheave pin is often welded to this cover plate and therefore the cover plate should be carefully pulled away from the mast whilst supporting the sheave. The second popular method is for the cover plate nearly to cover up the sheave pin hold and as a result when the two screws are removed the cover plate is free. In this case in order to remove the sheave pin, there should be a small hole drilled in the opposite side of the mast in line with the sheave pin. A small drift can be placed into this hole and the sheave pin gently tapped out.

Sheave pin cover plate

Fouled halyards. There are usually two ways in which halyards can become fouled and before any attempt is made to free the halyard it is important to establish the type of problem involved. The two causes are usually either twisting around other halyards or snagging on fittings inside the mast.

Twisted halyards. A twisted halyard usually becomes progressively tighter as the halyard is hoisted or lowered. If this is the case, there will often be more than one halyard that is difficult to hoist or lower. Firstly identify the halyard or halyards with which you are experiencing difficulty. Having identified the problem halyard, slacken the remaining halyards so that they are free to run. Then hoist or lower the fouled halyard whilst keeping a close eye on the slack halyards. Whilst this is being done, the halyards that are twisted will usually show signs of movement.

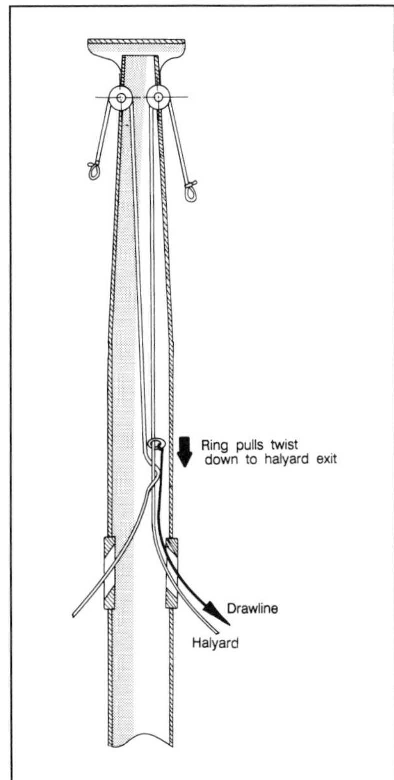

Untwisting halyards

Having identified the fouled halyards, there are two methods that can be used to free them. The first is:
1) Assuming the mast is in situ in the boat remove one of the fouled halyards completely.
2) Tighten the remaining halyards.
3) Rig the mast and/or trim the boat so that the re-reefed halyard will pass down the aft face of the mast. (If the sheave is close to the forward face of the mast it may be necessary for the halyard to run down the inside front face of the mast and therefore the rig must be racked forward and/or boat trimmed to suit).
4) Attach a plumb weight such as a lead fishing weight or a string of nuts to a suitable length of draw line and feed through the halyard sheave so that the weight pulls the draw line down through the mast.
5) Using a bent piece of wire, the draw line can then be hooked out through the appropriate halyard exit slot.
6) With the use of the draw line re-reeve the halyard.

During the re-reeving process with the draw line the boat should be kept as steady as possible in order that further twists do not occur. The second system is:
1) Attach two separate draw lines to the halyard tail at the exit position.
2) Pull the draw line through the mast by removing the halyard.
3) With the two draw lines in place remove one of the draw lines from the halyard tail and secure.
4) Draw the halyard back into the mast as if re-reeving the halyard.
5) Attach a small ring to the upper end of the remaining draw line. This ring will need to be small enough to pass through the sheave box. If this is not possible it may be necessary to remove the halyard sheave temporarily.
6) Pull the draw line and ring

back down through the mast until it emerges at the halyard exit position.
7) If a twist is present, the ring will draw the twist down towards the halyard exit where both halyards may be removed and untwisted.

Snagged Halyards. In most cases, it is the wire to rope splice that becomes jammed against the mast fittings inside the mast. The symptoms of this are usually that the halyard runs freely until it comes to an abrupt halt. If this is the case, the wire to rope splice will show signs of snagging as the rope part of the splice will appear burred. The following procedure will help to ascertain where the snagging is occurring.
1) Position the wire to rope splice so that it is at the position of the halyard exit.
2) Mark the halyard with a piece of tape or similar at the position where the halyard emerges from the sheave cage at the top of the mast.
3) Pull the halyard through until the snagging occurs.
4) Measure the distance from the sheave cage to the mark on the halyard.
5) Take the distance measured on the halyard and measure up from the halyard exit sheave to find the position of snagging.
6) The position of this snagging will usually correspond to the position of a fitting on the mast.
7) If possible remove the fitting and see if the snagging still occurs.
8) If this is not possible, try re-reeving the halyard in the manner set out above under 'Twisted halyards'.

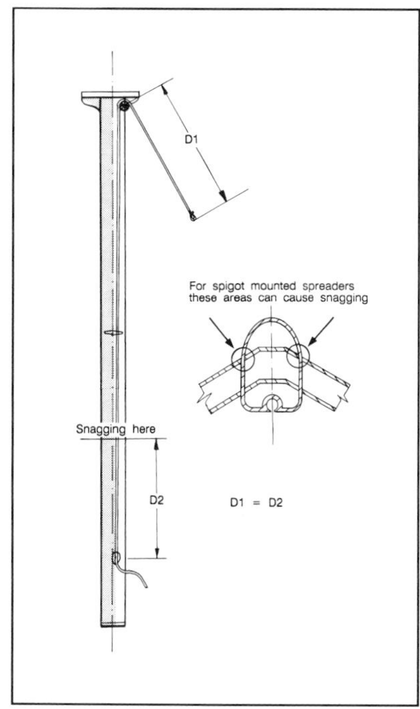

Snagging halyards

There are of course many fittings that are potential snags for halyards and it would be virtually impossible to detail each one and the remedy. However, one of the most popular fittings that causes snagging is the spreader mounting spigot. If the halyard has been reeved on the wrong side of the spigot (in most cases the halyard should be reeved so that they pass down the aft face of the mast) then the wire to rope splice can become jammed in the corner between the spigot and mast wall. The remedy for this is to re-reeve the halyard by using a plumb line and racking the mast aft to ensure that the plumb line passes down the aft face of the mast.

If the offending fitting cannot be removed or part of the halyard altered then it is worth remaking the wire to rope splice especially if the existing splice has been severely burred. The smooth tapered exterior of the splice will often allow it to travel across the fitting without snagging.

Track gate maintenance and conversions.

Whilst there is now a wide range of different track gate systems depending on the spar manufacturer, there are in existence a large number of stainless plate/thumbscrew type track gate in existence. This type of gate consists of a stainless steel plate which is formed to suit the shape of the section and is attached to the mast by means of a thumbscrew which is tapped into the mast wall. A common problem with this type of system is that because the thumbscrew is manufactured from stainless steel and the mast is aluminium, corrosion inevitably takes place and eventually strips the tapped thread in the mast wall. If this does occur, there are two simple ways of effecting a repair.

Track gates

a) Using a larger diameter bolt, drill and re-tap the hold to suit the larger size.
b) If there are halyard exits close by it is sometimes possible to bond a nut of the suitable size and thread type to the inside of the mast wall thus providing a more secure means for the thumbscrew. Alternatively the nut can be bonded on to the outside surface of the mast but in this case the shape of the stainless steel track gate may need to be slightly altered.

Many mast manufacturers nowadays provide a combined

Track gate conversion

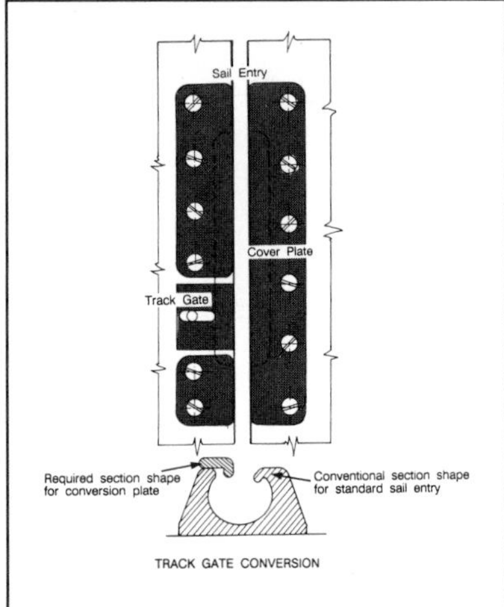

bolt rope sail feeder entry and track gate system. However, there are occasions where on older masts it is necessary to convert the existing bolt rope sail entry to a track gate system. This involves blanking off most of the cutaway that forms the bolt rope sail entry and replacing with a track gate system.

Maintenance checklist

This list is not by any means intended to be exhaustive but does provide a handy condensed guide to the key areas that should be checked on the spars.

1) Fastenings in good condition and seated correctly and secure.
2) Remove paint if necessary for inspecting cracks.
3) Check all welds.
4) Check clevis pins for flats, bends etc.
5) Check eyes for elongation and cracks.
6) Check free turning sheaves.
7) Check all exit boxes, sheaves cages etc. for cracks and snags.
8) Check all swage terminals.
9) Ensure adequate toggles in rigging terminations.
10) Check rigging screws, in particular for thread damage.
11) Check all areas for signs of chafe.
12) Check alignment of standing rigging.
13) Check spreader sockets and spigots.
14) Check for signs of cracks and denting.
15) Check spreaders for cracks, bends, dents etc.
Check end fittings secure. 16) Check for chafe especially forward and trailing edges.
17) Check end fittings secure.
18) Check shroud tangs for elongation, cracks, corrosion secure etc.
19) Check halyards and shackles.
20) Check articulation for rigging screws and that rigging screw is correct way up.
21) Check for corrosion in all areas but in particular around deck and heel areas.
22) Check mast step secure and corrosion free.
23) Check all areas for sharp edges.
24) Lubricate all moving parts.
25) Check standing rigging attached securely to ends of spreaders.

Spares checklist

a) Clevis pins
b) Split pins
c) Shackles
d) Nuts and bolts
e) Screws – machine screws and self-tap
f) Snap-shackles
g) Blocks
h) Toggles
i) Spacers
j) Rigging terminals – swage and swageless
k) Rigging screws
l) Thimbles
m)Sails slides
n) Mast and boom sleeving kit
o) Wire and rope
p) U-clamp bolt
q) Seizing wire

Tool checklist

a) Knives
b) Marlin spike
c) Files
d) Spanners
e) Screwdrivers
f) Pliers
g) Hammer
h) Hacksaw
i) Bolt croppers
j) Drill and bits
k) Tape measure
l) Tape

Index